Edited b

IAN BERG
JEAN NURSTEN

Unwillingly to School (4th edition)

GASKELL

British Library Cataloguing-in-Publication Data
A catalogue record for this book is available from the British Library

ISBN 0902241893

Distributed in North America
by American Psychiatric Press, Inc
ISBN 0-88048-648-1

Cover illustration by Louise Whalley
Phototypeset by Dobbie Typesetting Limited, Tavistock, Devon
Printed by Bell & Bain, Thornliebank, Glasgow

Jack Kahn (1905–1989)

Contents

Contributors

Ian Berg, Consultant in Child and Adolescent Psychiatry, Department of Psychological Medicine (Children), Clarendon Wing, Leeds General Infirmary and Senior Clinical Lecturer, University of Leeds

Howard C. M. Carroll, Course Director (Educational Psychology), Department of Education, University of Wales Swansea, Hendrefoilen, Swansea SA2 7NB

Dilys Daws, Consultant Child Psychotherapist, Tavistock Clinic, 120 Belsize Lane, London NW3 5BA

Judith Edwards, Child Psychotherapist, Wandsworth Town Child Guidance Clinic, London SW18 1TJ

David Farrington, Professor of Psychological Criminology, Institute of Criminology, University of Cambridge, 7 West Road, Cambridge CB3 9DT

Natalia Flakierska-Praquin, Child and Adolescent Psychiatry, Annedals Clinics, S-41345 Göteborg, Sweden

Ken Fogelman, Professor of Education, University of Leicester, 21 University Road, Leicester LE1 7RF

Christopher Gillberg, Professor, Child and Adolescent Psychiatry, Annedals Clinics, S-41345 Göteborg, Sweden

Betty C. Glasscock, Associate Professor, School of Public Health, University of Alabama at Birmingham, 112 Mortimer Jordan Hall, Birmingham, Alabama 35294-2010, USA

Jack Kahn†, 1904–1989 Formerly Director, Community Mental Health, Newham, London

Lorraine V. Klerman, Professor, School of Public Health, University of Alabama at Birmingham, 112 Mortimer Jordan Hall, Birmingham, Alabama 35294-2010, USA

Judith Lask, Family Therapist, Bethlem Hospital, Beckenham, Kent BR3 3BX

Marianne Lindström, Child and Adolescent Psychiatry, Annedals Clinics S-41345, Göteborg, Sweden

Margaret Murphy, Consultant Adolescent Psychiatrist, Gart Royal Naval Hospital, 1055 Great Western Road, Glasgow G12 0XH

Jean Nursten, Professor of Social Work, Department of Community Studies, University of Reading, Bulmershe Court, Earley RG6 1HY

David Reynolds, Professor, Department of Education, University of Newcastle, Joseph Cowan Hse, St Thomas Street, Newcastle upon Tyne NE1 7RU

Ian M. Robertson, Partner, Griffiths Robertson, Solicitors, 46 West Street, Reading RG1 1TZ

Judith Robertson, Department of Psychiatry, Washington University School of Medicine, Barnes and Reynard Hospitals, 4940 Children's Place, St Louis, Missouri, 63110, USA

Lee Robins, Department of Psychiatry, Washington University School of Medicine, Barnes and Reynard Hospitals, 4940 Children's Place, St Louis, Missouri 63110, USA

Frederick Stone, Professor Emeritus, University of Glasgow, President of Young Minds

Marlene Wardle, Head Teacher, London Inner City Primary School

John Werry, Emeritus Professor of Psychiatry, University of Auckland, 19 Edenvale Crescent, Mount Eden, Auckland 3, New Zealand

S. N. Wolkind, Formerly Consultant Child Psychiatrist, Department of Children and Adolescents, Bethlem Royal and Maudsley Hospital, Denmark Hill, London SE5 8AZ

Anne Worrall, Senior Lecturer in Child and Adolescent Psychiatry, Division of Psychiatry and Behavioural Sciences in Relation to Medicine, University of Leeds, 12a Clarendon Road, Leeds

Susan Elinor Wright, Senior Lecturer in Education, Department of Teaching Studies, University of North London, 166–220 Holloway Road, London N7 8DY

Foreword

FREDERICK STONE

It was an inspired thought to produce this commemorative volume of *Unwillingly to School* as a tribute to Jack Kahn. To those who knew him, the mention of his name at once conjures up an unmistakable picture – the corpulent, rather short figure, the beaming smile, the alert glance, the Yorkshire accent, more like one's idea of the beloved family doctor of yesteryear, which indeed he once was, than what he became, and how most of us knew him, the intuitive, sensitive innovator, one of the pioneers of British community psychiatry.

Like the majority of first or second generation specialists in the psychiatry of childhood, those who embarked on such a career in the twenties and thirties, Jack was essentially self-taught, though blessed with an innate aptitude for child and family guidance work as it was then known. To some extent by chance (a topic which fascinated him) his 16 years in general practice proved to be an excellent apprenticeship.

Jack grew up in Huddersfield in a traditional Jewish family and was active in community affairs. There was an early brief phase as a pharmacist's assistant from which he rebelled to enter Leeds medical school, where he graduated with Honours in 1928. For relaxation the busy family doctor found time to read widely, to become a playgoer, and quite often to appear in print as book reviewer or drama critic. We should not be surprised, therefore, to find numerous, highly apposite, literary and dramatic references in his professional writings.

The year 1948 was an eventful one for Jack Kahn. After general psychiatric training and obtaining the MD and DPM, he was appointed psychiatrist-in-charge of the Huddersfield Child-Guidance Clinic, and he and his wife Florence moved to Leeds where he obtained a part-time lectureship in the University Department of Psychiatry and also ran sessions at the Harrogate Child-Guidance Clinic. Rapidly his services began to be sought as adviser to the education authority, consultant to approved schools, and to the Ministry of Pensions. He became involved in the work of the National Association for Mental Health.

In retrospect all of this activity can rightly be viewed as preparation for the most significant part of his career when in 1960 he moved to London to take up the Medical Directorship of the Newham Child-Guidance Service. This post gave him a unique opportunity to develop in practice what were then very new ideas about mental-health services for families, namely services based in the community, provided by a multidisciplinary team whose psychotherapeutic skills included consultation to medical, education and social agencies serving children and parents. Interestingly it was only then that the name of Jack Kahn began to be known as the author of numerous articles and a succession of books, all of them enriched by the distillation of clinical experience, and psychodynamic insights from personal experience, biblical studies, general literature and drama.

Jack was a superb communicator, whether as lecturer, group-leader, or impresario organising highly original training events. No doubt he was equally impressive in court as an expert witness in custody disputes and child-abuse allegations for which he was much in demand well into his retirement years. His professional writing bears the hallmarks more of the essayist and philosopher than of the scientist, an engaging contrast for the reader who enjoys imaginative flair and literary allusion. While this may convey the impression of a 'Renaissance man', gifted but anachronistic, there is a paradox about Jack, for his concerns have major relevance for our times – the significance of human relationships for personality development, the broad potential of the school environment, the meaning of team-work between disciplines, the provision of community-based mental-health services for all age groups.

The range of his publications is indicated by a few selected titles: *Beyond the Determinacy Principle*; *Do not Interpretations Belong to God?*; *Recollected Grief*; *Human Growth and the Development of Personality*; *Job's Illness*; *The Cry for Help* (with E. Earle); *The Group Process and Family Therapy* (with S. Thompson).

In this volume we commemorate a scholar, a wise clinician and a lovable colleague.

Introduction

IAN BERG and JEAN NURSTEN

Although considerable changes have been made in this fourth edition of *Unwillingly to School*, it is intended that enough remains of the spirit which characterised previous editions to maintain a degree of continuity with the original text. The first and second editions by Jack Kahn and Jean Nursten, and the later third edition with Howard Carroll, were concerned with school refusal, rather than school attendance problems more generally and these embraced, and indeed advocated, a multidisciplinary method of working which at that time was based on the traditional child guidance clinic and staffed by a close-knit group of psychiatrist, social worker and psychologist, along with other professional workers concerned with children as well. In a very real sense this latest multi-authored version of the book is by way of a Festschrift for Jack Kahn who contributed so much to the speciality of child and adolescent psychiatry in his lifetime, particularly in the field of school attendance problems. It was considered important in the interests of continuity to include some of his writings from previous editions since these seem as valid and as fresh today as they ever were. Only slight modifications have been made to these to fit in with present-day terminology. The chapters by his co-authors of the third edition also keep the spirit of the previous editions alive. A welcome professional link is maintained through the Foreword by Professor Fred Stone, President of Young Minds, representing both a person Jack Kahn respected and an organisation with which he was clearly identified from its inception. A family feeling is engendered too by the happy circumstances that both Jack Kahn's daughters, Dilys Daws and Susan Wright, were well fitted to contribute chapters on this occasion.

This new edition aims to provide a broad perspective on a number of aspects of problems of school attendance. Symptoms of physical illness remain the principal acceptable reason for not going to school. Children with such symptoms may take more time off school than the particular condition would normally justify. Account needs to be taken, too, that physical symptoms may occur as manifestations of psychiatric disorders.

Up-to-date information on some important epidemiological studies has also been included since these studies provide a wider view than a sharply focused clinical perspective. Such studies help to identify possible causative factors. The book is privileged to have a report on several studies carried out in the USA, and also to have recent information from two British surveys: the Cambridge Study of Delinquent Development and the National Child Development Study. A contribution comes from New Zealand on diagnosis, and the most recent follow-up of Swedish children treated for school refusal many years ago gives invaluable information on long-term outcome.

School factors feature in two chapters. In an ideal world school should be so rewarding that no child would ever consider avoiding it. But it is a world that holds different values. Current law relating to school attendance is considered with regard to the UK, as changes in the law have occurred that need to be brought forward and the implications discussed. Child and adolescent psychiatry is increasingly attempting to systematise the assessment of disturbed young people, so place is given to the contribution on classification of disorders as it affects school refusal. Likewise, with greater independence of the different disciplines working with children and families, it is relevant to include a chapter that sets out what child and adolescent psychiatry can contribute to the understanding of the problem.

A general point to make is that it appears that the legal framework surrounding compulsory school attendance has changed in the direction of less coercion, thereby apparently reflecting less concern on the part of society that children should be made to go to school. Thus in 1993 in the USA, the Supreme Court of the State of Wisconsin ruled that compelling children to attend school is unconstitutional! A number of states have introduced legislation to permit children to be educated at home in the last decade and many others permit this as a form of private education. In stark contrast, only about 15 000 children were kept out of school and educated at home in the early 1980s in the USA but by 1992 the figure had grown to more than one-third of a million (*The Economist*, 11 June 1994). Change has occurred, too, in Britain since the Children and Young Person's Act of 1989 and later provisions came into force, where it is no longer possible for juvenile courts to remove children from home because they fail to attend school satisfactorily, although a recent judgement may change this to some extent. Parents may still be prosecuted, but there are often long delays before they are taken to magistrates courts for not ensuring that their children receive adequate education. Although a maximum fine of £1000 can be imposed, courts seem to give this problem little importance, often failing to fine at all, or fining parents only about £10 (*Daily Telegraph*, 3 July 1994).

Turning to the nature of each chapter in turn, Ian Robertson outlines the present legal framework surrounding school attendance in England and Wales at a time when new legislation is being implemented and the prolonged process of testing it by judicial appeal is just beginning. This followed the Appeal Court decision of Lord Denning in 1977 which clarified the law at a time when there was a simple legal equation: unjustified absence from school equals sufficient grounds for a child to be removed from home under a care order. Already there are some suggestions, as a result of a recent judicial decision, that there may be something of a return to the status quo despite the Children and Young Person's Act 1989 prohibiting children being taken to court under care proceedings. On the face of it the new Education Supervision Order does little more than put an official stamp on what the Education Welfare Service already does, or tries to do despite increasingly limited resources! The role of the education welfare officer is increasingly seen as that of a family counsellor rather than the strong arm of the law in relation to school attendance. School attendance is easy to measure, so the effectiveness of the legal framework surrounding it will no doubt be assessed on levels of absence in the future.

Anne Worrall provides a review of illness and school attendance at a time when there is much recent published research on the subject. Children in both Britain and the USA stay off school only a few days a year on average and this amount of absence is not greatly increased by chronic illness. This contribution will enable those such as family doctors faced with a child absent from school for long periods, with relatively minor physical symptoms, to judge the implications of the amount of time away from school. Factors other than the particular medical condition, such as sex of the child, parental attitudes and aspects of treatment, appear to be of particular significance in determining the amount of time spent out of school.

Lorraine Klerman and Betty Glasscock include illness among their wide-ranging survey of factors, such as sex, race, socio-economic status, provision of services and school, in relation to absence from school. They provide some interesting detail on ways in which absence from school is dealt with in the USA. These may have application elsewhere.

Truancy is beginning to be seen as a complex interaction between child, family, school and community. In the consideration of school factors, David Reynolds further suggests that contributions from this source may not be as great as supposed, nor may they be necessarily related to other features of schools, such as poor achievement or the attitude of pupils. He examines new approaches in relation to school effectiveness research and effective educational systems in other countries, as well as in different industries, particularly where the rigorous standards applied could become useful models for school effectiveness.

Susan Wright and Marlene Wardle confine their chapter to one particular primary school and give brief examples to illustrate the problems faced by teachers when an attempt to keep children with special needs within normal school is the order of the day. Illustrations are given of the way in which teachers try to cope and consideration is given to what outside agencies can do to help. A personal view of compulsory education is given.

Ian Berg gives a brief historical account of compulsory education in Britain. He then summarises a series of randomly controlled trials of children taken to juvenile court under the legal system operating in Britain in the 1970s and 1980s. These trials showed that when there is a predictable set of sanctions in operation, with the possibility of a child being removed from home if all else fails, summonses to attend court are helpful in restoring more normal school attendance. Such a summons to court may possibly reduce criminal offending as well. In addition, a survey of substantially poor attenders in normal high schools showed that only some had features of either truancy or school refusal. Among those categorised as truants only a proportion had a conduct disorder as described by the third edition of the *Diagnostic and Statistical Manual of Mental Disorders*, revised (DSM–III–R), and among those classified as school refusers only a proportion had a DSM–III–R anxiety disorder. It was significant that school refusers had not been referred for treatment. Finally, an outline is given of the recent large-scale survey of truancy in Britain.

The outcome of children who truant in later life is presented by Ken Fogelman using the findings of the National Child Development Study in Britain. Irrespective of social and educational factors, and after taking into consideration the increased absence from school that occurs towards the end of the compulsory period of schooling, truancy still acts as a predictor of adult mental distress, irresponsible adult relationships, poor employment prospects and excessive smoking. Girls are particularly prone to these outcomes. The nature of the study, employing a longitudinal national cohort, gives grounds for considering that some degree of causality underlies these relationships. The findings may be readily drawn upon due to the elegant presentation, especially through the use of relative odds showing the magnitude of the effects.

Fresh results in the long-term outcomes of boys, who comprised the sample in the Cambridge Study in Delinquent Development, are put forward by David Farrington. A unique combination of features is gleaned from several sources and a variety of theoretical constructs offered. Material from early work is taken further and truancy, as a predictor of adult dysfunction, is shown as a significant factor up to 32 years of age. Important indications emerge which suggest that although in small proportion, emotional disturbance as well as conduct disorder may play a part in the problems of truants. Following such a distinction, different pathways to truancy and different outcomes are further areas for study.

Lee Robins and Judith Robertson report on the Epidemiologic Catchment Area (ECA) study in the USA, which examined the adult recall of truancy. Half of the incidents of truancy were before the age of 14 years. It was found that adult personality disorder, and drug and alcohol abuse, were linked to previously reported truancy, in men and women. To a lesser extent depression, phobias, obsessive–compulsive disorder and schizophrenia were also linked to truancy. This was more likely to be the case in men when a personality disorder or substance abuse coexisted but it was less likely in women under those circumstances. They note that their findings relate to incidence of disorders not prevalence, and make it a point of principle that causes of a disorder should be distinguished from factors that maintain disorders.

The chapter by Margaret Murphy and Stephen Wolkind provides a comprehensive account of what the field of child and adolescent psychiatry can offer in the assessment and management of school attendance problems. The procedures used are particularly firmly based on research findings in the case of school refusal, but techniques are available also which aim to evaluate and modify inappropriate behaviours of children who truant. Where there is an emotional disorder, attention deficit disorder, bizarre behaviour, eating disorder, substance abuse or physical symptoms, then psychiatric referral is particularly appropriate. Mental illness affecting a parent is also an indication for the involvement of a psychiatrist.

Following this chapter there is a substantial contribution from the third edition, which takes up the clinical theme by presenting cases, offering a frame of reference and advocating a multidisciplinary approach to school refusal. A commentary is given before chapter 11.

John Werry's chapter on systems of categorising psychiatric disorders clarifies the recent methods of classification. Although school refusal is a criterion in the diagnosis of separation anxiety disorder and truancy a criterion of conduct disorder, many other disorders are associated with school attendance problems. He deals with the complex situation when two or more disorders are found to coexist.

A contribution from another discipline is presented by Howard Carroll, who demonstrates the changing role of the educational psychologist at a time when many demands are being made on this profession in the assessment of children with special educational needs. A critical account is given of the sequential strategy following the referral of a pupil absent from school. Different approaches are discussed and alternative practices mentioned.

The next three chapters cover treatment, drawing upon family therapy, cognitive therapy and psychotherapy. Judith Lask describes family therapy based on systems theory. Although this approach still awaits objective evidence for its effectiveness in school attendance problems, family therapy is seen as a valued approach that is often drawn upon. The description of it, illustrated by a case, will be useful to those who employ this form of treatment and use it as a template for other approaches.

Jean Nursten records meeting with both parents of a school-refusing adolescent where the principles of cognitive therapy were employed. This is illustrated by the detailed description of the case. The social worker's approach was carried out in the context of a multidisciplinary team and involved the anxious and depressed parents. The case was drawn upon in the third edition but here it is a fresh presentation where cognitive therapy is seen as an appropriate mode of help as each parent had, among other attributes, negative aspects of the situation of their daughter's school refusal.

A third chapter concerned with psychotherapy, by Judith Edwards and Dilys Daws, focuses on separation anxiety in children and its treatment by child psychotherapy. The view is taken that 'insecure' attachment of the child is a key factor. Various illustrative cases are vividly outlined of play, in a protected setting, enabling the expression of feelings and emotion for the child. Fathers' roles where present or absent are considered.

At the end of the book the chapter by Natalia Flakierska-Praquin, Marianne Lindström and Christopher Gillberg describes the longest follow-up study of children with school refusal that has been reported. Although the sample of children studied was limited to 7–12 year olds who had associated separation anxiety disorder, the findings after two to three decades were reassuring in that any difficulties in previous school refusers compared to controls were of only moderate severity. Nevertheless the greater use of psychiatric services and less independent life-styles of these patients indicated more evidence of psychiatric disturbance and more limited social adaptation in adult life than would otherwise be expected.

Finally we would like to recall the value that Jack Kahn placed on the multidisciplinary approach. Changes have taken place that often preclude the mutlidisciplinary team from working together under one roof. Sometimes this is due to organisational re-structuring, or the development of different disciplines, or because of lack of resources. However, the present edition of *Unwillingly to School* has been written, through collective collaboration, by a team from different countries drawn from the different disciplines that underpin child and adolescent psychiatry, educational psychology, psychotherapy, social work, family therapy, teaching, law, criminology and child health. It is intended that these contributions, relating to both truancy, school refusal and varieties of other school attendance problems, will further the hope held by Jack Kahn that, although it is not necessarily expected that each profession will accept every account as entirely representing their own form, such an enterprise acts as a way in which different points of view may be expresed.

Collaboration gives support to the idea that multidisciplinary points of view continue to address the issues of absence from school.

1 Legal aspects

IAN ROBERTSON

The law plays a major part in both seeking to enforce attendance at school and dealing with non-attendance. It does this by means of criminal sanctions and state intervention under the guise of child welfare/protection, but it is important to recognise and differentiate between the two aspects of legal intervention since different principles of law and indeed philosophy apply to the two spheres.

Criminal law

The criminal law is invoked by the state in broad terms to punish wrongs caused to the fabric of the state as a whole. The criminal law is the means by which the state protects its own cohesiveness by punishing those who step out of line. In the educational context prosecutions are brought by the local education authority and hearings take place in the Magistrates Court. The Magistrates Court is the lay arm of the judiciary and the magistrates have no qualifications in law but are chosen by the Lord Chancellor to reflect society as a whole. Many commentators would say that magistrates are too middle-aged, middle class and white to actually reflect society properly. Within criminal proceedings strict rules of evidence apply and it is for the prosecution to prove guilt beyond all reasonable doubt. If guilt is found then the court can levy criminal sanction.

Care or other proceedings

Proceedings brought by the state in its protection/child welfare role are civil in their nature and such proceedings are also brought initially in the Magistrates Court. They may be transferred to be heard by professional judiciary in the County Court or in serious cases the High Court. In all such proceedings the

1

court is governed by the principle set out in Section 1 (a) of the Children Act 1989 which states:

> "when a Court determines any question with respect to −
>
> a) the upbringing of a child; or
> b) the administration of a child's property or the application of any income arising from it, the child's welfare shall be the Courts paramount consideration."

A similar provision in Section 1 of the Guardianship of Minors Act 1971 was considered by Lord McDermot in the case of *J* v. *C* ([1979] 1 All E R 788) where he stated:

> "reading those words in their ordinary significance relating to the various classes of proceedings which the section has already mentioned, it seems to me that they must mean more than the child's welfare is to be treated as the top item in a list of items relevant to the matter in question. I think they connote a process whereby, when all the relevant facts, relationships, claims and wishes of parents, risks, choices and other circumstances are taken into account and weighed, the course to be followed will be that which is in the interests of the child's welfare as that term was now to be understood . . ."

The strict rules of evidence do not apply in civil proceedings and indeed in care and other proceedings the rule against the admission of hearsay evidence is specifically waived. The court also in deciding upon whether any statutory conditions are satisfied has to be satisfied on the 'balance of probability', as opposed to being beyond reasonable doubt in the criminal sphere.

Responsibilities of parents

There is a general duty laid down by Section 36 of the Education Act 1944 to do the following:

> "it shall be the duty of the parent of every child of compulsory school age to cause him to receive sufficient full time education suitable to his age, ability and aptitude and any special education needs he may have, either by regular attendance at school or otherwise."

The parent is defined for the purpose of this section by Section 114 (1D) of the Education Act 1944 as follows:

"includes any person –

a) who is not a parent of his but who has parental responsibility for him, or
b) who has care of him . . ."

This will include the mother and father of a child who are married to each other, the mother of a child who is not married to the father, the father of a child who is not married to the mother but has acquired parental responsibility by virtue of a court order or an agreement signed with the mother, and any other person who has acquired parental responsibility by virtue of a Residence Order under Section 8 of the Children Act or has been appointed guardian under Section 5 of the Children Act or had an adoption under the Adoption Act 1976. Also falling within this definition is the local authority to whom the child is subject when under a Care Order by virtue of Section 33 of the Children Act 1989. The term "who has care of him" is not defined by the Act but would include for example the father of a child who is not married to the mother but who is looking after the child, a step-parent who is looking after a child, or indeed siblings or other relatives with whom the child is living. The general guiding principle should be whether the child is subject to the guidance and protection of such a person (see Section 70 of the Children and Young Persons Act 1969 now repealed, which is helpful in providing guidance on this).

It is also important to define the phrase "compulsory school age": the expression means any age between 5 and 16 years. This is further clarified by Section 4(2) of the Education Miscellaneous Provisions Act 1948, which states that a child must attend school from the beginning of the term after they attain the age of 5 (which includes a term beginning on their fifth birthday); at the upper end of the scale compulsory school age is up to the end of the spring term if the child becomes 16 between 1 September and 31 January and the Friday before the last Monday in May if they become 16 between 1 February and 31 August (Section 9 Education Act 1962 as amended by the Education (School Leaving Dates) Act 1976). It can be seen therefore that the simple definition of being aged between 5 and 16 is insufficient and account therefore has to be taken of birth dates in determining when a child is able to leave school.

Parental responsibility

The Children Act 1989 introduced a new concept into English law, namely that of parental responsibility. This has replaced the old concept of custody, care and control, and changes the emphasis of rights over children to duties and responsibilities towards children. Parental responsibility rests with those people enumerated above. Parental responsibility is defined by Section 3(1) meaning:

"all the rights, duties, powers, responsibilities and authority which by law a parent of a child has in relation to the child and his property."

This helpful definition has not yet been expanded by case law but the old definition of parental rights and duties tells of the duty to educate. Education therefore is clearly a central feature of parental responsibility and will in due course be the subject matter of applications for Prohibited Steps and Specific Issue Orders under Section 8 of the Children Act.

Duty to educate

There are two means by which the parents can comply with their duty to educate a child, either by ensuring regular attendance at a school suitable to age, ability and aptitude and any special educational needs, or otherwise. As far as the otherwise is concerned, clearly this would be by means of home tutor or education by the parents themselves. Indeed one of the pressure groups supporting parents who educate at home is called 'education otherwise'. In order to satisfy Section 36 of the Education Act in those circumstances, the parent or responsible person would have to satisfy the education authority that the education which is being provided is indeed suitable. Failure to do so could lead the authority to make use of School Attendance Orders, or bring criminal proceedings. Given the introduction of the National Curriculum it may become increasingly difficult for parents and responsible persons to show that the education which they are providing is suitable, within the meaning of the section. It will be interesting to see whether prosecutions are built around failure to comply with the National Curriculum.

The vast majority of parents of course ensure compliance with Section 36 by registering their children at a school either in the public or private sector. Within the private sector such schools have to be registered with the Department of Education. Within the public sector, in broad terms, schools are either provided by the local education authority or have grant-maintained status and fall within the province of the Department of Education. Innumerable statutory provisions apply to the duties of the local authority in the provision of schools but in broad terms they should be of such diverse character as to meet the needs of the community as a whole, be sufficient in numbers as to provide efficient education and to be available free of charge to all who need them. Within those very broad perimeters it is up to the politicians, be they in central or local government, to determine the nature of the education system in operation in the public sector. The fact that some parents have an implacable opposition to a certain form of education does not give them lawful excuse not to send their child to that sort of school (see *Re: DJMS* (1977) 3 All ER 582 for example).

School Attendance Orders

Where the local authority is not satisfied that parents are providing education in accordance with Section 36 and the child in question is not registered with the school, it may serve upon those parents a notice requiring them to satisfy the authority that the child is indeed receiving the appropriate education. The parents in that situation have 14 days in which to satisfy the local education authority that the child is receiving appropriate education. If not satisfied the authority must serve a written notice on the parents of its intention to serve a School Attendance Order, specifying the school it intends to name in the order or, if it thinks fit, one or more schools regarded as suitable alternatives. The notice must state that if one or more alternative schools are offered and the parents select one before the expiration of 14 days then that school is named in the order. Also, if the parents apply and obtain a place at a school maintained by another local education authority or at a school where the local education authority agrees to provide education for the child, that school will be named in the order. Once that notice has been served and 14 days have expired the local authority must, if it is their view that it is expedient that the child should attend the school, name that school in a School Attendance Order. Such a School Attendance Order remains in force as long as a child is of compulsory school age unless revoked or amended by the authority. Failure to comply with the order renders the parent liable to prosecution.

Prosecutions for non-attendance at school

Non-compliance with School Attendance Order

As can be seen above, where a School Attendance Order has been served upon a parent they have a duty to ensure that the child becomes a registered pupil at that school. Section 37 (5) of the Education Act 1944 states:

> "if any person upon whom a school attendance order is served fails to comply with the requirements of the Order, he shall be guilty of an offence against this section unless he proves he is causing the child to receive sufficient full time education suitable to his age, ability and aptitude and to any special educational needs he may have otherwise than at school."

It should be noted that the defence outlined above is that efficient full-time education is being provided otherwise than at school. It is not a defence to show that the child is being educated at a school not named in the order. It should also be noted that, following the case of *Enfield London Borough Council* v. *F* [1987] 2 FLR 126) where a School Attendance Order had been served upon parents that had been prosecuted for failure to comply with it, the local education authority had no power to bring a second prosecution for continued failure to comply with the original order. The local authority immediately had to serve a second School Attendance Order complying with the provisions of Section 37 in order to bring a second prosecution. The case also stated that where a parent had complied with an order and registered a pupil at the school and then caused him or her to be removed and deregistered, in no matter how short a time, there was no power to prosecute under a School Attendance Order nor was there power to prosecute under Section 39 (see below) as the child was no longer a registered pupil. This lacuna in the law is still apparent.

Prosecution for non-attendance at school of a registered pupil

As indicated above the vast majority of pupils of compulsory school age in this country are registered pupils at a school. Under Section 36 it is the duty of the parent to ensure attendance at such a school and failure to comply with that duty renders them liable to prosecution under Section 39 of the Education Act 1944. The broad offence is as follows:

> "if any child of compulsory school age who is a registered pupil at a school fails to attend regularly there at, the parent of the child should be guilty of an offence against this section."

This section provides three statutory defences to the main defence:

(a) They were prevented from attending by reason of sickness or any unavoidable cause.
(b) They did not attend on a day exclusively set apart for religious observance by the religious body to which their parents belong.
(c) The parent proves that the school at which the child is a registered pupil is not within walking distance of the child's home and that no suitable arrangements have been made by the local education authority either for transport to and from school or boarding accommodation at or near the school or for enabling the child to become a registered pupil at a school nearer their home.

It is also a defence to show that there was leave of absence, and further that the parent is engaged in any trade or business of such a nature as to require travel from place to place and that the child has attended the school at which he or she was a registered pupil at least 200 times during the period of 12 months ending on the date on which the proceedings were instituted.

The local education authority therefore have to show firstly a failure to attend regularly. In *Hinchley* v *Rankin* ([1961] 1 All ER 692) it was held that even though the child had attended school his failure to arrive before the closing of the register amounted to a failure to attend regularly. Regular attendance means regular attendance at the times provided by the local authority. Additionally, where the pupil is excluded from school through breach of school rules, such as having unacceptable hair-styles, wearing earrings and make-up, etc., they are deemed to be not attending school regularly irrespective of the fact they have been excluded by the school. Thus it is no defence to argue that the child did attend at school as they were excluded by the school because their hair was deemed to be unacceptable. The responsibility lies therefore upon the parent to ensure attendance at school is in compliance with the school rules and regulations.

As far as statutory defences are concerned, it will be for the parents to raise the defence. Thus if they are arguing that the child was absent because of sickness it is for them to show that the sickness occurred and was of such a nature it rendered the child unfit for education. The best means for doing this is by using supporting medical evidence.

If a defence of unavoidable cause is raised, then the cause must be the cause of the child and not of the parent. Thus in the case of *Jenkins* v. *Howells* (1949 1 942) the fact that the mother was ill was not deemed to be sufficient justification for the child not attending school. Unavoidable cause would cover such situations as where the only means of transportation to school, such as parental car in a rural area, broke down or the child's clothings and effects were destroyed in a house fire rendering them unable to attend school on that date.

It is interesting to speculate with the proliferation of religious 'sects' to what extent the court will take into account religious festivals outside the norm of mainstream religions. The defence appears broad as set out and on the face of it could be used to justify significant non-attendance where the 'sect' deemed that holy days existed more frequently than the norm.

The third statutory defence set out in the Act is that the school is not within walking distance. Under Section 39(5) walking distance is defined to be 2 miles in relation to a child who has not attained the age of 8 years and in the case of any other child 3 miles, measured by the nearest available route. The nearest available route is defined in the case of *Essex County Council* v. *Roger* ([1986] 3 All ER 321) as being a route along which a child accompanied as necessary can walk with reasonable safety to school. The House of Lords in judgement in this case indicated that where the parent who had normally accompanied a child was unable to do so for reasons such as illness, a defence to a charge of non-attendance at school may arise under the heading of 'unavoidable cause'. However, the House of Lords did not go as far as many would have liked them to in stating that the route must be safe for an unaccompanied child. Thus it is still open to the authority to say that a route is less than 3 miles within a definition of the Act even though the route to school involves walking along a very dangerous main road or through dark and secluded woods populated by child molesters.

It should be noted that an offence created by Section 39 is a 'absolute' offence. In the normal situation one has to show that the defendant has a guilty mind or *mens rea*; under these provisions it is no defence for a parent to argue that they knew nothing of the child's absence.

As can be seen above there is a further defence where one can show that absence is with the leave of the school. Leave can only be given by a person authorised to give such leave, by the governors or propriety of an independent school: this will almost certainly include the head teacher. Pupils can be absent with such leave during term time for the purpose of going on an annual holiday with their parents for a maximum of 2 weeks (Education (Schools and Further Education) Regulations 1981).

Provisions upon conviction

Once a person has been convicted of an offence under either Section 37 or Section 39 they shall be liable to a fine not exceeding level 3 on the standard scale. This stands at present at £1000. Prosecutions can only be brought by the local education authority and before doing so it should consider whether to bring proceedings under the Children Act to apply for an Education Supervision Order. Additionally upon conviction under Section 37 or upon hearing of a case under Section 39 the court can direct the local authority to institute proceedings for an Education Supervision Order unless the authority, having consulted with social services, decides that the child's welfare will be satisfactorily safeguarded without such an application being made. If they make such a decision they must inform the court of their reasons for doing so within 8 weeks of the direction.

Child protection/welfare provisions

As can be seen, the preceding provisions have been aimed at ensuring the attendance of children at school by applying sanctions to their parents. The provisions do not tackle the fundamental issue of what to do where a child simply will not attend school and there is nothing the parent can do to enforce such attendance. It is clear that the child cannot be prosecuted in those circumstances and the criminal courts therefore have no role to play. There are those of course who advocate that children should be punished for not attending school but it is submitted that such an approach rather misses the point. As things stand at present the authorities, be they the local education authority or social services, have the ability to make use of the welfare provisions of the civil law as set out in the Children Act 1989.

Under the 1969 Children and Young Persons Act one of the grounds for care proceedings was the failure of the child to receive sufficient full-time education suitable to his age, ability and aptitude. Lord Denning in the case of *Re: DJMS* said that this in itself was sufficient to satisfy the secondary ground of care proceedings, namely that the child was in need of care and control. As a result of the existence of such grounds and his decision, there were constant battles between the education and social services departments as to whether care proceedings should be initiated in respect of non-attendance at school. These arguments were heightened by the ability of the education department to bring proceedings in their own right on the education ground, although responsibility for a child under a Care Order made under this provision rested with the social services department. Many social workers took the view that their limited resources were better used dealing with social problems rather than effectively acting as education welfare officers in an attempt to ensure school attendance. In this somewhat confrontational situation, social services departments often failed to look behind the non-attendance at the environmental circumstances that had caused it.

In the review of the Children Act it was recognised that a separate provision should be created to deal specifically with the problems of children not attending school. Accordingly a new order called an Education Supervision Order was created by Section 36 of the Act. Such an order can only be applied for by a local education authority and can only be made if the court is satisfied that the child concerned is of compulsory school age and is not being properly educated. This means that the child is not receiving efficient full-time education suitable to age, ability and aptitude and any special educational needs he or she may have; in other words a repetition of the standard duty under Section 36 of the Education Act 1944. Before making the application the local education authority should consult with the social services department. The effect of such an order is set out in Schedule 3 Part 3 of the Act. Where such an order is in force it will be the duty of the supervisor to advise, assist and befriend and give directions to the supervised child and parents in such a way as will in the opinion of the supervisor secure that the child is properly educated. Where any such directions given to a child or parents have not been complied with, it shall be the duty of the supervisor to consider what further steps to take in the exercise of the powers under the Act. In making such directions the supervisor shall as far as practicable ascertain the wishes and feelings of the child and parents and to have appropriate regard to those. The making of an Education Supervision Order revokes any School Attendance Order previously made. An Education Supervision Order shall last for 1 year although it can be extended on more than one occasion for periods of up to 3 years at a time. It shall then cease to have effect when the child ceases to be of compulsory school age or if a Care Order is made in respect of the child.

An Education Supervision Order carries with it criminal sanctions. Thus if the parents of a child in respect of whom an Education Supervision Order is in force persistently fail to comply with a direction given under the order they shall be guilty of an offence. Unless they can prove they took all reasonable steps to ensure directions are complied with or they can show that the direction is unreasonable if convicted of such an offence, the person should be liable to a fine not exceeding £1000. Where a child persistently fails to comply with directions then the social services department shall be notified. Where such a notification is received they shall investigate the circumstances of the child. There is no duty upon the social services department in those circumstances to initiate care proceedings and no criminal sanctions apply to the child. It can be seen therefore that the purpose behind the Education Supervision Order is to provide a framework within which the educational welfare services can work with the child and parents in an attempt to solve the problems of their non-attendance at school in a constructive and co-operative manner. It was felt that when the provisions were enacted that many of the conflicts which existed with social services would be eradicated because there would be much less pressure upon the social services department to bring care proceedings as the only alternative to Sections 37 and 39. Thus the education department had been provided at a stroke with a whole range of civil options to fulfil their functions. It was not envisaged by many commentators that the care and supervision provisions of the Children Act would be used in education cases because of the very specialist threshold criteria as set by Section 31 of the Children Act. It was felt that educational matters would therefore be dealt with quite separately. However those commentators spoke before the decision of Mr Justice Ewbank in the case of *Re: O* ((1992) 2 FLR 7). Before looking at *Re: O* it is necessary to spend some time looking at the child protection provisions of the Children Act. Under Section 31 of the Children Act, care proceedings can only be initiated by the social services authority or the NSPCC; it is not open for the police or the education department to bring care proceedings. In order to satisfy the court that a Care or Supervision Order (as distinguished from an Education Supervision Order) should be made, the local authority have to satisfy the court that:

(a) the child concerned is suffering or is likely to suffer significant harm;
(b) that harm or likelihood of harm is attributable to
   (i) the care given to the child or likely to be given to him/her if the order were not made, not being what it would be reasonable to expect a parent to give to him/her or
   (ii) the child being beyond parental control.

Having satisfied these two conditions (now commonly known as the threshold criteria), the court has to be satisfied that it is in the interest of the child that an order shall be made and further that there is a positive benefit to the child in making an order. The Children Act has within it a general principle that where orders are unnecessary no order should be made.

As can be seen, the wording of Section 31 allows for state intervention in the child protection sphere in limited circumstances, those circumstances being where harm can be shown to have occurred or is likely to occur due to a lack of reasonable parenting or failure of such parenting due to the fact that the child is beyond control. It was assumed that simple failure to attend school where prevailing social circumstances were reasonable and family life was present and supportive would not in itself constitute significant harm of a degree that would satisfy the threshold criteria. However, Mr Justice Ewbank in *Re: O* took a different view. That case involved a girl aged 15 years 4 months who for the previous 3 years had effectively failed to attend school at all. After numerous attempts at working with the child by the education welfare officer the decision was taken to initiate proceedings for a Care Order. Proceedings were initiated in the Magistrates Court and the magistrates found on the evidence that the child had suffered such an impairment of educational, social and intellectual development as to warrant a Care Order being made. The child appealed this order and her appeal was dismissed by Mr Justice Ewbank. He states the following in his judgement:

> "The first point made on behalf of M is that a Care Order under the Children Act 1989 is not really the appropriate way to deal with truancy from schools. Truancy was a specific ground for the Care Order under 1969 Act but is not a ground for a Care Order under the 1989 Act, whereas under S36 Education Supervision Orders have been introduced to deal with children who are not going to school. It is said on behalf of M that this is the approach that the Local Authority should have taken. The local education authority rather than the Social Services Department, should have brought an application under S36.
>
> It is said on behalf of M and her parents that the conclusions that her intellectual development and social development have suffered significant harm are unjustified. It is said that the conclusion is speculative and that, being at home it does not establish that she has suffered in her social and intellectual development. This, I have to say, seems to me to be a totally unrealistic approach to a case of truancy. In my view, it was entirely open to the Magistrates to come to the view, as they did, that M's intellectual and social development was suffering and was likely to suffer, and that the harm she was suffering from, was likely to suffer from, was significant.
>
> The second threshold condition is that the harm or the likelihood of harm, is attributable to the care given to the child not being what it would be reasonable to expect a parent to give him, or the child is beyond parental control. In my Judgement, where a child is suffering harm in not going to school and is living at home it will follow that either the child is beyond her parent's control or that they are not giving the child the care that it would be reasonable for the child to receive."

It is clear therefore that the decision of Lord Denning in *Re: DJMA* has been followed and applied under the regime of the Children Act. It will be interesting to see whether this will be tested in due course in the Court of Appeal.

Other provisions of the Children Act

Given the decision in *Re: O* it is clear that failure to attend school can amount to significant harm. It follows therefore that it is open to the social services department in consultation with the education department to make use of other provisions of the Children Act, in particular Child Assessment Orders under Section 43 of the Children Act. This provision enables the social services department to apply to the court for an order that the child be assessed by specified persons at specified times for a period of up to 7 days to ascertain whether there is a need to bring proceedings. The grounds for such an application are firstly that the applicant has reasonable cause to suspect that the child is suffering or likely to suffer significant harm, and secondly that such an assessment will ascertain whether or not this is the case, and further that it is likely that such an assessment is required to enable the applicant to determine whether or not the child is suffering or likely to suffer significant harm, and further that it is unlikely that such an assessment will be made or will be satisfactory in the absence of an order under this section. Such an order can include provision for the child remaining away from home for the period of assessment. Thus where a child is not attending school and the social services department in consultation with the education department are concerned about what is happening at home, particularly where they are not receiving cooperation from the parents, application could be made for a Child Assessment Order using the non-attendance at school as their primary ground for proceedings. It is possible also that this could form the basis of an application for an Emergency Protection Order under Section 44 of the Act, although it is submitted that there will be very few if any circumstances where non-attendance at school in itself will be sufficient to justify immediate removal from home under the statutory provisions.

Section 8 orders

As stated previously the Children Act 1989 makes provision for two sorts of orders, namely a Specific Issue Order and a Prohibited Steps Order which have relevance in terms of education provision. Such orders specify steps that should be taken by the person having parental responsibility or prohibit persons with such responsibility taking specified steps. Thus it is open to an estranged parent to apply for a Specific Issue Order determining where a child should be educated or alternatively applying for a Prohibited Steps Order setting out a prohibition on certain types of education. It is open to any person with the leave of the court to apply for such orders and there are already examples of the social services department seeking such leave and making application for orders under these provisions rather than instituting care proceedings under Section 31. The question therefore arises as to whether the local education authority may in due course contemplate applying for leave to make use of these orders as opposed to the provisions in the public law sphere outlined above.

Effect of Education Act 1993 upon Sections 37–40 of the Education Act 1944

The above sections of the 1944 Act are repealed by the Education Act 1993 Sections 192–203. As far as the School Attendance Orders are concerned these are covered by Sections 192–198. The procedures remain the same except that the period of 14 days is replaced by a period of 15 days beginning on the day upon which the notice is served. Interestingly, provisions that took up three sections under the 1944 Act now take up seven lengthy sections under the new Act. The provisions of Section 39 of the Children Act now appear at Section 199 of the 1993 Act. This does not alter the effect in any way.

Conclusion

The law relating to education is an ever-expanding field and the issue of attendance is just one small area of it. There is no doubt that this aspect of the enforcement will continue to attract the legislators' attention, particularly given the emphasis placed upon truancy by the current government. Whether this will include the extension of juvenile justice provisions into this area, we will have to wait and see.

2 Chronic disease and school non-attendance

ANNE WORRALL

This chapter looks at absence rates in children with chronic disease compared to their healthy peers, at absence in specific diagnostic groups, and at the reasons for absence. A specific cause of absence, school refusal in children with chronic disease, is reviewed.

Absence rates in children with chronic disease

It has been stated that physically ill children miss more school than do their healthy peers (Charlton *et al*, 1991; Eiser, 1990); However, the issue is not straightforward. The variability in severity and the course of certain conditions, such as asthma, makes comparison between children, and between studies, difficult.

Epidemiological studies of school non-attendance in children with chronic disease

Several studies have shown high rates of non-attendance in groups of children with different chronic diseases. Four national surveys of children in the USA between 1959 and 1981, using absence rates estimated from parental reports, showed that children with chronic conditions missed significantly more days at school and had longer periods of absence than did their healthy peers (Weitzman, 1986). In Britain, Rutter *et al* (1970) also reported that children with chronic disease missed significantly more days at school than did healthy children. Weitzman *et al* (1986) suggested that children with certain chronic conditions, namely asthma, learning disability, arthritis, epilepsy and cerebral palsy, missed substantial periods of time, from 13 to 33 days in a school year.

Case-control studies of school non-attendance in children with specific chronic conditions

Cardiac disease

In a case-control study of children with either congenital or acquired cardiac disease, and their healthy peers, Fowler *et al* (1987) found that the cases and controls missed twice as many days at school as the national average but there was no significant difference in absence rates between the two groups.

Haemophilia

Studies of haemophiliac boys have produced conflicting findings. Lineberger (1981), reviewing four studies, found that between 23 and 72% of the boys had had prolonged periods of school absence. Kvist *et al* (1990) took a cross-sectional group of haemophiliac children and their healthy class-mates at two time points. In 1971–2, the haemophiliac children had significantly more school absences than did their healthy peers but this was not the case in 1987–8. The authors suggested that this could be due to the advances in treatment of the condition (prior to the risk of HIV infection through transfusion). However, Woolf *et al* (1989) found that despite an educational programme to help haemophiliac boys with specific learning problems and home-based treatment, they still missed an average of 18 days a year, three times the national average for children with chronic disease in general, and 4.5 times the national average for well children. It should be remembered that both studies necessarily had small samples, which may explain the conflict in findings.

Insulin-dependent diabetes mellitus

Orr *et al* (1984) found an excess of school absence, depression and school isolation in adolescent diabetics with poor glycaemic control compared with healthy peers.

Asthma

Non-attendance in children with asthma has been examined in several large-scale studies. Parcel *et al* (1979) examined school records and found that children with asthma had a significantly higher absence rate (8.4% school time) than did their healthy class-mates (5.9%). Anderson *et al* (1983) conducted a postal survey of 5100 parents of a cohort of 9 year olds and then interviewed a sample of 284 parents who had reported wheezing in their children over the previous year. Absence was reported in 58% of children, with 12% having missed at least 30 days in the school year. Hill *et al* (1989) surveyed parents of 4750 children aged 5–11 years. The 668 children who had asthma or a wheezing illness were absent for 7 days a year on average due to wheezing. In the following groups the proportions of absence were: 66% of asthmatic children, 46% of wheezy children on medication, 51% of wheezy children not taking medication and 73% of all the asthmatic and wheezy children.

Cancer

Charlton *et al* (1991) looked at absence in three groups: children with cancer, orthopaedic problems and other chronic diseases. School attendance rates were calculated after accounting for absence due to initial treatment. Children with cancer had a significantly higher proportion of time off school due to follow-up treatment than did children with chronic disease and orthopaedic problems. A study of 91 children with cancer in Italy found that teachers reported significantly poorer school attendance in the children with cancer compared with healthy controls (Mancini *et al*, 1989).

Summary

For most of the chronic conditions examined, school non-attendance was higher than in the healthy population, but there are exceptions. School absence has not been looked at in some conditions. There is a need for further research to integrate the conflicting findings and look further at the factors affecting absence rates.

Factors affecting absence rates

Several factors influence attendance rates: (a) the chronic condition itself; (b) the course and severity of the condition; (c) treatment procedures; and (d) psychosocial factors.

The chronic condition itself

Conditions that are life-threatening or require extensive and unpleasant treatment regimens are likely to result in a child having extensive periods of time off school (Mulhern *et al*, 1989). Cook *et al* (1985), using linear regression, found that the diagnostic category did not predict the number of school days missed by children with chronic conditions.

The course and severity of the condition

It is not clear whether the severity of a condition is associated with school absence rates. Studies provide conflicting results, and use different measures of severity, such as the frequency of clinic visits, the amount of time spent in hospital, unremitting symptoms and having a severe form of the disease.

Frequency of clinic visits

Assuming that children who visit clinics frequently have more severe disease, Fowler *et al* (1985) found that increased clinic visits (and by implication more severe disease) were associated with increased school absence in a group of children with a variety of chronic conditions.

Time in hospital

Increased absenteeism has been shown to be associated with increased time spent in hospital in children with cardiac disease (Fowler *et al*, 1987).

Unremitting symptoms

Continual symptoms such as chronic pain may lead to poor concentration in school, prevent children taking part in physical activities (Dworkin, 1989) and contribute to children being reluctant or unable to attend school. The degree of activity limitation also seems to increase absenteeism. In children with a variety of chronic conditions (Cook *et al*, 1985; Fowler *et al*, 1985), and specifically cardiac disease (Fowler *et al*, 1987), increased absenteeism was associated with severe limitation of physical activity rated in the clinic.

Severe form of illness

While some studies found no association between school non-attendance rates and severity of disease in children with a variety of chronic conditions (Stein & Jessop, 1984; Weitzman *et al*, 1986) and with haemophilia (Woolf *et al*, 1989), other studies showed that high absence rates were associated with a more severe form of juvenile rheumatoid arthritis and asthma (Anderson *et al*, 1983; Billings *et al*, 1987; Howland *et al*, 1988). This could be explained by the nature of the condition, or the way in which severity is measured. In some chronic conditions, children are unwell even between acute exacerbations. If severity is measured in terms of number of exacerbations, an association is unlikely to be found between absenteeism and severity, since children may be absent a great deal with minor ongoing problems but have few flare-ups of disease. It should also be remembered that school absence itself may contribute to poor social adjustment (Parcel *et al*, 1979), further exacerbating the condition. The final outcome of the condition was shown to predict the number of days absent from school in children with solid tumours (Cairns *et al*, 1982).

Treatment procedures

Length and nature of treatment programme

The length of many chemotherapy programmes for children's cancer may require extended periods of absence (Mulhern *et al*, 1989). In particular, central nervous system chemotherapy for solid tumours was more likely to lead to higher levels of absence (Cairns *et al*, 1982) perhaps because this treatment is often given over a year, so side-effects are prolonged over that period. The length and nature of a treatment programme will obviously affect return to school. Charlton *et al* (1991) looked at absence in three groups of children, with cancer, orthopaedic problems and other chronic diseases, and showed that a child was more likely to have more days off school not due to treatment if the treatment period was longer.

Drug syndromes

School refusal has been noted as a feature of a phobic-anxiety disorder, apparently induced by neuroleptics, specific to children with Tourette syndrome (Mikkelson *et al*, 1981; Linet, 1985).

Drug side-effects

Many of the problems children had on returning to school were related to drugs, e.g. increased appetite and Cushingoid appearance due to steroids; nausea, mouth ulcers and increased likelihood of infection due to cytotoxic drugs (Cairns *et al*, 1982; Larcombe *et al*, 1990). Anticonvulsants causing drowsiness may make a child more difficult to wake for school in the morning (Weitzman, 1984).

Psychosocial factors

Age, sex and racial origin

Charlton *et al* (1991) looked at absence in three groups of children: with cancer, orthopaedic problems and other chronic diseases. Regression analysis showed that a child was more likely to have more days off school not due to treatment if the child was a girl. This was supported by Cairns *et al* (1982) in children with solid tumours, but not by a study of children with a variety of chronic conditions (Weitzman *et al*, 1986). Cairns *et al* (1982) also found that racial origin did not predict the length of absence from school.

Parental health beliefs

Parcel *et al* (1979) showed that in asthmatic children absence rates were higher for those children whose mothers regarded their asthma as severe than for those whose mothers regarded it as mild. Charlton *et al* (1991) looked at absence in three groups of children: with cancer, orthopaedic problems and other chronic diseases. Regression analysis showed that a child was more likely to have more days off school not due to treatment if the child's mother had finished her education before the age of 18, suggesting that level of knowledge may be important. In children with cardiac disease (Fowler *et al*, 1987) increased absenteeism was associated with parental patterns of absenting the child from school for minor disorders, and a low belief in the child's ability to improve its health status. Mothers who absented their children from school for colds or headaches did not have high levels of sick leave themselves, suggesting that they responded differently to their own illness. It could be that these mothers regard their children as more vulnerable to minor disorders because of the chronic disease.

Parent and teacher anxiety and attitudes

The anxiety of a teacher about dealing with a chronically ill child in class and how the child's presence will affect other children in the class may add to the anxiety of the child and its parents. The anxieties of teachers and parents may lead them to encourage the child, overtly or covertly, to miss more school than is necessary (Weitzman, 1984). A vicious cycle may be set up, with the child feeling hopeless and having poor motivation to work, exacerbated by missing large areas of the curriculum, leading to less inclination to return to school. However, Dworkin (1989) suggests that excessive absenteeism contributes little to the underachievement of children with chronic disease, other factors such as altered expectations of teachers and poor psychosocial adjustment being more important.

School placement

If children are placed out of mainstream school or receive home or alternative tuition, they may receive education of an inferior quality in terms of curriculum breadth and social and personal development (Dworkin, 1989). Absence may be longer if the illness and treatment occur at the start of the child's schooling (Charlton *et al*, 1986). However, Parcel *et al* (1979) in asthmatic children found that school grade did not predict days missed at school.

Child's anxiety about missed curriculum

Charlton *et al* (1986) found that children with cancer worried about time missed from school, and especially about missing work, particularly mathematics.

Child's anxiety about physical/sexual development

Chronically ill children have the same kinds of worries about school and difficulties with friendships as do healthy children, but the worries and difficulties may be magnified. Concerns about physical appearance and sexual development will be intensified in a child whose growth is stunted and whose hair has fallen out due to chemotherapy. Teasing by peers about physical changes has been shown to be significantly important for children with cancer (Charlton *et al*, 1986).

Different range of social experiences

Social isolation may be made worse in a child whose social range of experiences includes prolonged hospital stays, contact with adult professionals and discussions about death and dying.

Loss of contact with peers

School refusal may result from the stress of re-integrating into school after a long absence due to treatment, for instance in leukaemia (Lansky *et al*, 1975).

Socio-economic group

Absence has been shown to be associated in asthmatic and wheezy children with absence of one or both natural parents from home, living in rented accommodation, more than three children in the house, not owning a car, maternal previous depression and mothers working in a 'white-collar' occupation (Anderson *et al*, 1983), findings not supported by Parcel *et al* (1979) who showed that children with asthma did not have significantly higher absence rates than their healthy class-mates, regardless of ethnic origin, school grade, sex or socio-economic group. Lower educational level of mothers was shown to predict the amount of school non-attendance in children with solid tumours (Cook *et al*, 1985). Children with cancer living in small towns or less than 100 000 people were absent from school significantly less than children living in large towns (Cairns *et al*, 1982).

Behavioural, emotional and learning difficulties

Weitzman *et al* (1986) found that children with chronic disorders who also had learning difficulties, or behavioural and family problems, were more likely to be absent from school than children with chronic disease without these additional problems.

Reasons for absence

Weitzman (1984) states that many chronically ill children miss much more school than can be attributed to the severity of their problems. In a study of 270 children with a variety of chronic conditions (Fowler *et al*, 1985), the most common reasons given by parents for time off school were minor illnesses, the chronic condition itself and hospital visits. The reporting of minor illnesses or physical symptoms unrelated to the chronic condition may represent the health beliefs of parents. They may regard their children as particularly vulnerable to acute infections (Weitzman, 1984) and therefore keep them away from school. Alternatively such symptoms may be part of unrecognised school refusal or depression. Hill *et al* (1989) found that the most common reasons given for absence were bronchitis, chest infections or cough, but it should be noted that parents were asked the reason for absence *due to wheezing* and therefore it is impossible to assess school non-attendance due to other than health reasons. Mancini *et al* (1989) asked the teachers of children with cancer about reluctance to attend school and found that although the ill children attended school less often than did their healthy counterparts, they were not reluctant to attend. The authors state that this suggested that the non-attendance was not due to school refusal.

School refusal in chronic disease

It is well known that physical symptoms are commonly presented by children who are refusing school, so-called masquerade syndrome (Waller & Eisenberg, 1980). It is less clear whether school refusal is a significant problem in children with chronic diseases. Lansky *et al* (1975) studied a group of 100 children with cancer and found that 11 met their criteria for school refusal, which were (a) refusal to attend school, (b) fear of separation and (c) somatic complaints. Since these are not standardised criteria, it is difficult to compare the prevalence with other groups. In addition the authors may have biased their findings by using their own criteria. A case report of school refusal in a 7-year-old girl with leukaemia describes the onset of illness during an overtly asymptomatic relapse and resolution of the problem when there was a bone marrow response to treatment (Futterman & Hoffman, 1970). The authors comment that of the 25 children with leukaemia in their sample, there was only one case of school refusal, although separation anxiety was common. However, Deasy-Spinetta (1981) did not find an excess of school refusal in leukaemic children. Skuse (1987) reports that school refusal occurs, if rarely, in hypopituitarism despite these children having particular difficulty with academic skills, poor self-concept, emotional immaturity and a lack of interest in school work.

School refusal was investigated in children with learning disabilities associated with infantile autism and other pervasive developmental disorders (Kurita, 1991). Overall, school refusal was found in 24% of the group, but was significantly more common in children with learning disabilities associated with autism or pervasive developmental disorder than mental handicap alone. It was suggested that obsessional tendencies and higher intellectual level needed to be present to allow the child to perceive stressful classroom situations and for the problem to develop.

School refusal secondary to chronic disease

School refusal has been reported as the presenting symptom of a fourth ventricle tumour (Blackman & Wheler, 1987) and associated with a mitral valve prolapse (Casat *et al*, 1987). It has also been described as being common in, and a presenting feature of, Tourette syndrome (Comings & Comings, 1987; Plapp, 1990).

Summary

It is misleading to make a blanket statement about school non-attendance in children with chronic disease. Some children with certain chronic conditions probably miss more school than do their healthy peers. This is particularly the case for those with severe disease, requiring prolonged periods of hospital treatment, and for children who find it difficult to readjust to school. Parental and teachers' expectations, attitudes and beliefs about illness are important factors in affecting readjustment. The special case of school refusal occurs in many disease groups but it is not clear whether chronically ill children are more prone to school refusal than are their healthy class-mates. Rarely, school refusal may mask a physical condition. There is a lack of work assessing the extent of absenteeism and the reasons for it in children with chronic disease.

Related studies

For several conditions, studies have looked at performance but not attendance but this does not give a comprehensive picture of children's difficulties in school (Johnson, 1980). Children with diabetes and renal and sickle cell disease have been shown to have poor school attainment, but it is not clear whether this is due to reduced attendance or other factors (Gath *et al*, 1980; Eiser, 1990). Adedoyin (1992) found that nearly 58% of his sample of adolescents with sickle cell disease were worried about the amount of time they had missed at school.

References

ADEDOYIN, M. A. (1992) Psychosocial effects of sickle cell disease among adolescents. *East African Medical Journal*, **69**, 370–372.

ANDERSON, R., BAILEY, P. A., COOPER, J. S., *et al* (1983) Morbidity and school absence caused by asthma and wheezing illness. *Archives of Disease in Childhood*, **58**, 777–784.

BILLINGS, A. G., MOOS, R. H., MILLER, J. J. III, *et al* (1987) Psychosocial adaptation in juvenile rheumatic disease: a controlled evaluation. *Health Psychology*, **6**, 343–359.

BLACKMAN, M. & WHELER, G. H. T. (1987) A case of mistaken identity: a fourth ventricular tumor presenting as school phobia in a 12 year old boy. *Canadian Journal of Psychiatry*, **32**, 584–587.

CAIRNS, N. U., KLOPOVICH, P., HEARNE, E., *et al* (1982) *Journal of School Health*, **52**, 152–155.

CASAT, C. D., ROSS, B. A., SCARDINA, R., *et al* (1987) Separation anxiety and mitral valve prolapse in a 12-year-old girl. *Journal of the American Academy of Child and Adolescent Psychiatry*, **26**, 444–446.

CHARLTON, A., PEARSON, D. & MORRIS-JONES, P. H. (1986) Children's return to school after treatment for solid tumours. *Social Science and Medicine*, **22**, 1337–1346.

——, LARCOMBE, I. J., MELLER, S. T., *et al* (1991) Absence from school related to cancer and other chronic conditions. *Archives of Disease in Childhood*, **66**, 1217–1222.

COMINGS, D. E. & COMINGS, B. G. (1987) A controlled study of Tourette syndrome I. Attention-deficit disorder, learning disorders and school problems. *American Journal of Human Genetics*, **41**, 701–741.

COOK, B. A., SCHALLER, K. & KRISCHER, J. P. (1985) School absence among children with chronic illness. *Journal of School Health*, **55**, 265–267.

DEASY-SPINETTA, P. (1981) The school and the child with cancer. In *Living with Childhood Cancer* (eds J. J. Spinetta & P. Spinetta). St Louis: Mosby.

DWORKIN, P. H. (1989) School failure. *Pediatrics in Review*, **10**, 301–312.

EISER, C. (1990) *Chronic Childhood Disease*. Cambridge: Cambridge University Press.

FOWLER, M. G., JOHNSON, M. P. & ATKINSON, S. S. (1985) School achievement and absence in children with chronic health conditions. *Journal of Pediatrics*, **106**, 683–687.

——, JOHNSON, M. P., WELSHEIMER, K. J., *et al* (1987) Factors related to school absence among children with cardiac conditions. *American Journal of Diseases of Children*, **141**, 1317–1320.

FUTTERMAN, E. H. & HOFFMAN, I. (1970) Transient school phobia in a leukemic child. *Journal of the American Academy of Child and Adolescent Psychiatry*, **9**, 477–494.

GATH, A. & BAUM, J. D. (1980) Emotional, behavioural and educational disorders in diabetic children. *Archives of Disease in Childhood*, **55**, 371–375.

HILL, R. A., STANDEN, P. J. & TATTERSFIELD, A. E. (1989) Asthma, wheezing, and school absence in primary schools. *Archives of Disease in Childhood*, **64**, 246–251.

HOWLAND, J., BAUCHNER, H. & ADAIR, R. (1988) The impact of pediatric asthma education on morbidity. *Chest*, **94**, 964–969.

JOHNSON, S. B. (1980) Psychosocial factors in juvenile diabetes: a review. *Journal of Behavioural Medicine*, **3**, 95–115.

KURITA, H. (1991) School refusal in pervasive developmental disorders. *Journal of Autism and Developmental Disorders*, **21**, 1–15.

KVIST, B., KVIST, M. & RAJANTIE, J. (1990) School absences, school achievements and personality traits of the haemophilic child. *Scandinavian Journal of Social Medicine*, **18**, 125–132.

LANSKY, S. B., LOWMAN, J. T., VATS, T., *et al* (1975) School phobia in children with malignant neoplasms. *American Journal of Diseases of Children*, **129**, 42–46.

LARCOMBE, I. J., WALKER, J. J. P., CHARLTON, A., *et al* (1991) Impact of childhood cancer on return to normal schooling. *British Medical Journal*, **301**, 169–171.

LINEBERGER, H. O. (1981) Social characteristics of a hemophilia clinic population. *General Hospital Psychiatry*, **3**, 157–163.

LINET, L. S. (1985) Tourette syndrome, pimozide and school phobia: the neuroleptic separation anxiety syndrome. *American Journal of Psychiatry*, **142**, 613–615.

MANCINI, A. F., ROSITO, P. & CANINO, R. (1989) School-related behavior in children with cancer. *Pediatric Hematology and Oncology*, **6**, 145–154.

MIKKELSEN, E. J., DETLOR, J. & COHEN, D. J. (1981) School avoidance and social phobia triggered by haloperidol in patients with Tourette's disorder. *American Journal of Psychiatry*, **138**, 1572–1576.

MULHERN, R. K., WASSERMAN, A. L., FRIEDMAN, A. G., *et al* (1989) Social competence and behavioral adjustment of children who are long-term survivors of cancer. *Pediatrics*, **83**, 18–25.

ORR, D. P., WELLER, S. C., SATTERWHITE, B., *et al* (1984) Psychosocial implications of chronic illness in adolescence. *Journal of Pediatrics*, **194**, 152–157.

PARCEL, G. S., GILMAN, S. C., NADER, P. R., *et al* (1979) A comparison of absentee rates of elementary schoolchildren with asthma and nonasthmatic schoolmates. *Pediatrics*, **64**, 878–881.

PLAPP, J. M. (1990) Tourette's and school refusal. *Journal of the American Academy of Child and Adolescent Psychiatry*, **29**, 149–150.

RUTTER, M., TIZARD, J. & WHITMORE, K. (1970) *Education, Health and Behaviour*. London: Longman Press.

SKUSE, D. (1987) The psychological consequences of being small. *Journal of Child Psychology and Psychiatry*, **28**, 641–650.

STEIN, E. K. & JESSOP, D. J. (1984) Psychological adjustment among children with chronic conditions. *Pediatrics*, **73**, 169–174.

WALKER, D. K. (1984) Care of chronically ill children in schools. *Pediatric Clinics of North America*, **31**, 221–233.

WALLER, D. & EISENBERG, L. (1980) School refusal in childhood – a psychiatric paediatric perspective. In *Out of School* (eds L. Hersov & I. Berg). Chichester: John Wiley.

WEITZMAN, M. (1984) School and peer relations. *Pediatric Clinics of North America*, **31**, 59–69.

——— (1986) School absence rates as outcome measures in studies of children with chronic illness. *Journal of Chronic Disease*, **39**, 799–808.

———, WALKER, D. K. & GORTMAKER, S. (1986) Chronic illness, psychosocial problems and school absences. *Clinical Pediatrics*, **25**, 137–141.

WOOLF, A., RAPPAPORT, L., REARDON, P., *et al* (1989) School functioning and disease severity in boys with hemophilia. *Developmental and Behavioral Pediatrics*, **10**, 81–85.

3 Features of children who do not attend school

LORRAINE V. KLERMAN and
BETTY C. GLASSCOCK

Almost all pupils are absent from school a few days during any school year. In the USA the National Center for Health Statistics (NCHS) annually reports the number of 'school-loss days' for children 5–17 years of age caused by an acute or chronic health condition[1], according to information collected in its ongoing National Health Interview Survey. The NCHS estimated that in 1993 acute and chronic health conditions caused almost 250 million days of school to be lost or 5.3 days per child. This rate has varied little over the last 5 years. It was 4.9 in 1988, 4.6 in 1990 and 4.6 in 1992 (Table 3.1) (Benson & Marano, 1994). The NCHS statistics do not distinguish between an occasional absence or one of short duration and frequent or prolonged absences, which are more likely to affect school achievement.

The NCHS data, moreover, do not include absences for reasons other than medical conditions, such as avoiding classes or going to a sports event. These types of absences are usually called truancy, although this term is not always defined precisely. Not even all the absences due to medical causes are justifiable. A child who is kept home because of an asthmatic attack that could have been prevented or stopped quickly, or an adolescent girl who is allowed to stay home because of dysmenorrhoea, are examples of absences that need not occur.

Another potential reason for absence is a psychological reaction to the experience of violence or disaster. In the USA, increasing numbers of children and adolescents are victims of kidnappings, shootings, hostage situations and domestic violence. A survey in an inner-city Chicago

---

1. A condition is considered chronic if it was first noticed more than 3 months before the reference date of the interview or it is a type of condition that ordinarily has a duration of more than 3 months, such as diabetes or a heart condition. An acute condition is defined as a type of illness or injury that ordinarily lasts less than 3 months and was first noticed less than 3 months before the interview. To be included, an acute condition must have resulted in at least one physician visit or at least 1 day of restricted activity.

25

TABLE 3.1
School-loss days per individual 5–17 years old, 1988–93, USA

	Acute and chronic conditions	Acute conditions only
1993	5.3[1]	4.1[1]
1992	4.6	3.5
1991	5.1	4.1
1990	4.6	3.8
1989	5.7	4.6
1988	4.9	4.1

1. Estimate.
Source: National Health Interview Survey, National Center for Health Statistics.

elementary school found that 4% of all fifth to eighth grade students (ages 10–14) had witnessed a shooting; 31%, a stabbing; and 22%, a murder (Dyson, 1990). National crime statistics indicate that between 25 000 and 100 000 children a year are victims of parental kidnapping (Shetky & Haller, 1983). Although the exposure of children and adolescents to violence has become a significant public health concern, the empirical literature on the psychological sequelae of such experiences is surprisingly meagre (Forehand *et al*, 1989) and only a few longitudinal studies were found (Nader *et al*, 1990). No studies described a decline in school attendance of more than minimal duration.

Studies of the psychological impact of natural disasters (fires, earthquakes, floods, hurricanes, cyclones and tornadoes) on children and adolescents have found varying amounts of emotional and behavioural consequences (Earls *et al*, 1988; Bradburn, 1991; Jones & Ribbe, 1991; Sullivan *et al*, 1991). In general, the acute effects diminish over time, with minimal long-term effects. Again, the studies did not mention any significant relationship between disaster and school absence.

In this chapter we examine the reasons for absences, particularly those that are so frequent or so prolonged that they interfere with school work, as well as some programmes designed to reduce absenteeism, with an emphasis on health-related causes.

A theoretical perspective

Absence should be viewed as the result of interactions between pupils, their families, their peers, the schools and the community's social environment, rather than as a behaviour based entirely on the health status and other characteristics of the student. A pupil's health complaint may only lead to absence if the family sanctions it. If the family decides that the health complaint can be treated and takes the child to a physician and then insists that the physician's advice be followed, absences are avoided or reduced.

If the school is unpleasant or boring, or if pupils are not treated with respect, pupils will elect more attractive pursuits. This frequently leads to punishment of pupils, which leads to additional absences and eventually to dropping-out, with the blame being placed on the pupils when the school played a major role (Fine, 1991).

Finally, community expectations play a major role in whether pupils attend school. Attendance in suburban schools is better than that in inner-city schools not only because the schools are better, but also because there is a community expectation that pupils will attend school. A school-age child on the streets or in a mall during school hours on a school day in the suburbs elicits comments from other parents, if not from the police. Moreover, middle-class pupils are expected to graduate from high school and move on to college, expectations that may not be realised if pupils are excessively absent. The strong role of the community was shown in the Gautreaux Housing Demonstration project in which families from public housing in Chicago were moved to private apartments either in mostly white suburbs or mostly black urban areas of Chicago. The very low income families were predominantly headed by black women. Adolescents and youths in the families that moved to the suburbs, and their superior schools, as compared with those that stayed in the city, were more likely to be in high school and in a college high school track or in a four-year college (Rosenbaum & Kaufman, 1991).

In the review that follows, we attempt to show that absence should not be considered only in terms of the characteristics of the pupils, but also in terms of peer, family, school and community forces acting upon them.

Factors leading to excessive absenteeism

The research on school absence has made it clear that some pupils are more likely to be absent than others.

Demographic factors

In terms of demographic factors, the NCHS data show that females and whites have higher rates of absence for acute conditions only and for acute and chronic conditions combined than do males and blacks. For acute conditions only and for acute and chronic conditions combined, rates of absence are inversely related to income except for acute conditions in families with incomes of $35 000 or more (Table 3.2) (Adams & Benson, 1992).

A 1983 study of six middle schools (grades 6–8) in Boston analysed school record data to determine student characteristics. The researchers found that

TABLE 3.2
School-loss days per individual 5–17 years old, by sex, race and income, 1993, USA

	Acute and chronic conditions	Acute conditions only
Sex		
Male	5.0	3.8[1]
Female	5.5	4.5
Race		
White	5.3	4.2
Black	4.9	4.0
Income		
Less than $10 000	8.2	5.3
$10 000–$19 999	6.0	4.8
$20 000–$34 999	5.6	4.6
$35 000 or more	4.4	3.6
All	5.3	4.1

1. Estimate.
Source: National Health Interview Survey, National Center for Health Statistics.

problem absence pupils[2] were more likely than other pupils to be white, older, in higher grades, one or more years behind their appropriate grade, in special education classes and bused to school. Absence also varied markedly by school. When these variables were analysed using a mutliple logistic regression, age, white race, school attended and inappropriate grade for age remained significant and special education placement marginally so. Gender was not significant in this study (Weitzman *et al*, 1985).

The National School Health Services Program, a 1979–82 study of 23 school districts in medically underserved areas in four states, administered a questionnaire to the parents of almost 2000 children. Included in the study was the question, "How many days was your child absent due to illness in the past two weeks?" The results showed that girls were more likely to be absent than boys and white and American Indian children less than black and Latino children. There was an interaction between gender and race/ethnicity: black and Latino males were more likely to be absent than white or American Indian males, but Latino females were more likely to be absent than any other racial/ethnic group of females. Being absent was inversely related to maternal education. This relationship was more pronounced for females, blacks and Latinos. Being absent was also inversely related to family income (Kornguth, 1990).

Health-related factors

The NCHS data show that acute conditions cause more days of school loss than chronic conditions. The most frequent cause of school loss days due to

2. Problem absent students were those who during the study or preceding three-quarters had been absent: (a) six or more consecutive days; (b) 10 or more non-consecutive days in any quarter (representing absence of 25% or more for any given quarter); or (c) half or more of any particular weekday in any quarter (patterned absence).

acute conditions is respiratory conditions, particularly influenza. This is followed by infective and parasitic diseases, including the common childhood diseases. Injuries are the third most common cause, followed by digestive system conditions and ear infections. Gender and race interact with illness. Female rates are higher than the rates for males in most categories except injuries and digestive system conditions, and white rates are higher than black ones for most major categories except digestive system conditions (Adams & Benson, 1992).

The National School Health Services Program asked parents whether their children had any of 14 health problems. As expected, those with health problems were more likely to be absent and the likelihood increased with the number of problems from one to four or more. Older children (12–17 years of age) with two or more health problems were more likely to be absent than younger children (5–11 years of age) with the same number of health problems.

As part of this study, over 2000 children received a complete physical examination by a nurse. Diagnosed health conditions that led to absence were heart problems (including murmurs), spinal and bone problems (including scoliosis), and dental problems (including caries). One diagnosed health problem had little or no effect on absence, but two or more did. Health problems were diagnosed in more older than younger children, but the two absence rates did not differ, given the same number of problems. Mother's education was inversely related to absence due to diagnosed health problems.

Absence was related to source of medical care. Those most likely to be absent had a hospital or health department clinic as a regular source of care, even though they were least likely to have a diagnosed health problem. Among families whose regular source of care was a private physician, low-income children were more likely to be absent. A large percentage (34%) of children covered by Medicaid missed one or more days of school compared with those covered by private insurance (21%) or no insurance (30%) (Kornguth, 1990).

A study of 745 eighth-grade pupils attending public schools in two rural counties in Maryland provides some insights into possible reasons for gender differences in absence. Pupils were asked about health status, school absence for illness, school attendance when feeling ill and concerns about 28 health-related topics. They were asked whether each topic was of concern to them rarely or never, sometimes, or often. Using factor analysis, five 'concern' factors were developed: emotional, social, physical, drug and body image.

Physical health concerns were most important for boys and emotional concerns for girls. For both boys and girls, physical health concerns were positively associated with school absence, school attendance when ill and physician visits in the prior year, but the correlation was stronger for girls. Emotional concerns were associated with all three indicators for girls only, while body image concerns showed a weak but positive association with school absence and school attendance for boys only, suggesting that body image problems were not considered appropriate for a physician visit. Social concerns were associated weakly with absence for girls only. Drug use concerns were strongly associated with absence and for boys only (Alexander, 1989).

Asthma is a major cause of school absence. Taylor & Newacheck (1992) estimated that 2.7 million American children under 18 years of age have asthma and that it leads to 7.3 million days restricted to bed and 10.1 million days missed from school, or an average of 5 days per asthmatic child per year. Absence from asthma is not related exclusively to the severity of the health problem; psychosocial problems, frequent physician visits and activity limitations may also contribute (Celano & Geller, 1993).

Environmental factors can influence health and, through that, absence. In a study of respirable particulate pollution in the Utah Valley, an increase in pollution was associated with an increase in absence in all grades, but more in grades 1–3 (ages 6–9) than in grades 4–6 (ages 9–12) (Ransom & Pope, 1992).

Family

The family may influence absence directly by requiring that the pupil stay home for some reason, such as caring for a young sibling or an adult; or indirectly by not encouraging attendance or by creating an atmosphere not conducive to education generally. The adolescent children of depressed mothers are more likely than those of psychologically healthy ones to develop types of problem behaviour including excessive absence and dropping-out (Weissman & Siegel, 1972).

In a study of eighth-grade pupils (generally ages 13–14), caring for oneself after school without adult supervision was found associated with greater school absence. The pupils were asked, "Within the last month, how many days did you stay out of school when you were not sick?" Those with one or more such days were listed as truants and truancy was significantly greater among those in self-care for more than 10 hours per week than for those not in self-care. There was no difference, however, in truancy rates for those who had initiated self-care in elementary as compared to junior high school. Other types of behaviour associated with self-care of 10 or more hours were risk-taking, anger, family conflict and stress. Self-care pupils were also more likely to report that their friends were their major source of influence and that they attended more parties (Dwyer *et al*, 1990).

School

The Boston study of six middle schools found marked variation in absence among the schools, even when the sociodemographic characteristics of the students were controlled (Weitzman *et al*, 1985). Rutter's (1980) study of 12 secondary schools in an inner London borough also found that the particular school attended was associated with attendance, even after controlling for verbal reasoning scores and parental occupation. The school variables that affected attendance most strongly were the balance of pupils at intake in terms of academic ability, parental occupation and behaviour; and the social organisation of the schools and their environment for learning. Rutter believed that these latter variables, which include use of rewards and praise of pupils, a pleasant and comfortable environment, opportunities for pupils to assume responsibility, positive teacher role models, and a consistent academic curriculum and discipline, could be modified to foster positive student outcomes even in disadvantaged areas.

For schools that consider themselves overcrowded or burdened with pupils who are difficult to teach, poor attendance provides a way of excluding pupils from the school, particularly those who are over the age at which dropping-out is permitted. Writing about a comprehensive high school in New York with about 3200 pupils, Fine (1991, p. 65) reported:

> "At this high school the discharge process was rationalized – honest, efficient, and ultimately devastating to the student body. The law was followed precisely. Phone calls home, conducted by a taped message TELSOL machine, efficiently informed parents or guardians of their child's absence. Then letters were sent after ten days of absence, and again after twenty, indicating that the student must, with his or her parent or guardian, attend a meeting at school to discuss truancy or she or he would be dismissed summarily. When these letters went unanswered, because many students 'take it out of the box before my mother can see it,' the discharge category 'overage' [seventeen-year-olds (plus)] was activated. Such was the fate of almost a thousand students during the year."

Fine also noted that most pupils were unaware of their legal entitlement to education, to an exit interview, or to not being failed or discharged because of truancy or suspension. In fact, some believed that only if they "acted good" could they remain in school after age 17.

The relative importance of health, family and school influences was shown in the Boston middle school study. When problem absence pupils were asked an open-ended question about the reasons for their absences, almost half cited a health reason, almost always physical health. The remainder of the reasons offered related to attitudes towards school (dislike of school, poor relationships with teachers, etc.), laziness or missing the school bus. When offered a list of 15 possible reasons for absence, health and attitudes towards education remained important, but reasons suggesting a low priority given to school attendance by pupils or the family were chosen by about two-fifths of the pupils; these included bad weather, frequently missing the bus, or not being awakened. In addition, about one-quarter of the pupils reported missing school to care for a younger member of the houshecold or an adult.

Violence in the schools was given as a reason for absence by 23% of pupils. Parents were asked the same open-ended question and given the same list. Their spontaneous responses were similar to the pupils but showed somewhat more emphasis on negative attitudes towards school and less on laziness and waking up late. Using the check-list, parents were more likely than pupils to mention emotional problems, violence and racial problems. They were less likely to mention weather conditions, no one waking up the student, or the need to care for a child or an adult in the household. This pattern suggests that parents were less willing to mention reasons for absence for which they might be considered as, or more, responsible than the student (Klerman *et al*, 1987).

It seems clear that there are characteristics of schools that make it more or less likely that pupils will not attend on a regular basis.

The association between absence and other types of deviant behaviour

Pupils who are frequently absent from junior and senior high schools often have problems in other areas of their lives as well. Dryfoos (1990) in her summary of studies of high-risk adolescents notes that truancy and school misbehaviour are related to substance abuse, dropping out and delinquency. A study of 300 African-Americans 9–15 years of age in six public housing projects found self-reported truancy to be significantly associated with selling and delivering drugs and having sexual intercourse, as well as being suspended from school (Stanton *et al*, 1993).

In a 7-year follow-up of fifth-grade pupils in a semi-rural area, frequent school absences and aggression were found to be correlated with grade retention, truancy and school drop-out (Kupersmidt & Coie, 1990). (For an earlier review of studies of the association between excessive absence and other types of risk-taking behaviour see Klerman, 1988).

Programmes that attempt to reduce absence

Researchers have studied some programmes whose only intent was to reduce school absence, particularly truancy. Also of interest, however, are studies of programmes targeted at broader social problems that used absence as one of the indicators of success.

Truancy reduction

Many American schools have adopted a mechanical, impersonal approach to unexcused absence. A machine is installed that is programmed to dial the home numbers of all absent pupils. The tape, activated by a voice at the other end, informs the person on the phone that the student has been absent for a certain period of time and requests that a reason for the absence be given after the tone. Fine (1991) tallied the responses to 421 calls on a day in September when the tape was still only available in English, although at least 40% of the parents were Spanish-speaking: 58, no answer; 123 answers, but no verbal response; 35, disconnected lines; 10, Spanish responses; 28, transfers; 30, doctors appointments, with six in the hospital; 40 sick; 17, "I didn't know, thank you"; 14, "my child wasn't absent", or "stop lying, nobody's been absent all the time"; 8, wrong numbers; 8, living elsewhere; 4, taking care of my baby; 4 "needed at home"; 2, having a baby; 2, relative died; and miscellaneous others. Fine (1991, pp. 166–7) comments:

> "TELSOL machines, now well institutionalized across high schools, represent a complex 'advancement' in school–family relations. More parents are contacted, with more information gathered about student absenteeism. But the replacement of a standardized tape contact for 'real' human interaction reveals a crisp message about the nonreciprocity of parental involvement for low-income parents in public schools. Only one question is asked. Fifteen to thirty seconds are allotted to respond. And no challenge is possible. A sobering metaphor for parent involvement."

Problem related

Pregnancy and parenting among women of school age remains a major problem in the USA. In 1992, the last year for which data are available, the birth rate for females under 15 years of age was 1.4 per 1000, 37.8 for those 15–17 and 94.5 for those 18–19 (Ventura *et al*, 1994).

Two states have developed programmes whose purpose is to encourage young parents to attend school or discourage them from being absent. The first such programme to be initiated was LearnFare in Wisconsin. Preliminary reports on LearnFare indicate that it is not increasing school attendance.

Ohio has developed a programme entitled Learning, Earning, and Parenting (LEAP). All pregnant women and custodial parents under 20 years of age who are receiving welfare and do not have a high school diploma or a General Equivalency Diploma (GED) certificate must enrol in LEAP. Those who enrol in school and attend regularly (no more than four absences with two or fewer unexcused absences in a month in a full-time high school [absences excused by a physician are not counted]) receive a $62 bonus in their monthly welfare grant, while those who fail to enrol or attend poorly have their grants reduced by the same amount. The student is assigned a case manager who monitors compliance with the programme and helps the student overcome barriers to attendance. Pupils are also eligible for assistance with child care and transportation as needed to attend school. Interim study findings show that LEAP promoted retention in high school and induced some drop-outs to return to school, as well as improving the attendance of pupils enrolled in high school. The researchers believe that the LEAP programme was assisted by the Ohio Department of Education's initiative called Graduation, Reality and Dual-Role Skills (GRADS), which enables home economics teachers to provide special instruction to pregnant and parenting pupils (Bloom *et al*, 1993).

The Ounce of Prevention Fund, a public–private partnership in Illinois, uses two programmes to reach pupils before high-school age and help them stay in school, delay sexual activity and pregnancy, and develop realistic career goals. Peer Power is addressed to sixth through eighth grade (ages 11–14 generally) females and Awareness and Development for Adolescent Males (ADAM) is for males. Small groups meet with an adult leader (a schoolteacher or counsellor and a teacher's aide, usually a parent) once a week for 2 or 3 hours over two school years. Meetings provide time for homework and tutoring; sessions on subjects such as decision-making, self-esteem, human development and reproduction, substance abuse, peer pressure, intimacy and relationships, communicating with parents, career awareness, community resources; and a recreational period. Field trips and various incentives are also employed and parent involvement is encouraged. An evaluation conducted in 1989–90 found that the average number of school days missed by participants in Peer Power and ADAM was less than among comparison group pupils even after controlling for differences in attendance before the programme, for differences among schools, or for differences in grade (Fitzgerald & Ruch-Ross, 1990).

An intensive family support intervention in New Haven, Connecticut in the 1970s had a positive impact on school attendance. A family team (home visitor, paediatrician, primary child care worker and development examiner) provided social work, paediatric care, child care and psychological services tailored to the needs of 17 impoverished families from pregnancy through 30 months postpartum. A 10-year follow-up which compared the study families with a matched control group found that the study children had better school attendance than did the controls (Seitz *et al*, 1985).

School-based health programmes

An on-site school health demonstration project based on a family practice model has reported success in reducing absenteeism in an elementary school located in a medically underserved, health manpower shortage area in Brooklyn. The school health office was open 5 days a week during the school year and 2 days a week during holiday and vacation periods. Emergency cover was available through the 24-hour on-call system of the Department of Family

Practice of the local medical school. All children who entered the programme received a complete physical examination. Care was provided by the project director, a family physician, a nurse practitioner, two health technicians, a part-time clerical assistant, and residents and professional pupils. Absentee rates were lower among participants than non-participants in each of the three study years with participants' rates dropping and the non-participants' rates remaining somewhat stable. In addition, immunisation rates improved and vision and hearing defects were corrected (Birrer *et al*, 1991).

Although school-based clinics were originally promoted as a means of reducing adolescent pregnancy, the expansion in their numbers over the last 10 years is probably related to an acknowledgement of the magnitude of adolescent health problems and a belief that school-based health centres (SBHC) might be a way of meeting those needs, particularly in poor and medically underserved areas (Office of Technology Assessment, 1991). Since absences are related both to physical health problems and to psychological problems, both of which are addressed in high-quality SBHCs, it was expected that schools with such centres would experience a reduction in absence.

However, a recent study of pupils in 19 of the schools participating in the Robert Wood Johnson Foundation's School-Based Adolescent Health Care Program found significant differences in absence depending on the characteristics of the SBHC. Between schools with stronger and weaker overall SBHC programmes (defined in terms of staff–student ratios, turnover, access [location within school and quality of environment], SBHC's relationship with school leaders and provision of health education in classroom and school-wide events), there was a 5.3 percentage point difference in absence for more than 5 days for sickness in the previous months and a 4.2 percentage point difference in skipping more than 5 days of school (truancy) in the same period. In addition, employing an extra person to provide psychosocial services (per 1000 pupils) was associated with a 0.4 percentage point difference in absence and in truancy. These analyses were controlled for differences in student characteristics among the schools (Kisker & Hill, 1993). The authors of this report note:

> "The lower absenteeism levels are consistent with the higher utilization rates experienced by the stronger SBHCs and the importance of treatment of illnesses and injuries among the services for which pupils went to their health center."

For an earlier review of studies of school-based programmes, see Rude & Klerman (1992).

Conclusions

Excessive school absence remains a major problem in the USA. Many days of school absence not only interferes with a student's ability to learn but, particularly in junior and senior high school, a chronic absence problem is often the precursor of dropping-out of school, a behaviour with dire consequences for future productivity.

Attempts to reduce absenteeism have not been very successful. Although individual demonstration projects may have a positive effect, these are seldom replicated on a large scale. Many senior high schools, often suffering with large class sizes and 'difficult' pupils, find it easier to ease pupils with excessive absence out of the system, rather than to try to discover and remedy the causes of the absence.

In addition, the associations between excessive absence and poverty, poor-quality schools and deviant behaviour suggest that reductions in chronic absence may require modifications in family structure and dynamics, as well as societal changes, e.g. reduction of poverty, improvement in the school systems and sources of stimulation other than alcohol, drugs and sex. Nevertheless, it is clear that some progress in reducing absence can be made if a school is willing to devote attention to the subject, rather than to ignore it, handle it superficially, or push out the chronically absent pupils.

As the USA seeks to upgrade the quality of its work-force and to reduce the number of individuals dependent upon its welfare system, increasing attention is being paid to the educational system. While much of that attention is still on curriculum and testing, some spill-over to the problem of absence can be expected. If that occurs, the systems may begin to adopt programmes shown to be successful in demonstration studies, as well as to experiment with new concepts.

References

ADAMS, P. F. & BENSON, V. (1992) Current estimates from the National Health Interview Survey, National Center for Health Statistics. *Vital and Health Statistics*, **10** (184).

ALEXANDER, C. S. (1989) Gender differences in adolescent health concerns and self-assessed health. *Journal of Early Adolescence*, **9**, 467–479.

BENSON, V. & MARANO, M. A. (1994) Current estimates from the National Health Information Survey, 1993. National Center for Health Statistics. *Vital and Health Statistics*, **10** (190).

BIRRER, R. B., FLEISHER, J. M., CORTESE, L., *et al* (1991) An urban primary school health program. *New York State Journal of Medicine*, **91**, 339–341.

BLOOM, D., FELLERATH, V., LONG, D., *et al* (1993) *LEAP. Interim Findings on a Welfare Initiative to Improve School Attendance among Teenage Parents*. New York: Manpower Demonstration Research Corporation.

BRADBURN, I. S. (1991) After the earth shook: children's stress symptoms 6–8 months after a disaster. *Advances in Behavior Research and Therapy*, **13**, 173–179.

CELANO, M. P. & GELLER, R. J. (1993) Learning, school performance, and children with asthma: how much at risk? *Journal of Learning Disabilities*, **26**, 23–32.

DRYFOOS, J. G. (1990) *Adolescents at Risk*. New York: Oxford University Press.

DWYER, K. M., RICHARDSON, J. L., DANLEY, K. L., *et al* (1990) Characteristics of eighth-grade students who initiate self-care in elementary and junior high school. *Pediatrics*, **86**, 448–454.

DYSON, J. L. (1990) The effect of family violence on children's academic performance and behavior. *Journal of the National Medical Association*, **82**, 17–22.

EARLS, E., SMITH, E., REICH, W., *et al* (1988) Investigating psychopathological consequences of a disaster in children: a pilot study incorporating a structured diagnostic interview. *Journal of the American Academy of Child and Adolescent Psychiatry*, **27**, 90–95.

FINE, M. (1991) *Framing Dropouts: Notes on the Politics of an Urban Public High School*. Albany, New York: State University of New York Press.

FITZGERALD, P. T. & RUCH-ROSS, H. (1990) *Peer Power/ADAM in the 1989–1990 School Year: Final Report (Overview)*. Chicago: The Ounce of Prevention Fund.

FOREHAND, R., LONG, N., ZOGG, C., *et al* (1989) Child abduction. Parent and child functioning following return. *Clinical Pediatrics*, **28**, 311–316.

JONES, R. T. & RIBBE, D. P. (1991) Child, adolescent, and adult victims of residential fire: psychosocial consequences. *Behavior Modification*, **15**, 560–580.

KISKER, E. E. & HILL, J. (1993) *Healthy Caring: An Outcomes Evaluation of the Robert Wood Johnson Foundation's School-Based Adolescent Health Care Program*. Princeton, New Jersey: Mathematical Policy Research, Inc.

KLERMAN, L. V. (1988) School absence – a health perspective. *Pediatric Clinics of North America*, **35**, 1253–1269.

———, WEITZMAN, M., ALPERT, J. J., *et al* (1987) Why adolescents do not attend school. *Journal of Adolescent Health Care*, **8**, 425–430.

KORNGUTH, M. L. (1990) School illnesses: who's absent and why? *Pediatric Nursing*, **16**, 95–99.

KUPERSMIDT, J. B. & COIE, J. D. (1990) Preadolescent peer status, aggression, and school adjustment as predictors of externalizing problems in adolescence. *Child Development*, **61**, 1350–1362.

NADER, K., PYNOSS, R. S. & FAIRBANKS, C. (1990) Children's PTSD reactions one year after a sniper attack at their school. *American Journal of Psychiatry*, **147**, 1526–1530.

NATIONAL CENTER FOR HEALTH STATISTICS (1993) Advance report of final natality statistics, 1991. *Monthly Vital Statistics Report* **42**(3) (suppl.). Hyattsville, Maryland: Public Health Service.

OFFICE OF TECHNOLOGY ASSESSMENT (1991) *Adolescent Health – Volume I: Summary and Policy Options*, OTA-H-468. Washington, DC: United States Government Printing Office.

RANSOM, M. R. & POPE, C. A. (1992) Elementary school absences and PM_{10} pollution in Utah Valley. *Environmental Research*, **58**, 204–219.

ROSENBAUM, J. E. & KAUFMAN, J. (1991) Educational and occupational achievements of low-income Black youth in white suburbs. Paper presented at the Annual Meeting of the American Sociological Association, August 1991.

RUDE, C. S. & KLERMAN, L. V. (1992) School avoidance: excessive absenteeism and dropping-out. In *Comprehensive Adolescent Health Care* (eds S. B. Friedman, M. Fisher & S. K. Schonberg), pp. 892–898. St. Louis, Missouri: Quality Medical Publishing.

RUTTER, M. (1980) School influences on children's behavior and development: the 1979 Kenneth Blackfan Lecture, Children's Hospital Medical Center, Boston. *Pediatrics*, **65**, 208–220.

SEITZ, V., ROSENBAUM, L. K. & APFEL, N. H. (1985) Effects of family support intervention: a ten-year follow up. *Child Development*, **56**, 376–391.

SHETKY, D. H. & HALLER, L. H. (1983) Parental kidnapping. *American Academy of Child Psychiatry*, **22**, 279–285.

STANTON, B., ROMER, D., RICARDO, I., *et al* (1993) Early initiation of sex and its lack of association with risk behaviors among adolescent African-Americans. *Pediatrics*, **92**, 13–19.

SULLIVAN, M. A., SAYLOR, C. E. & FOSTER, K. Y. (1991) Post hurricane adjustment of preschoolers and their families. *Advances in Behavior Research and Therapy*, **13**, 163–171.

TAYLOR, W. R. & NEWACHECK, P. W. (1992) Impact of childhood asthma on health. *Pediatrics*, **90**, 657–662.

VENTURA, S. J., MARTIN, J. A., TAFFEL, S. M., *et al* (1994) Advance report of final natality statistics, 1992. Monthly Vital Statistics Report, **43**(5) (suppl.). Hyattsville, Maryland: National Center for Health Statistics.

WEISSMAN, M. & SIEGEL, R. (1972) The depressed woman and her rebellious adolescent. *Social Casework*, **53**, 563–570.

WEITZMAN, M., KLERMAN, L. V., LAMB, G. A., *et al* (1985) Demographic and educational characteristics of inner city middle school problem absence students. *American Journal of Orthopsychiatry*, **55**, 378–382.

4 School factors

DAVID REYNOLDS

Even the most cursory review and examination of the literature on truancy for the last two decades is bound to pick up a substantial change in the way that truancy is described and explained. Whereas in the 1970s the great majority of studies explored truancy as due to factors within the nature of the truant's own personality, family or community environment (see reviews in Reid, 1985, 1986; Reynolds, 1987; Carlen *et al*, 1992), by the early 1980s the explanatory focus had shifted to the educational system in general and to individual schools in particular as explanatory factors (see reviews in Mortimore, 1991; Reynolds & Cuttance, 1992) and as the foci for remediation.

Indeed, in many different educational houses, it seems that school effectiveness research and school effectiveness researchers are now in the 1990s a part of the furniture. In the world of politics in the UK, the Labour Party fought the 1992 election on a policy platform to establish arrangements for local educational authorities to monitor the standards and the effectiveness of their schools, and for these authorities to be monitored likewise. The Conservative Government also has clearly been influenced by, and has been receptive to, the messages concerning the variation in school quality and teacher quality that have emanated from the effectiveness research base.

In the world of educational policy-making also, it is clear that the work of the Office for Standards in Education (OFSTED), in for example its 'check-lists' for school inspectors, reflects the influence of effectiveness research and indeed OFSTED is commissioning a series of publications on topics related to school effectiveness, ranging from reviews of the characteristics of 'good' schools to reviews that survey the apparent lessons for Britain of the international surveys of educational achievement that are becoming increasingly numerous. Mechanisms of utilising routinely collected individual pupil and contextual data to enable true comparisons of schools' 'added value' have also been a recent focus of attention at both OFSTED and at the Schools' Curriculum and Assessment Authority.

In the world of educational practice, there is also evidence of some take-up of the insights of school effectiveness by school managements, although none of this seems to be as direct as that of the head teacher in the north of England who after the publication of the seminal *Fifteen Thousand Hours* (Rutter *et al*, 1979) study spent literally scores of pounds on flowers in classrooms because of the book's findings of an association between pupils' academic achievement and the attractiveness of classroom decor!

The popularity of this perspective on the school's role in creating, and therefore in also potentially combating, truancy is of course closely linked to the emergence of both a distinctive 'school effectiveness' research paradigm and to an associated and linked 'school improvement' paradigm (both of whose tenets are outlined in Reynolds *et al*, 1993). These paradigms are now buttressed and supported by the disciplinary apparatus by which 'normal science' is maintained: for example, there is an international journal *School Effectiveness and School Improvement*, an international professional association and the publication of annual meeting proceedings. The perspective of 'school effectiveness' correspondingly features in virtually all of the recent reviews of the field (see Reid, 1989; Carlen *et al*, 1992), since the rise of the discipline of school effectiveness has coincided with the increased attention given to variation in the quality of the educational system within more general political discussion of the system's problems.

There are, according to those within the school effectiveness field such as Mortimore (1991) and Reynolds & Cuttance (1992), a number of positive effects that the school effectiveness research perspective and its associated findings have had upon the general tenor of educational thinking. Firstly, the research can be argued to have destroyed the 'alibis' of family background, social deprivation and social disadvantage that educational practitioners may have used as an excuse for schools' own failings. Findings that 'effective' schools can succeed in enhancing pupils' results, even in disadvantaged catchment areas as shown by Rutter *et al* (1979) and by Mortimore *et al* (1988), have helped to combat the fatalism that saw pupils' problems such as truancy as irremediable.

Secondly, the knowledge accumulated within the school effectiveness paradigm concerning those school and classroom factors that are associated with positive pupil academic and social outcomes in areas such as academic achievement, delinquency, behavioural problems and truancy has now begun to form a body of good professional practice that is available for educational practitioners and policymakers to utilise within schools. Indeed, some of the most interesting 'cutting edge' scholarship within the field of educational studies is currently taking place at the interface where the knowledge about 'good practice' is interacting with the body of knowledge concerning school improvement (see, for example, the work of Hargreaves & Hopkins, 1991).

There is no doubt that, in many ways, the rise of the school effectiveness perspective has facilitated the demise of explanations which located the causes of problems like truancy as within the nature of pupils' home backgrounds and communities. The limited amount of variance in the dependent variable of 'attendance' or 'truancy' that these studies explained, the absence of predictive power that followed from even very detailed assessment of numerous child, family and environmental factors, the reduced utility of key background variables such as social class and, indeed, the demise of 'internally' based causal explanations for truancy and their replacement with an emphasis upon 'situation' and 'opportunity' as determinants of patterns of behaviour have been reviewed and noted elsewhere (e.g. Reynolds, 1984, 1987).

The popularity of the knowledge base in the furnishing of explanations for truancy has had one significant negative effect, however, in that it has encouraged the growth of national evaluation systems of school performance that permit invalid comparisons between schools. The extensive publicity given to research findings concerning school effects upon academic achievement and truancy rates has encouraged, in the view of commentators such as Hargreaves (1994), the introduction of managerially orientated evaluation systems that have been based upon the publication of 'raw' unadjusted school truancy rates. Even though a school's truancy rate will reflect a variety of familial, community and environmental influences as well as the effects of the particular school regime, these rates were published for individual schools in 1993 without any attempt being made to separate out the school's effect, or 'added value', that it may give in terms of generating low truancy rates, from the contribution or effects of the many other influences on patterns of attendance/non-attendance. The 'educational market' (Hargreaves & Reynolds, 1989) whereby parents are encouraged to 'shop around' for those schools that are performing well on academic achievement and attendance measures is therefore being based upon information about the quality of the schools competing in that market that is woefully inadequate for the purposes of demonstrating school quality that it was meant to facilitate.

It is also important to note that the popularity of the school effectiveness paradigm has also tended to obscure many of the continuing arguments concerning the validity of the knowledge base that continue to rage within the discipline itself. Indeed, the school effectiveness knowledge that one can access in the reviews of truancy noted at the beginning of this chapter are 5–7 years out of date in most cases. Often what is presented as a simple, straightforward and valid body of knowledge about the school factors associated with truancy and other educational outcomes is now in reality very complex, is increasingly contested and is often seen as an increasingly partial view of a very much more complex interaction between the child, the family, the community and the school. These 'cutting edge' debates within the field and their implications for knowledge about, and policy prevention of, truancy form the subjects of the next section of this chapter. Applying the more complex knowledge base in programmes of school improvement is an issue discussed later.

The context specificity of school effectiveness factors

The first area of major controversy concerns the potential 'context specificity' of the educational factors that are associated with pupil performance on academic outcomes and on the more social outcomes such as truancy. Because the early work in the field of school effectiveness was located exclusively in socially deprived catchment areas (because of a commitment to equity for disadvantaged children in the case of research in the USA and because of the location of research units in the case of the British research), there was never enough variation in the 'context' or 'catchment area' variable for any discontinuities between areas in the factors responsible for effectiveness to become apparent. What emerged was a correspondingly simple 'steampress' perspective that saw a fixed set of school factors as generating effective educational outcomes. In the American context, a 'five factor' model was generally accepted, involving in most formulations (e.g. Lezotte, 1989):

(a) high expectations for students, based upon the belief that all children could learn;
(b) assertive leadership and a commitment to the importance of basic academic skill achievement from the principal;
(c) frequent monitoring of students' achievement test scores in such areas as reading and maths, with the results of the monitoring being fed back into decisions concerning curricular placement, option choice, and the like;
(d) an ordered school environment, in which communal areas were 'safe' and in which classrooms had considerable time for learning because of the absence of disciplinary interruptions, problematic transitions between lessons, and the like;
(e) a commitment to instructional goals by the school staff.

From the British literature, the studies of Rutter *et al* (1979), Reynolds (1982), Reynolds *et al* (1987) and Mortimore *et al* (1988) generated factors that appeared to be present in schools with high levels of academic achievement and low levels of pupils' behavioural problems and truancy problems. These factors included:

(a) headteacher management and leadership that involved a blend between a 'top down' determination of goals and motivation of staff, linked with high levels of involvement in the management of the school by the teaching staff;
(b) a climate of high expectations of what pupils could achieve, combined with a strong 'academic press' to enable the attainment of the academic goals, the latter involving high 'time on task' in classrooms, the

utilisation of homework to expand learning time and the entry of a high proportion of pupils into public examinations;

(c) the management of the pupils through the offering of rewards for good behaviour rather than the punishment of poor behaviour, in a climate where purposive and proactive policies were preferred to orientate pupils towards educational goals, rather than reactive or punitive ones;

(d) pupil involvement in the day-to-day life of the school generated by a proliferation of leadership positions, society positions and within-classroom positions, such as classroom monitorships;

(e) close links with parents, designed to involve them in the life of schools and designed to ensure that if there were a need to intervene with any pupil problems such as truancy, then parents would be supportive of the school;

(f) a caring orientation to pupils' learning and behavioural problems in which pupils felt able to approach staff with their needs;

(g) a controlled and cohesive environment, exhibiting cohesion, consistency and constancy, thereby generating a controlled socialisation process for children.

However, these 'recipes' of factors associated with 'effectiveness' defined in terms of low levels of truancy and high levels of academic achievement have appeared to be increasingly intellectually vulnerable from the mid 1980s. A study from the USA (Hallinger & Murphy, 1986) showed that effective schools in severely disadvantaged catchment areas may be significantly different from those in other areas in their characteristics, particularly in their distancing of themselves from their parents rather than relating directly to them as in the effective schools 'model' above. Work from New Zealand by Galloway (1983) in four schools with an apparent absence of behavioural problems showed a variety of headteacher management styles, all apparently equally effective when aligned with the particular history, culture, personalities and ethos of their schools. Recent research from the Louisiana School Effectiveness Project (Teddlie & Stringfield, 1993) again shows variation between schools in different catchment areas in the ways in which schools are improved over time by their principals.

The danger of the application of 'recipe' knowledge concerning the effectiveness characteristics of schools to schools in widely divergent catchment areas and of widely different history, culture, ethos and managerial arrangements within countries has recently been increased by the simplistic application of factors effective within one country into the educational systems of others. Demands in the UK for head teachers to take on a more managerial, assertive and central role within their schools are often buttressed by the American effective schools research noted earlier, yet European research (van de Grift, 1990) has consistently failed to replicate the American findings. A further example would be the proposed lengthening of the school day and the reduction in the number of days of school holidays that is apparently being discussed in some American states due to the popularity of explanations of Japan's effectiveness that point to high 'time to learn' and 'opportunity to learn' (see, for example, *Business Week*, 14 September 1992), even though simply transplanting extra learning time into American settings with low rates of pupil 'time on task' may be highly unlikely to transfer educational achievements or levels of pupils' attendance! (Further discussion of problems of context specificity are to be found in Reynolds *et al*, 1994.)

The independence of attendance from other outcomes

If major concern about the past simplistic application of the knowledge base is raised by the possible specificity of 'effectiveness' factors in relation to certain cultural contexts, then even more concern is likely to be generated by the recent evidence concerning the dependence/independence of school outcomes. Early research that had utilised a variety of academic and social outcome measures (e.g. Reynolds, 1976, 1982; Rutter *et al*, 1979) had argued for 'effective' schools being so across a wide range of outcomes, and therefore that the aetiology and factors which were responsible for the generation of high attendance were the same as those responsible for the generation of high academic achievement.

While knowledge in this area is hampered by the still rather limited number of school effectiveness studies that utilise pupil attendance as an outcome variable (none of the large number of Dutch studies do so, for example), in the British *Junior School Project* of Mortimore *et al* (1988) it is clear that the attendance rate variable in their sample of junior schools has an apparently different aetiology and constellation of associations by comparison with other outcome variables. Firstly, this study found that the effects of school upon cognitive and non-cognitive outcomes were virtually completely independent of each other, with the cognitive outcomes utilised in this study being reading, mathematics, writing quality, writing length and oracy, and with the non-cognitive outcomes used being self-concept, behaviour, attendance, attitude to school, attitude to mathematics, attitude to reading and attitude to writing.

Secondly, the study found that if one utilises customary forms of factor analysis to explore the possible structures that underlie the data, then the two independent dimensions that are generated (of cognitive and non-cognitive factors) exclude the attendance-rate variable completely, suggesting that school effects upon attendance are significantly different from those upon the other outcome variables.

Thirdly, the distribution of explained variance between the three levels of pupil, class and school is different in the case of attendance from all the other outcome variables. The school and class level explain significantly less variation in attendance rate (1.9%) than is the case with all the other outcome variables (where the comparable figure for reading, for example, is 15.8%, for mathematics is 18.7% and for attitude to school is 8.6%).

Fourthly, the actual factors that make a significant contribution to the explanation of the school effects upon attendance are both very small in number and very different to the factors explaining variation in the other outcome measures. At *school* level, one factor was found: pupil demeanour and behaviour around the school. At *classroom* level, four factors were found:

(a) The average percentage of teacher time spent discussing pupils' work.
(b) The average percentage of teacher time spent marking work silently in front of pupils.
(c) The average percentage of teacher time spent on higher order communication.
(d) The levels of inter-pupil cooperation.

By comparison, the school-level variable concerning 'demeanour' was not related significantly to any other of the outcome measurements, cognitive or non-cognitive. At classroom level, the variable 'extent of inter-pupil co-operation' only features as significantly related to one other outcome measure and the variable relating to 'the amount of time that teachers spend marking work silently in front of their pupils' is not significantly related to any other outcome variable, except attendance.

The strong indication from this study, widely argued to be the most detailed and comprehensive in its measurement and specification of school/classroom variables of recent years (see Scheerens, 1992 for further elaboration of this point), is that truancy/non-attendance from school may be a complex of types of behaviour that may have a different, distinct aetiology by comparison with other conventionally utilised cognitive and non-cognitive school outcomes. It may be substantially independent from other outcomes, may be differently caused and may relate to a different complex of within-school factors than other customarily used 'effectiveness' or outcome measures.

Some further caveats

Concerns about the simple and simplistic portrayals of truancy and its remediation within the early school-effectiveness literature are further magnified by a wide range of other recent findings in that literature. Specifically:

(a) On the size of school effects, early 'Messianic' beliefs that the effects of schools might be as large as the effects of family and community influences are misplaced, since a large number of studies in recent years show only 6–14% of the variation in pupil outcomes as due to educational factors, whether school or classroom based (see Bosker & Scheerens, 1989; Cuttance, 1992).

(b) On the consistency of school effects, early beliefs that 'effective' schools stayed in that status consistently over time have been put in doubt by studies showing quite rapid changes in effectiveness status, over 2 or 3 years in some instances (Nuttall *et al*, 1989).

(c) On the effectiveness of schools across different subgroups of pupils, the earlier belief that schools were effective or ineffective equally for all groups of pupils within them is no longer tenable in view of the evidence of the differential effectiveness of schools for children of different ethnic groups, ability ranges and socio-economic status groups (Aitken & Longford, 1986; Nuttall *et al*, 1989).

Most recent studies and reviews (e.g. Fitz-Gibbon *et al*, 1989; Cuttance, 1992; Scheerens, 1992) note that the classroom level seems to explain more of the variation in pupil academic and social outcomes than the school level, yet much of the emphasis within school effectiveness research has been, as the name suggests, upon the school.

There is no doubt, then, that the study of truancy as a school-effectiveness variable and its relationship to various school and classroom process factors within schools is an infinitely more complex intellectual and practical business than the early simplistic accounts of research and practice in the field suggested. The school-process factors associated with problems like truancy may be different in different ecological and situational niches. Truancy may be a symptom complex substantially different from other school outcomes in its aetiology and causal factors, and independent of other outcomes in numerous other ways also. If research on school outcomes can be generalised to the truancy outcome, then school effects on truancy may be relatively small, may be inconsistent over time and across different groups of children within schools, and may relate more to the classroom level than to the school level.

The need for new approaches in school effectiveness research

If we were to accept that the emergence of the evidence noted above calls for novel and more advanced methods and conceptualisations than evident hitherto in the study of school and classroom effects upon children's attendance levels, then it must be admitted that rather little of the necessary adjustments in our disciplinary procedures for the study of the school have taken place. In most recent studies of school effectiveness (e.g. Teddlie & Stringfield, 1993) there is, indeed, rather little evidence of the emergence of enhanced understanding by comparison with that generated by earlier studies (e.g. Brookover *et al*, 1979; Rutter *et al*, 1979; Reynolds *et al*, 1987). From studies of *international* variation in the effectiveness levels of schools rather than of *within-nation* variation, we are again deficient in understanding, partly because the use of resource-based or organisationally simplistic descriptions of schools and classrooms (generated and used clearly because of the need for cross-cultural reliability) does not do justice to the complexity of schools as organisations.

The need for more advanced conceptualisation, operationalisation and measurement of educational processes would seem to be particularly acute in the following respects:

(a) The rapid changes in the organisation of educational systems both in Britain and internationally (for example, the decentralisation of power to school level and the increased volume and importance of routine school assessment of student progress) has generated a need for new measures of school organisational functioning appropriate to the changed nature of the organisation's role. The widespread use of school development planning, now virtually universal within all cultures, is not matched by use of variables related to these activities as school-level variables.

(b) The use of a variety of multiple-level methodologies and analyses has been rightly regarded as revolutionising the study of educational effects, but researchers have been unwilling or unable to generate the associated revolution in data gathering needs at school level. The exposure of within-school variation in effectiveness by class, by pupil ability group, by social class, by ethnicity and by subject department that has been revealed for the first time in multiple-level studies needs to be matched by the introduction of 'class/school interface' variables concerned with how this variation is maximised or minimised within different types of 'effective' or 'ineffective' schools.

(c) The absence of any 'running through' of the same variables at classroom, school and school/educational community levels reduces the explanatory power. The variables measured at the two levels tend to be very different, and although there is no reason why certain school-level variables may have effects upon other different class-level variables, in the present state of knowledge the 'opening up' of the interface between the school and the classroom is more likely to take place if the *same* variables are studied at school and within-school level, with the difference or lack of difference between the two levels on the same variables being used to open up the management of the school/class interface.

(d) Where studies have utilised multiple measures of outcome by the adoption of 'social' or 'affective' outcomes such as truancy, it is noticeable that the number of school-level variables that are associated with variation in these outcomes are notably less for the social outcomes such as truancy as compared to the academic outcomes, suggesting that we are not at the moment tapping the school variables (climate? emotional tone? relationships?) necessary to explain variation.

(e) The power of the classroom level as a determinant of outcomes shown by many reviews of the literature has not been matched by the necessary re-conceptualisation of the nature of the school level. Rather than having strong *direct* influences upon development, the school may now more usefully be seen as facilitating or hindering the classroom level to potentiate student learning. Adoption of this re-conceptualisation would lead to a different focus on somewhat different variables at school level (and probably to a focus upon the interface and the interaction between the various schools' organisational arrangements and their classroom levels).

(f) The conceptualisation and measurement of variables at school level has been inadequately sensitive to the range of possible factors that may have effects. Most studies (see review in Reynolds, 1992) have used formal organisational factors (e.g. mixed ability teaching as against streaming by ability) but few of these, and few in total, have used the 'culture' of schooling in terms of teachers' attitudes to mixed ability/streaming. The third dimension of school life, that of the psychological or psychosocial which is concerned with the relationships between individuals, and the 'psycho-history' of the patterns of relationships found has been rarely studied (in this case, the variable would be operationalised as factors such as the friendship patterns of the teachers who use/have attitudes to mixed ability teaching and those who use/have attitudes to streaming by ability). The use of sociometric techniques to explore this third 'dimension' of schooling, and the adoption of an associated 'micropolitical' perspective, have been much neglected within school effectiveness research.

(g) The role of the head teacher in British schools has changed considerably in the last decade, with this person now being responsible for a range of new responsibilities (organising school finances, determining school in-service budgets, etc). It would be wrong to proceed with the customary measurement of the role of the head teacher in British schools, for example, without developing new instruments to measure what the new role features are.

(h) The changed nature of schools, and the changed interactions and relationships between schools and other socialising agencies, also make new approaches to the study of the school important. In the USA, the large number of 'add on' programmes is a noticeable educational feature: the planning and 'co-ordination' of the educational enterprise may now be important concepts to operationalise and measure. Also, the increased heterogeneity within societies, and the decrease of power within the socialising agencies of the family and the community, combine to potentially elevate a variable such as the consistency of the school's socialisation process to an importance it would not formerly have had.

(i) A final point, implicit in most of the above but in need of emphasising, is that school effectiveness needs to be much more concerned with 'cross-level' issues than before. The unidimensionality and restricted nature of one-level analyses are clear, but it is also important to realise that the *interactions* across and between the levels of the educational process (classroom, school, local educational structure, national educational structure) need to be modelled and ultimately measured and analysed. The product could be a multi-level, dynamic and interactive account of schooling, of a much more advanced nature than those at present on offer within school effectiveness research.

School effectiveness research at the cutting edge

In the last 4 or 5 years, it is clear that effectiveness and improvement researchers and practitioners have begun to make considerable advances in their fields, advances which take account of the nature of the new educational and social contexts outlined above, and which build on the insights into school and classroom processes noted above.

Useful American insights have come from some of the work conducted within their school improvement tradition, particularly from the work on schools such as the 'stuck' or 'moving' schools of Susan Rosenholtz (1989). The American work is now notable for its consistent use of multiple methods that utilise both quantitative and qualitative data, as they are deemed appropriate to the particular problem being investigated, and shows none of the anodyne 'either quantitative or qualitative' mentality that seems to still excite the intellectual trailing edge within British educational research.

American work is now also increasingly strong on the potential context specificity of the factors that promote effective schools, and on the potential variation that there may be in what makes for effectiveness in differing contexts, either urban/rural or low socio-economic status/high socio-economic status. It also has much to contribute at the level of the experimental study of the causal status of correlational school effectiveness factors when they are applied within school improvement or school change programmes. Since over 50% of American school districts are routinely using school effectiveness programmes of one kind or another (General Accounting Office, 1989), there is considerable scope for work of this kind, although the experimental situation is usually clearly based upon 'experiments of nature' involving non-random allocation to experimental and control groups rather than on random allocation as in classical experimental design.

From The Netherlands have come major contributions in three areas. Firstly, the Dutch have been particularly keen to explore the nature of effective instructional practices at the classroom level (Creemers, 1992), in part because of the absence within their culture of any sociological traditions of research at the school level, and also in part because of the important influence in their culture of psychological perspectives from the cognitive psychologists emphasis upon learning and instruction. Secondly, the Dutch have consistently utilised large sample sizes, drawn representatively from a full range of social and economic contexts, a marked contrast to the research base in Britain, which has been based almost exclusively on inner London and the Welsh Valleys. Thirdly, the Dutch have begun to attempt to generate some middle range theoretical models that can begin to causally order the school/classroom variables and which can act both as a guide to entrants to the field (who do not have time for the reinvention of the wheel) and as a codification of knowledge that makes it more accessible and ultimately understandable by practitioners than the frankly grubby empiricism of purely statistical approaches (see Scheerens, 1992 for an example).

While there have also been some contributions from Australia, Scandinavia and continental Europe, a considerable variety of contributions have come from Britain recently. They are of three main types:

(a) Studies that systematically attempt to measure the school and the classroom factors associated with effectiveness, as in the recent work of Sammons *et al* (1994). These studies use both academic and social outcome measures, and define effectiveness much more broadly than research traditions in other countries.

(b) Studies utilising already existing datasets that are concerned with academic achievement solely, with public examinations results at age 16 or 18 being related to prior measures of achievement at age 11, or age 16 in the case of A-levels. These studies focus upon 'school against school' effects (see Gray *et al*, 1990).

(c) Studies that combine use of academic intake data and public examination data with other measures of pupil outcomes (such as attitudes) and which focus particularly upon the within-school variation that exists by department within schools, hoping to develop indicator systems to help schools themselves develop their own insights concerning effective practice at classroom, department and school levels that are relevant to the particular school context, history, culture, phase of development and educational personalities involved (see Fitz-Gibbon *et al*, 1989).

From school effectiveness to school improvement?

The most difficult of the problems within the field of school effectiveness may not be the improvement of the knowledge base to deal with both the doubts and uncertainties noted above and with the changed educational and societal contexts of advanced industrial societies. Judging by experience so far, the most difficult problems may be the introduction of the findings into the educational system in general and into ineffective schools in particular, a process that is important for reasons of ideology (this research field is an applied science like medicine or engineering) and for the potential increments in knowledge that can be generated by the interaction between school effectiveness research and the needs of schools to improve.

It is this area of the application of knowledge that has produced the biggest disappointments in the UK. Taking the findings from the *Fifteen Thousand Hours* study (Maughan *et al*, 1990) back into some of the schools that had participated in generating them produced minimal improvement in pupil outcomes. My own attempts to take the knowledge base into schools have also often generated little improvement and have been described in some detail (Murgatroyd & Reynolds, 1984, 1985; Reynolds, 1987).

The implications of these failures may be that we need to start studying the *ineffective* schools with the same fervour and purpose that we have attached to the problem of conceptualising and operationalising school *effectiveness*. We must become the discipline of school effectiveness *and* ineffectiveness.

The task is urgent because the educational context is probably that a higher proportion of schools are now falling below the threshold of 'basic organisational adequacy', because the props from local educational authorities that kept some schools from 'bottoming out' have been taken away as local authority roles change and as their personnel retrench. Increased responsibilities for head teachers may actually make some incompetent who were not so formerly, because the enhanced pressure will expose deficiencies that were hidden before. Superimposing on schools a range of responsibilities such as managing teacher appraisal, starting school development planning and running ambitious improvement programmes is likely to result in the raising of the educational ceiling by competent persons in competent schools but is also likely to result in the floor of incompetence being left increasingly far behind, both relatively and absolutely.

Ignorance about these schools is stark. School improvement persons do not visit them because the ineffective school and its pathologies are far more problematic than the effective school. School effectiveness researchers often lose these schools and the knowledge that they could furnish because they fail to participate in research through dropping out. Besides, effectiveness researchers have implicitly 'back mapped' the characteristics of the effective school onto the ineffective school, thinking that what the ineffective school has is the absence of the things that made the effective school effective. We have not entertained the possibility that the ineffective school itself has factors that are unknown in the effective school which require distinctive approaches. We have, in short, only viewed failure as not being successful, not as failure. Indeed, some of the effectiveness factors that come out of the study of effective institutions may be the *results* of effectiveness rather than the cause and the ineffective school simply may not be able to generate them.

Those schools that are ineffective are likely to provide very stern tests of our professional capabilities. They are likely to be missing the prior competencies that are needed to do precisely the kinds of things that we at present wish them to do to become more effective, like development planning for example. They may be, in fact, thoroughly non-rational institutions, where all sorts of delusions may flourish as a means by which ineffective and ineffectual individuals avoid the brutal truth of their own ineffectiveness. Catchment areas, local authority housing estates, local social and economic conditions, and parents may be projected upon and used as excuses for failure.

There may well be in these schools various pathologies — there may be fear of outsiders, which is likely to be masked by strong defences both personal and group based. There may be a reluctance to risk change, not because the school does not need it (which is the reason the ineffective teachers will give) but actually because of fear that the change will be unsuccessful and further hurt teachers who have in reality low self-esteem. The ineffective school may also have inside itself 'multiple schools' formed around cliques and friendship groups, cliques that act to reflect and in turn mould differences in competence. There will be none of the organisational, social, cultural and symbolic 'tightness' of the effective school.

Our actions with these schools would need to be appropriate to what they are and to where they are coming from. Firstly, in the short term, we would need to be directive with them, telling them what to do, independent of whether they agree or not. There is little point in attempting to use principles of 'ownership' or 'collegiality' in our early help attempts — people who have collectively permitted a school to hit educational rocks are unlikely to be those who steer it off them.

Secondly, we should build on whatever it is that these schools themselves have as 'good practice'. All of these schools will have individuals and departments who are relatively more effective than others. Some ineffective schools will have individuals and departments who are absolutely effective when seen in the context of what is effective across all schools. Using methods of 'buddying' and 'pairing' the ineffective with the more effective schools may be productive of a school that can generate its own knowledge of itself and that can slowly replace the reliance upon outside knowledge that is needed in the short term.

There are numerous other ways in which we may want to act with these schools to improve their levels of effectiveness:

(a) We might want to bring our knowledge into them by using the 'Trojan Horse' philosophy of school improvement, where the bringer of these good things is not an outsider but a member of school senior staff who has been trained to become a change agent (as in the successful pilot schemes of Reynolds *et al*, 1989).

(b) We might want to eliminate the negative first, to do something about the floor before reaching for the ceiling and accentuating the positive.

(c) We might want to use micropolitical skills to build a coalition for success that will increasingly isolate the rump of poor practice (see Reynolds, 1991 for further development of this theme).

(d) We might want to use psychotherapeutic techniques to deal with the ineffective schools' abnormality and pathology. These techniques – group work, the use of 'confessionals', physically recreating interactive situations to shake people free from the mental ecology that can enslave them in prisons of pathology – can exorcise the ghosts or psychosocial 'shadows' of ineffective schools' past histories. It was Elizabeth Richardson (1973) who first suggested this way of 'treating' schools, informed by the psychoanalytic tradition.

Beyond the conventional boundaries of school effectiveness research

Whatever we may learn from our involvement with schools that are ineffective, and it is indeed ironic that in our dealings with them we are likely to need the help of the psychology and psychiatry that school effectiveness research has supplanted as a 'popular' explanatory paradigm for truancy and school failure, it may be that we need to go beyond our current intellectual boundaries in the search for educational institutions that can combine the high achievement, high attendance and positive social outcomes that were the original goals of the effective schools movement. In short, the answers of how to avoid low efficiency and effectiveness for our educational institutions may lie within those societies and within those organisations that have, for different reasons, been forced to generate no fault, right first time, organisational processes.

To take the cross-cultural example first, it is clear that many societies have been forced to generate highly reliable forms of schooling to develop themselves as nations. Taiwan is a case in point, where a society has been created by a particular interaction between culture, economy, education and society. Education there is part of national planning, is a central state responsibility, is adequately funded (indeed funding is tied to gross national product), and has educational professionals who behave somewhat differently to ours. There is routine quality monitoring of the staff by principals involving the collection of all the pupils' homework books and the random selection of some for checking by the principal every term. Each child takes home at the end of school to their parents or caretakers a book in which the child has described in detail the educational experiences and the curriculum knowledge acquired in the day, for parents to see and act on as they see fit. In lessons, teachers routinely attempt to ensure that all children pass over the hurdles of basic skill acquisition, since the aim is to ensure that all children are educated without failure. Children who fail to complete work continue to work during lesson transitions, in lunch hour or after school, the aim being to reduce the range of intellectual variation to make it possible for teaching to be a pleasant, stress-free job for teachers, and a productive learning experience for children.

At the moment, school effectiveness research in Britain celebrates only the utility of the more effective institutions within a very small range of degrees of effectiveness. Looking to those societies that generate both high mean scores of academic achievement, high attendance levels and also a reduced spread or range of scores may be necessary in order for us truly to see educational possibilities hidden if we restrain ourselves to the study of our own culture.

The second possibly useful direction for us to take in the search for school excellence beyond our country and disciplinary boundaries is to study those organisations that are not permitted to fail and see if there are useful lessons for schools. They are known as HROs or high reliability organisations. They are usually taken to be airline traffic controllers, nuclear power plant operatives, electricity supply operatives and all those other organisations and their employees who have to generate 100% reliable functioning (see Stringfield & Slavin, 1991).

The characteristics of HROs are as follows:

(a) They train extensively, pre-service and in-service, in order to eliminate operational flaws. When training, all levels of an organisation act as respondents on the effectiveness of all levels, in a process of mutual monitoring.
(b) The goals of the HROs are few and are explicit.
(c) There is a body of knowledge about practice that is codified into standard operating procedures (SOPs), which tell people how to behave in the event of any contingency.
(d) Great attention is given to minor errors, since the belief is that these could cascade into major system failure.
(e) Simulations to identify weak links are always being run, with direct action being taken to identify the trailing edge and to make it more effective.
(f) The organisations are well resourced and equipment is kept in good order.

Underlying the reasons for the existence of all the organisational procedures is the belief that system failure or unreliability would generate costs that are too heavy for a society to bear. One must ask why that belief does not apply to educational failure also.

Conclusions

In this chapter attempts have been made to review the existing state of our knowledge in the fields of school effectiveness and school improvement, and in particular to assess the utility of the research paradigm of effectiveness research to the understanding of truancy. The great popularity of school effectiveness approaches in the literature on truancy, and some of the simplification that has often taken place of the nature of the findings, have been noted. Problems of the context specificity of effective schools' factors and the different aetiology of attendance as a school outcome variable from the other customary outcome variables have been particularly noted.

Various educational and social changes are argued to have increased the need for a considerable re-conceptualisation of school effectiveness research in its focus upon 'the school', yet considerable improvements in the nature of the research enterprise are clear in the knowledge base generated within the USA, in The Netherlands and in the UK over the last few years. It is argued that our remaining problem is to improve the take-up of knowledge within practice communities, and to particularly focus upon the ineffective school as a research site. Looking outside the current range of relative effectiveness, to samples where there is absolute effectiveness, is suggested as useful, especially in the cases of societies and organisations that have to exist without any apparent failure or ineffectiveness.

It should be clear from this chapter that school effectiveness research has in many ways probably subsumed into its disciplinary arrangements many of the approaches, and indeed some of the people, who might formerly have been expected to explore the interface between educational achievement and non-attendance problems, and educational achievement and delinquency also. Indeed, in recent years there has been little of the flowering of research into *specifically* school links with patterns of non-attendance that were seen in the early 1980s (see, for example, Fogelman, 1978, 1983; Farrington, 1980) and there has been a more general treatment of truancy as one of a number of educational outcomes related to generalised educational factors.

This may be in the long term a retrograde step, however, in view of the evidence of the distinctive aetiology of truancy by comparison with other outcomes from schools. The bodies of knowledge that are related to when one treats truancy as an important outcome in its own right are many and varied: the literature on deviance and delinquency or on abnormal family dynamics are but two examples of these. As school effectiveness begins to look outside its conventional disciplinary boundaries in search of the insights that can improve the quality of its explanatory power, a revival in the historically important area of the truancy/school processes interaction is more desirable than ever.

References

AITKEN, M. & LONGFORD, N. (1986) Statistical modelling issues in school effectiveness studies. *Journal of the Royal Statistical Society, Series A,* **149,** 1–43.

BOSKER, R. J. & SCHEERENS, J. (1989) Issues in the interpretation of the results of school effectiveness research. *International Journal of Educational Research,* **13,** 741–751.

BROOKOVER, W. B., BEADY, C., FLOOD, P., *et al* (1979) *School Social Systems and Student Achievement.* New York: Praeger.

CARLEN, P., GLEESON, D. & WARDHAUGH, J. (1992) *Truancy: the Politics of Compulsory Schooling.* Buckingham: The Open University Press.

CREEMERS, B. (1992) School effectiveness and effective instruction – the need for a further relationship. In *School Effectiveness and Improvement* (eds J. Bashi & Z. Sass). Jerusalem: Hebrew University Press.

CUTTANCE, P. (1992) Assessing the effectiveness of schools. In *School Effectiveness* (eds D. Reynolds & P. Cuttance). London: Cassell.

FARRINGTON, D. (1980) Truancy, delinquency, the home and the school. In *Out of School* (eds L. Hersov & I. Berg). Chichester: John Wiley.

FITZ-GIBBON, C., TYMMS, P. B. & HAZELWOOD, R. D. (1989) Performance indicators and information systems. In *School Effectiveness and Improvement* (eds D. Reynolds, B. P. M. Creemers & T. Peters). Groningen: RION.

FOGELMAN, K. (1978) The effectiveness of schooling. In *Perimeters of Social Repair* (eds W. H. G. Armytage & J. Peel). London: Academic Press.

—— (1983) *Growing Up in Great Britain.* London: Macmillan.

GALLOWAY, D. (1983) Disruptive pupils and effective pastoral care. *School Organisation,* **13,** 245–254.

GENERAL ACCOUNTING OFFICE (1989) *Effective Schools Programmes – Their Extent and Characteristics.* Gaithersburg, MD: General Accounting Office.

GRAY, J., JESSON, D. & SIME, N. (1990) Estimating differences in the examination performance of secondary schools in six LEA's – a multilevel approach to school effectiveness. *Oxford Review of Education,* **16,** 137–158.

HALLINGER, P. & MURPHY, J. (1986) The social context of effective schools. *American Journal of Education,* **94,** 328–355.

HARGREAVES, A. (1994) *Changing Teachers, Changing Times.* London: Casell.

—— & REYNOLDS, D. (eds) (1989) *Education Policy: Controversies and Critiques.* Lewes: Falmer Press.

HARGREAVES, D. & HOPKINS, D. (1991) *The Empowered School.* London: Cassell.

LEZOTTE, L. (1989) School improvement based on the effective schools research. *International Journal of Educational Research,* **13,** 815–825.

MAUGHAN, B., OUSTON, J., PICKLES, A., *et al* (1990) Can schools change: outcomes at six London secondary schools. *School Effectiveness and Improvement,* **1,** 188–210.

MORTIMORE, P. (1991) School effectiveness research: which way at the crossroads? *School Effectiveness and School Improvement,* **2,** 213–229.

——, SAMMONS, P. & ECOB, R. (1988) *School Matters: The Junior Years.* Salisbury: Open Books.

MURGATROYD, S. J. & REYNOLDS, D. (1984) Leadership and the teacher. In *New Directions in Educational Leadership* (ed. P. Harling). Lewes: Falmer Press.

—— & —— (1985) The creative consultant. *School Organisation,* **4,** 321–335.

NUTTALL, D., GOLDSTEIN, J., PROSSER, R., *et al* (1989) Differential school effectiveness. *International Journal of Educational Research,* **13,** 769–776.

REID, K. (1985) *Truancy and School Absenteeism.* London: Hodder and Stoughton.

—— (1986) *Disaffection from School.* London: Methuen.

—— (ed.) (1989) *Helping Troubled Pupils in Secondary Schools*. Oxford: Blackwell Education.

REYNOLDS, D. (1976) The delinquent school. In *The Process of Schooling* (ed. P. Woods). London: Routledge and Kegan Paul.

—— (1982) The search for effective schools. *School Organisation*, **2**, 215–237.

—— (1984) Creative conflict: the implications of recent educational research for those concerned with children. *Maladjustment and Therapeutic Education*, Spring, 14–23.

—— (1987) The effective school: the 1986 Association of Educational Psychologists Lecture. *Educational Psychology in Practice*, October.

—— (1988) The consultant sociologist: a method for linking sociology of education and teachers. In *Sociology and Teaching* (eds P. Woods & A. Pollard). London: Croom Helm.

—— (1991) Changing ineffective schools. In *Effective Schools for All* (ed M. Ainscow). London: David Fulton.

—— (1992) School effectiveness and school improvement in the 1990s. In *School Effectiveness* (eds D. Reynolds & P. Cuttance). London: Cassell.

——, SULLIVAN, M. & MURGATROYD, S. J. (1987) *The Comprehensive Experiment*. Lewes: Falmer Press.

——, DAVIE, R. & PHILLIPS, D. (1989) The Cardiff programme – an effective school improvement programme based on school effectiveness research. *Developments in school effectiveness research. Special issue of the International Journal of Educational Research*, **13**, 800–814.

—— & CUTTANCE, P. (1992) *School Effectiveness: Research Policy and Practice*. London: Cassell.

——, HOPKINS, D. & STOLL, L. (1993) Linking school effectiveness knowledge and school improvement practice: towards a synergy. *School Effectiveness and School Improvement*, **4**, 37–58.

——, CREEMERS, B. P. M., STRINGFIELD, S., *et al* (1994) *Advances in School Effectiveness Research and Practice*. Oxford: Pergamon Press.

RICHARDSON, E. (1973) *The Teacher, the School and the Task of Management*. London: Heinemann.

ROSENHOLTZ, S. (1989) *Teachers' Workplace*. New York: Longman.

RUTTER, M., MAUGHAN, B., MORTIMORE, P., *et al* (1979) *Fifteen Thousand Hours: Secondary Schools and their Effects on Children*. London: Open Books.

SAMMONS, P., THOMAS, S., MORTIMORE, P., *et al* (1994) Understanding the processes of school and departmental effectiveness. Presented at the *Annual Meeting of the British Educational Research Association*, Oxford.

SCHEERENS, J. (1992) *Effective Schooling*. London: Cassell.

STRINGFIELD, S. & SLAVIN, R. (1991) Raising societal demands, high reliability organisations, school effectiveness, success for all and a set of modest proposals. In *Interuniversitair Centrum Voor Onderwijsevaluie*, October.

TEDDLIE, C. & STRINGFIELD, S. (1993) *Schools Make A Difference: Lessons Learned from a Ten Year Study of School Effects*. New York: Teachers College Press.

VAN DE GRIFT, W. (1990) Educational leadership and academic achievement in secondary education. *School Effectiveness and School Improvement*, **1**, 26–41.

5 Absences in a primary school

SUSAN ELINOR WRIGHT and
MARLENE WARDLE

The plan of this chapter is as follows: we first discuss the type of absences that were a cause of concern in recent years to the teachers in a London primary school; then pick out indicative factors that may have precipitated these absences; and outline the kind of policies and support that we believe need to be in place. Finally, we place the discussion within a wider philosophical debate about the justifications for compulsory schooling.

Introduction

We are writing from our own experience. Marlene Wardle has from the early 1970s onward been a teacher in a London inner-city primary school — first a class teacher, then deputy head and latterly head teacher. Susan Wright became acquainted with the school in the early 1980s through her role of supervising students who were carrying out teaching practice in the school. She became a school governor, co-opted from higher education and is currently vice-chair of the governing body.

Stirling Street School (not its real name) is what is known as a maintained primary school. This means that it is what would probably be thought of as an 'ordinary' school: it is funded entirely by public money, at present a mixture of government and local authority funding, and is not a designated school for children with special educational needs.

In the UK, the primary school caters for children between the ages of 5 and 11. The overall age group is subdivided into infant (5–7) and junior (7–11). In some schools there is also a nursery class, which takes children from 3 years old. Compulsory education begins in the term after the one which the child has had her, or his, fifth birthday. At 11 children transfer to a secondary school. Compulsory schooling ends at 16. Some pupils stay on for a further two years, to gain a higher level of leaving qualification.

One striking difference that has occurred since the former editions of *Unwillingly to School* were published is that there are now a large number of children who have special eduational needs who are being educated within the maintained school. The ground-breaking Warnock Report (DES, 1978) advocated both a wide interpretation of the notion of a special educational need and the integration, wherever possible, of children with special needs into the maintained classroom. The 1981 Education Act encouraged local education authorities to implement such integration. Nationally, the integration has been patchy, and very much dependent on the level of resources available. However, the principle of integration is now widely accepted, and it is a common experience to find children with special needs in the maintained classroom and to expect the class teacher to be able to deal effectively with such children, perhaps with some specialised help. The amount and nature of the support available varies from one local authority to another. The greater variety of need being catered for within the one classroom often puts stress on both teacher and children. It will be a feature of this chapter that there will be a major focus on children with special needs, as we believe that most children who have substantial absences also have some kind of special need.

Since 1981 it has become the norm for schools to have a well worked out special needs policy. In the primary school at least, this was not necessarily the case 5–10 years ago. Stirling Street School has been developing policy and practice over the last few years, and the brief case histories that follow should be seen against this background.

One of the advantages of the school perspective is that it gives an overview of the entire population that comes within its community. Stirling Street School is a small school of about 200 pupils with an additional 50 children attending either morning or afternoon nursery sessions. In common with most London schools, its community includes children and parents with a number of different ethnic backgrounds, home languages and religions. Over half of the children speak at least two languages. The two languages other than English that predominate are Bengali and Arabic. There are a few children from European Community or East European countries and a smattering of recent refugees, from Eritrea, Somalia and latterly Bosnia. There is also a substantial number of children from an Afro-Caribbean background.

Stirling Street School is not necessarily representative of all UK primary schools. Schools of a different size, a different location, or a different type of catchment would all have different factors affecting them. So would secondary schools within the same type of area.

The six cases that have been picked out for discussion are of children who were on the school roll in the recent past and who had sufficient absences from school to alert the attention of the teachers. In all of the cases, the names of the children have been changed and identifying details have been omitted. Some of the absences had officially sanctioned explanations; some did not. Some of the children came to the notice of agencies other than the school; some did not.

The children have now all left the school. Several of them were identified as giving cause for concern relatively late in their primary school career. In some cases this was because the factors that precipitated the absences were not present until this stage. In others, the school believes that had its present policy and practices been in place, difficulties could have been identified earlier, and preventative action taken.

Six brief case studies

The cases chosen are representative of the kinds of unapproved absences that have occurred at Stirling Street School over the last 10 or 12 years and therefore can be regarded as representative of those that have occurred since the 1981 Education Act.

Case 1

Wayne was 10 years old and the third of six children in a one-parent family. Going to school for Wayne was something that happened on the whole regularly, but with frequent interruptions.

Wayne's mother was caught between at least two cultural systems. Her own parents were born in the Caribbean, and carried with them the values of their country of origin. She herself had been educated in the UK and therefore exposed to the institutionalised racism that characterised the education system and the wider society of her generation. This made it difficult for her to co-operate with school authorities. She was not wholly convinced that schooling could be a beneficial experience. In addition to this, Wayne had pressures from his elder brother who was a school avoider and, according to the local grapevine, involved in criminal activities connected with drugs and stealing.

Frequent and often unsuccessful struggles to cope with the 'system' led to Wayne sometimes appearing at school unkempt and without socks. Other times he arrived late, on his own initiative, while his mother was still asleep.

Wayne wanted to come to school. At school, however, he often bullied other children and made a general nuisance of himself. His teachers had picked out learning difficulties that constantly frustrated him. They also felt that to be of lasting help to Wayne someone would have needed to supply his mother with the experience of parenting that she had never had (impossible for a school to do) and to have had resources to give him one-to-one attention for a large part of the week.

At one stage they thought they had made a real breakthrough, when, through a scheme the school regularly takes part in, a visiting performing arts company tapped some real natural talent. This fizzled out – his mother's life was too chaotic for her to be able to follow it up and when Wayne transferred to secondary school, contact was lost. Informal feedback from younger siblings suggested that he became a regular truant.

Case 2

Joanne was from a local working class family, resident in the area for many generations, with a wide network of friends and extended family. She had attended the school from the nursery stage onwards and became a cause for concern only at the later primary stage. She attended school regularly and her absences were 'authorised' in the sense that they were always duly covered by notes from her mother. She was the younger of two girls and her parents were in the process of breaking up. She had learning difficulties that had been assessed by the educational psychologist and for which she was receiving regular additional support.

Joanne often displayed physical symptoms such as a stomach ache or a headache, which prevented her from attending, or which developed at school, and led to the class teacher asking her mother to come and collect her.

Joanne's mother was fully co-operative with the school, but Joanne seemed unwilling to attend. She frequently visited an infant teacher who had been her class teacher at an earlier stage of her education. The school gradually came to suspect that she was badly disturbed by the parental break-up: she seemed to be bearing the brunt while her elder sister sailed through it with no visible ill effects. She also had an overt fear of failure at school, which seemed to arise from her learning difficulties.

She left for the secondary stage with her learning and home difficulties both very much still in existence, and the school expected her pattern of absences to continue.

Case 3

William was an only child of older parents who were both professionals, and very anxious to further their child's education. He was 6 when he joined the school and 8 when he started to give cause for concern. He strongly resisted all his parents' efforts to get him to school, often creating temper tantrums. To the school, when this behaviour began, he seemed at first to be a spoiled brat well able to manipulate his parents to his own advantage.

Investigations and dialogue with his parents revealed learning difficulties, which were addressed by moving him to a school that has small classes and specialises in learning difficulties. It is an independent school and the local authority paid the fees. This was a case where the school felt it had been able to negotiate an ongoing satisfactory outcome that brought an end to the pattern of absence.

Case 4

Mariam amd Mohammed had a father who seemed unwilling to accept that he was now living in a country where schooling is compulsory. Mariam was 6 years old and Mohammed 8 when the family moved into the school's catchment area. The children were rarely at school, to the point where the father was under threat of being taken to court. Even this threat did not alter his apparent refusal to send his children to school. He understood the system enough to give illness as the reason for one particular absence, but for an absence during a time when a teacher had spotted the children out and about in the local streets. This case remained unresolved because the family moved out of the area within two years.

Because the family was with the school for a comparatively short time, many factors will necessarily stay unknown. However, before they left, Mohammed had had learning difficulties identified through the operation of the school's own special needs support system.

Case 5

Claire and Jacqueline were more like the stereotype of the truant. They were close friends, 10 years old, and subject to inducements to truant from older neighbourhood friends. The difference here was that neither school nor parents knew they were truanting before it was discovered in the course of a routine check. On the face of it here were two sub-adolescent girls who had found something more desirable than going to school and who were, in a very straightforward way, taking advantage of it. They were two lively girls who had no learning difficulties. However both had difficult circumstances in their family backgrounds that may have been a factor.

For both girls there was a close relationship between school and home, and as soon as the absences were discovered they were promptly returned to the school system. Thereafter their attendance was carefully monitored. Their transition to secondary school was smooth, and as far as the school knows no further absences have occurred.

Case 6

Michael and Brian seldom came to school. Brian, who had just turned 5, had not really got the idea of school and needed to be constantly monitored to make sure he stayed on the premises. Michael, who was 8, was eager to learn. When at school, he soaked up any morsel of learning that came his way. His family never stayed in one place long enough for him to settle down, or build on learning from previous schools. Both Michael and Brian were cheerful children and the school was sorry to lose them when their family moved on. The family was permanently short of money, had no settled home and was riven by dissensions between various family members. The children were shunted around, not just from one home to another but also from one set of family members to another.

Precipitating factors

The children in these six cases differed in age, sex, social class and ethnic origin. None of these factors seems to be a determinant for the avoidance of school. However, all of the children had understandable reasons for not being at school. In one case, sexual abuse by a near relative was suspected but without sufficiently clear indications for an investigation to be made. Nearly all the children seemed to be low in self-esteem. Learning difficulties were frequently in evidence before the pattern of absence emerged. (Prolonged absence can of itself cause learning difficulties, through the tendency to fall behind class-mates.)

Some of the children quite badly wanted to be at school. For some children, school can be intrinsically desirable, in spite of countervailing opinions held by the home. In other cases it can be a refuge from serious abuse, involving either the child or one of the parents (usually the mother).

Several features occur with some regularity in cases where there is a pattern of unapproved absences. We have classified these as follows:

Differing home/school values

These may occur where there are differences in culture, class, religion or nationality between the home and the school, each offering a model of correct usage, behaviour or opinion. Sometimes children cope very well with the competing models as for instance when they automatically switch from one 'dialogue' to another, from the classroom to the playground to the home. However, there can be fundamental clashes of perception between home and school, even over the value of schooling itself. Such differences can be very difficult for children to cope with. So can the situation where the neighbourhood provides a third set of values, different from those of both home and school, and sometimes introducing a criminal element. Some children solve the dilemma of having to reject and therefore be disloyal to either school or home by rejecting both in favour of the neighbourhood.

Second-generation immigrants, i.e. the children of the original migrants, can have particular difficulties in finding a way of reconciling the competing models of home and the wider society. Third-generation children may find they have to cope with second-generation parents, still caught in their own conflicts.

Where there are strongly held religious beliefs at stake, as for instance with fundamentalist subdivisions of any religion, it can be particularly difficult for the children, because they feel sinful as well as disloyal if they reject the home values.

Inadequate parenting

Some parents seem to find it difficult to conform to the normal standards of adequate care for their children. While it is to some extent subjective to make such a judgement about a parent, it can also be useful inasmuch as it directs attention towards support of the parents as well as the child. If the parents are not supported, then the so-called cycle of deprivation can arise: because they have lacked a model of adequate parenting, the children in their turn become inadequate parents.

Bullying

In the past, bullying has often gone unrecognised or has not been dealt with by schools. This is an area where there has been a shift in both perception and practice in recent years. Stirling Street School has a strong policy, well disseminated to parents and children, who know that any incident will be taken seriously. The school therefore has some confidence that most cases of bullying do come to its attention.

Family trauma

A parent may be seriously ill, have recently died or have recently left the family home. A child may be emotionally abused by parental fighting, or physically abused by either parent. Alcohol or drug abuse by a parent can also result in physical abuse of the child or the other parent. In many of these cases a child finds it difficult to leave home because of a fear of what might happen during the absence. This can be an emotionally grounded fear of the death or desertion of a remaining parent, or a realistic fear of physical abuse to one parent. Sometimes, however, the school provides a refuge, a place where the child feels safe.

Families under stress

Poverty, poor housing, unemployment and a large number of children within a family are factors that can cause stress to all family members. These factors often appear in conjunction and can produce associated problems of poor physical or mental health. In a recession, such problems come to the fore and particularly affect those who in any case tend to be at the bottom of the economic heap. This often applies to families from ethnic minority backgrounds, who may also be facing direct or indirect discrimination in many areas of their lives.

Children from such families who are having problems connected with school might have had these problems irrespective of the family circumstances. None the less there is no doubt that the external circumstances make it much harder for both family and child to cope.

Pure truancy

Pure truancy occurs when there is no obvious reason for a child to avoid school, but there is something intrinsically desirable that she or he wants to do instead. This might well include inducements from peer groups or from older children to join in activities that have the added attraction of being, through the very act of missing school, illicit.

Learning difficulties

As already suggested, these will occur inevitably once a regular pattern of non-attendance is established. Additionally, we often find that there have been learning difficulties clearly identified *before* the absences began. Learning difficulties often seem to be accompanied by low self-esteem, and a vicious circle is set up. The more the child is frustrated in efforts to learn, the lower her or his self-esteem becomes; and the lower the self-esteem, the harder it is to learn. In this situation, absence becomes an avoidance tactic, removing the child, temporarily at least, from a painful situation.

School strategies

Just as the causes of non-attendance are many and complex, so are the strategies the school uses in response. The children come to the school's attention in a number of ways. Initially, they may be picked out by the class teacher or by an education welfare officer (EWO). An EWO is a part of the local authority's education service, who visits the school regularly and always inspects the registers. EWOs are often the first to detect a worrying pattern of absence. Where concern has been aroused, they are able to make a home visit, and this will be a starting point for the school's own investigations and enquiries.

Often it is the parents who are the first to voice concern and to initiate investigations.

For each case, the school tries to build a relationship with the parents. This is not always easy. The parents are bringing a great deal of 'baggage' to the situation, from their own past history, from current power relationships within our society, from the competing values of the multicultural society. Somehow the school has to find a way through all of this and, of course, through whatever 'baggage' the teachers are carrying, in order to work out a joint policy that is agreed to be in the best interests of the child. Almost always this is possible. A vital element is the recognition that parents need to be listened to and supported, just as much as children do.

Once a relationship has been established, it may be necessary to pursue investigations with the help of the Schools Psychological Service, and through them to gain support where appropriate from the local authority's Special Needs Panel. Sometimes as little as one informal conversation with an educational psychologist can allay parents' fears and point a way forward.

In whatever way concern is raised, the school tries to work out a programme that meets the needs of the individual child. Where learning difficulties are involved, this will include extra support within or outside the classroom, sometimes on a one-to-one basis for a small part of the school week. For emotional difficulties, help is sought from the Schools Psychological Service or from a child guidance clinic. Where bullying is part of the problem, there are routines that automatically come into effect. All offending children are reported to their parents and excluded from the school for 2 or 3 days, if the bullying is repeated.

Because of the intimate knowledge it has of children and parents, a small primary school is often able to identify problems before they escalate into serious non-attendance and to take preventative action.

Policies

The organisation and particularly the funding of education in the UK is very much in a state of flux. The present Government has introduced local management of schools, a policy that devolves the administration of school funding to the level of the individual school. It is also Government policy to encourage schools to opt out completely from local authority control. At present, services like the Schools Psychological Service are still administered and funded by the local authority. In the future, such services may be hived off, privatised or completely disappear.

The policies that are in place at Stirling Street School, and which we are advocating, demand a certain level of available funding and of outside support for their implementation. Both within and outside the school, there needs to be money available for the support of individual children and their families. There is never, of course, enough funding and schools will always have to set priorities. Here, we wish only to point out that, as in so many areas of policy, spending more money on preventative work would save much more elsewhere. It is with a certain amount of foreboding for the future that we articulate the elements of policy that we believe to be necessary.

Early identification and intervention

If absences are being caused by learning or emotional difficulties, then it is essential to diagnose these as soon as possible so that appropriate action can be taken. Children who are left with problems not only unresolved but also unaddressed are often subject to levels of stress that can cause permanent damage to health and to family relationships.

Continuity of policy and practice

In inner-city schools there are large demands on available resources for the support of children with special needs and, often, a high turnover of staff from year to year. It is therefore necessary to renegotiate policies with new staff as they arrive and to make sure that priorities are preserved. For instance, it would be easy to overlook the needs of a child like Joanne, who was not causing the school any trouble. On the other hand, a child like Wayne, who one way or another caused a good deal of trouble, could turn out to be very expensive to support, and there could be a danger of lowering his priority to save money.

Affording a high level of support

This follows from the previous point. In Stirling Street School, the support of children with worrying patterns of absence comes under its special needs policy. It has a long-standing policy of releasing the deputy head from class teaching and allowing her to devote much of her time to the support of children with special needs. As financial constraints bite harder, it may not be possible to continue this level of support.

General requirement for special needs' policies

If many schools opt out from local authority control it becomes all the more necessary for all schools to be committed to the support of children with special needs. Schools that opt out can, to a large extent, determine their own selection criteria. Many of the children in our case studies could be unwelcome additions to a school community. There is a danger that 'problem' schools could develop for 'problem' children, and if such children become segregated and stigmatised their futures will be bleak. It is our belief that the implementation of special needs policies in schools should be externally monitored, nationally or locally, to ensure access for all children.

The 1988 Education Act and entitlement to education

This is the Act that established the National Curriculum and Standard Attainment Tests. One of its basic tenets is that all children are entitled to education and, within education, to a broad and balanced curriculum.

Teachers welcomed the language of entitlement. It is a long-standing problem, not just in the UK but also in all countries with a developed system of education, that some children seem to get more benefit from the system than do others.

Up to one-third of all children in inner-city areas have some kind of special need. The background circumstances of all the children in our case studies could easily be found within one classroom. In addition, primary schools nowadays are often faced with children displaying challenging behaviour, sometimes to the extent that outside help needs to be brought in. This was not common in earlier generations. It is partly brought about by the (welcome) less authoritarian methods that nowadays prevail in the primary school and partly by the stresses of living in the inner-city in a time of recession.

Our argument here is that any government, of whatever political persuasion, which wishes all of its children to have access to high-quality education must supply the necessary resources. It is not enough that the total cake should be adequate. Unless a slice of it is earmarked for children with special needs, some children will continue to miss out. Those who effectively drop out of school, through persistent absence, however caused, will not easily make up lost ground.

The irony is that most children, including persistent absentees, actually want to go to school. This is particularly true at the primary stage of education, before children have developed adolescent interests that could entice them away. However, even at the secondary stage, it is still true that the vast majority of children understand the value of gaining leaving qualifications and want to be in school. A recent survey carried out by the Truancy Research Unit at the University of North London found that most truants were 'bunking off' from specific lessons, but staying within the school campus (O'Keefe & Stoll, 1993). Far from fitting the stereotype of the truant as an adolescent youth hanging around the streets, and all too easily recruited into petty crime, most of them valued what the school had to offer and preferred to remain on its premises.

We should not forget that the vast majority of children leave school with the basic skills and knowledge that are necessary for survival as adults within our society. It is the minority who do not who are our concern.

Why compulsory education?

Absence becomes a problem only if school is compulsory. If school is somewhere where children want to go, and if it is reasonably successful in turning out coping adults, why should it need to be compulsory? Why do we need to bring the whole apparatus of the state and its legal system to bear on making people do something that the vast majority of them want to do anyway?

The historical background

We often forget that compulsory education arrived fairly late on the scene. By the time the Industrial Revolution was starting in the late eighteenth century, most middle-class children and a substantial proportion of working-class children were having some schooling, if only for a year or two. Indeed, it is necessary to have a substantial number of adults able to read and write before industrialisation can take off. The famous 1870 Education Act established school boards and allowed local authorities to levy a rate for education. This led to a great increase in the number of schools available for working-class children. However it was not until 1880 that education became compulsory between the ages of 5 and 11. It is interesting to note that in the nineteenth-century novel *David Copperfield*, the hero sometimes attends school and sometimes does not, according to the vicissitudes of his life.

When looked at sociologically, the education system is often viewed as one that serves children differentially, almost processing them as in a factory and releasing them into differential occupational outlets, which vary in line with their socio-economic origins. In all developed countries, children's occupational destinies correlate heavily with those of their parents. This is often called *social reproduction*.

It would be a mistake, however, to look at the development of the school system solely in terms of social reproduction. Things are rarely that simple or that pure. One can trace a number of trends that led to the development of mass schooling even before it was compulsory. As well as the need for a literate work-force, there were genuinely idealistic motives among many of the 'establishment' who wanted to provide for all children what had previously been available only for those able to pay. At the same time, many of the working class had a desire for education and for the wider horizons it could offer. (See Kahn & Wright, 1980, p. 116 for a further discussion of these points.)

In the UK, because industrialisation was early and widespread and because it led to swift migration of most of the work-force from country to town, large urban centres were created, where the population had little contact with their roots and little in common with any local institutions such as church or school. A situation grew up in which the recipients of mass schooling did not have shared values with the providers of it. Added to this, there were in effect two systems of education: one for the élite, which initiated them into 'high culture' within a prestigious grammar school; and one for the masses, which schooled them in the '3 Rs' and in religious instruction to inculcate the appropriate moral values, within an elementary school, whose pupils left it at the first possible opportunity.

As well as two systems of education, there were two types of teacher. Those for the élite were scholars with high levels of education, usually to honours degree standard, but also usually without any teacher training. Those for the masses were trained rather than educated, at a training college not a university, over a much shorter period of time, and gained a certificate rather than a degree.

Vestiges of these differences remain even now. Teaching has an all graduate entry, but there is a difference in public perception between those who have a BA or BSc honours degree and those who have a BEd (Bachelor of Education) honours degree. The latter involves 3 or 4 years of study, and incorporates Qualified Teacher Status, but becase the BEd is a latecomer to the academic scene, and because BEd graduates teach most often in primary schools, the difference in perception remains. Similarly, although there are now a large number of leaving qualifications that young people can work towards, many of them much better related to the world of work than the traditional ones, it is still those who gain the more academic levels of leaving qualification who stay on to gain further qualifications and perhaps university entrance who have the status.

A new vocational qualification which will eventually provide an integrated system of qualification covering students from the lower part of the secondary school up to university Higher Degree level is at present being introduced. In 1995, some 18-year-olds left school with a General National Vocational Qualification (GNVQ). It is too early to judge what the effects of this will be. It seems likely that, within the overall system of secondary education, tensions between the needs of different types of pupil will remain.

Freedom versus equality

Because of these tensions within the system, differing sets of beliefs about the nature and purposes of education have developed. These have become associated with specifically political points of view. It would be a gross oversimplification to suggest that all the holders of one viewpoint belong to a particular political party or, conversely, that the members of a specific political party all line up behind a particular educational viewpoint. None the less, the generalisation holds good.

The Conservative Party's political philosophy holds that governments should interfere with the individual freedom of its citizens as little as is consistent with safeguarding them from dangers to themselves or their property. Legislation should be restricted to a necessary minimum. There has also been a belief that it is always right to try to conserve whatever is held to be valuable in the status quo, and this gives the party its contemporary name.

Conversely, one part of the Labour Party's tradition (which derives from the nineteenth-century Liberals) is a much more recent belief that it is part of any government's remit to enact what might be called welfare legislation, i.e. laws that interfere with the freedoms of citizens, not to protect them from others but for their own good. Laws requiring people to be connected with public sewage systems, or to wear seat belts in moving vehicles, would come under this heading. Added to this, there is a belief that certain systematic inequalities in society are unjust and should be remedied. Historically, many of these inequalities, such as not having the right to vote, pertained predominantly to manual labourers, thus giving the Labour Party its name.

In practice, even in the days of 'New Labour', 'Thatcherism', 'Majorism' and the 'New Right', there is an all-party consensus about a large part of the legislation any government wishes to enact.

It is ironic that the contemporary Conservative government, while committed to the increase of parental choice over what schools their children may go to, and to increasing the extent to which market forces operate within education, has assumed powers over the *content* of education unparalleled in the history of education in this country. Government can now dictate not only what subjects must be taught but also the content within those subjects, right through from 5 to 16.

The reason for this involves the notion of entitlement referred to above. The origins of the 1988 Act lay partly in the belief, common across the political spectrum, that many children were underperforming at school, and that this applied particularly to those groups who historically do less well out of the education system: children from black and ethnic minority backgrounds; children with parents in unskilled occupations or unemployed; and girls. Interestingly, the gender gap does not seem to exist in Scotland, where there has always been much more of a comprehensive system.

The 1988 Act, by specifying the content of education, was intended to improve the outcomes of education for all children, but especially for the traditionally disadvantaged. Because the language of entitlement rather than that of disadvantage was used, this was not always apparent. However, when the background of widespread concern over standards is taken into account, it is not surprising that the introduction of the National Curriculum has been widely accepted, even though it has meant much extra work for teachers. Dissension has focused on specific features of content and on the nature of the Standard Attainment Tests and the ways in which they were introduced.

One result of all this is that children are now, nationwide, following roughly the same syllabus at the same age. Before 1988, at the primary stage, although the basics of English and mathematics were taught everywhere, there was also a great deal of variation both in what was taught and at what age. If children were away from school for any length of time, because there was no national system, it would not matter greatly if what was missed was not made up.

Nowadays, a child who has missed a substantial amount of work will need to make it up or will have been deprived of some part of the educational diet that everyone else is getting.

Conclusion

If we are talking about entitlement to education, we need some means of making sure that all children can take up their entitlement. This is where the argument comes together. Education is both good in itself, and useful. For the vast majority it is intrinsically desirable, and it provides the necessary skills and knowledge for coping, as an adult, within our society. So essential is it in the latter respect that anyone who has not had it is severely disadvantaged.

The argument has been all along that children with special needs, and particularly those who are in danger of missing substantial amounts of schooling, need to be identified as early as possible. The earlier problems are picked out, the more likely it is that preventative rather than remedial measures can be taken. For this, adequate and earmarked resources are needed. As is so often the case, spending money early on saves the necessity of spending much more money later on.

In order to make sure that everyone takes up his or her entitlement, it is necessary to have some element of compulsion. This is because it is the very children who are already disadvantaged on whom (or rather on whose parents) the greatest pressures fall. It would be difficult to envisage about half the children in our case studies actually getting any schooling if everything were left to parental choice and market forces. Wayne, Michael, Brian, Mariam amd Mohammed would all miss out, and they are by no means the most disadvantaged of children. We need to add the language of disadvantage and of equality to the language of entitlement.

References

DES (1978) *Special Educational Needs: The Report of the Committee of Enquiry into the Education of Handicapped Children and Young People* (The Warnock Report). London: HMSO.

KAHN, J. & WRIGHT, S. E. (1980) *Human Growth and the Development of Personality* (3rd edn). Oxford: Pergamon Press.

O'KEEFE, D. J. & STOLL, P. (1993) *Truancy in English Secondary Schools*. London: HMSO.

6 Unauthorised absence from school

IAN BERG

Historical aspects

Like other developed countries (Debusse, 1951; Lester-Smith, 1951), Britain has a legally enforced system of compulsory schooling. However, it emerged rather gradually in its present form and has only really existed for a century. The current situation is that all children are expected to go to school regularly from age 5 to 16. State education is basically free. There are various measures to deal with unauthorised absence, namely absence not due to illness or, to a limited extent, associated with religious and family holidays (Berg *et al*, 1988).

Until the third quarter of the nineteenth century in the UK, poverty, child labour, high mortality rates and a widespread lack of interest in education meant that for most of that period only a small proportion of children went to school and then only for a very limited number of months or years. In 1850, about 50% of children were enrolled at a school. The provision of schools was patchy throughout the country, and those that did exist were often of poor quality in terms of buildings, teachers, curricula and ethos. Even so, attempts were sometimes made to keep up the attendance of those who were registered with the school, by giving out welfare benefits at school, linking job opportunities to completing a period of schooling and by displaying publically lists of absentees and even fining parents when their child failed to attend (Curtis, 1967; Pallister, 1969; Ball, 1973).

A national system of education for all began to emerge after the Elementary Education Act of 1870. When the Education Act of 1918 came into force all children aged from 5 to 14 were required to be appropriately educated. Subsequently, the age at which compulsory education ceased was raised to 15. In the last 20 years or so, it has been set at 16. School attendance on average during this century has remained remarkably constant at about 90%, although there is considerable variation due to a child's age, sex and social circumstances as well as the part of the country where the school is situated (Fogelman *et al*, 1980).

There were various developments in the early part of the twentieth century that were relevant to the enforcement of school attendance. Industrial schools were available where a child could go to learn a trade. Special day and residential schools were set up. Remand homes and reformatory schools were established where truants could be placed.

The Education Act of 1944 made it the legal responsibility of parents to ensure that their children received appropriate schooling. In the majority of instances, this meant that the child would attend the local state school regularly. However, sometimes, when parents could afford it, private education could be arranged. Local authorities had a duty to prosecute parents who failed in their responsibilities to ensure that their child received appropriate education. Under the Children and Young Persons Act 1969, failure to attend school was a sufficient reason for a Juvenile Court to place a child in the care of the local authority. Until quite recently (Newell, 1983) this meant that many thousands of children were in foster homes or children's homes ostensibly because of failing to go to school.

Following the Elementary Education Act of 1870, local authorities were empowered to set up school attendance committees and to appoint officers to look into instances of frequent absence. In the 1944 Education Act these employees were called education welfare officers. Their role was partly to help families by arranging transport when necessary and clothing when this was needed. However, their main function was to attempt to find out why a child was missing school and to help remedy the situation. When it seemed appropriate, they could institute legal proceedings against parents and/or a child. Children could be taken to Juvenile Court under care proceedings but this only happened occasionally in the case of persistent absentees. Since the Children's Act of 1989, it has no longer been possible to take care proceedings because of failure to attend school. Parents may still be prosecuted and children may still be taken to a Juvenile Court, but the magistrates can then only make an Education Supervision Order, which merely puts on a more formal footing the education welfare officer's regular meetings with the child. It remains to be seen whether the abandonment of the use of care proceedings, which enabled courts as a last resort to remove a child from home when school attendance was very poor, will be seen as a 'truants' charter' in the years to come.

The Leeds Truancy Project

The effectiveness of Juvenile Courts to improve attendance in severe school attendance problems was evaluated by a series of randomly controlled trials of court procedures over several years in the city of Leeds (Berg *et al*, 1988). Magistrates in that city in the early 1970s, led by their chairman Dr Roy

Hullin, were dissatisfied with the standard procedure that was normally used when children were taken to court under care proceedings for persistent and severe failure to go to school. The procedure in question was the Supervision Order. When this order was made there were no further appearances in the court unless the education department reinstituted legal proceedings, which rarely happened. A social worker or probation officer took charge of the problem. School attendance figures did not appear to be improving and magistrates suspected that despite regular contact with a counsellor, children were remaining away from school. The courts began to employ another method called adjournment. No court order was made when a child appeared before the magistrates because of failure to go to school. The case was simply adjourned for a specified period, usually a few weeks, and the situation was then reviewed. Repeated adjournments of the proceedings could go on for months with the magistrates monitoring school attendance and varying intervals between attendances at court according to progress made in returning to school. Eventually, when they were satisfied that sufficient improvement had occurred, no further action was taken. The end result was that no court order had been used. The procedure relied on regular contact with the court. However, at any stage, if the court learned that school attendance was not improving or indeed deteriorating, an Interim Care Order could be made. This meant that the child would spend a few weeks in a social services residential assessment centre for a comprehensive enquiry to be carried out. Repeated adjournments could then be continued when the child returned home. Exceptionally, when all else failed and particularly when other problems were evident, a Full Care Order was made and the child's future care handed over to the social services. This might mean residence in a foster home or children's home.

In 1973, a retrospective survey looked at the outcome of children dealt with by repeated adjournments and compared them to those who were put on Supervision Orders. It appeared that, despite the fact that there were similar circumstances, children did substantially better, in returning to regular attendance at school, when they were on adjournment than when they were on a Supervision Order.

In 1977 magistrates carried out the first randomly controlled trial of court procedures in children taken to Juvenile Court because of persistent and severe failure to attend school. The use of random allocation ensured that any child had an equal chance of being managed by either of the two procedures. Before coming to court, average attendance at school was only 25% of possible attendances. Following the first court appearance, the children under adjournment were going to school 65% of the time over several months, while the children under a Supervision Order were only going 50% of the time. There was also evidence that children under adjournment committed less criminal offences than those under a Supervision Order. Full Care Orders were occasionally made, usually on grounds other than school attendance, and the two groups did not differ in this respect. Following the successful completion of this trial, the magistrates virtually stopped using the Supervision Order. Subsequently, after several other studies, it became increasingly likely that it was not so much the effects of the adjournment procedure that improved school attendance but the adverse effects of the Supervision Order that led to the deterioration in outcome. It seemed that if nothing had been done, the children who had been put on a Supervision Order would have done better.

There then began a whole series of similar experimental investigations of court procedures in Leeds. In 1980, flexibly used adjournments that tailored intervals between court appearances according to progress in returning to school were compared with a system of letters excusing appearances in court when school attendance was improving substantially. No differences between the four methods (1, flexible interval, letters; 2, inflexible interval, letters; 3, flexible interval, no letters; 4, inflexible interval, no letters) of handling the school attendance problems emerged. It seemed that it was just the process of having to go to court that produced the desirable effects rather than what happened once the child came there. Looking at school attendance prior to coming to court, it was found that improvements in school attendance occurred after the summons to attend court was sent. There was a 20% improvement in the 5 weeks before court attendance.

It appeared that there was a group of children with school attendance problems who responded particularly well to having to come to court. Another randomly controlled trial was set up confined to those children whose school attendance was 85% by the time they first came to court. These children were assigned randomly to one of two subgroups. Those on the 'no order made' procedure did not have to come back to court and those on the 'continued adjournment' procedure did return regularly. Both groups had good school attendance subsequently and it was concluded that nothing was to be gained by having these good responders appear in court more than on a couple of occasions. About half of all children brought to court because of failure to go to school fell into this category.

One problem in dealing with those children who failed to respond well to being taken to court was the misgivings many people had about the use of Interim Care Orders. Official records did not distinguish between these and Full Care Orders, where the children became the responsibility of the social services department and could be placed in a foster home or children's home indefinitely. The use of assessment centres in this way caused a certain amount of disquiet. Yet magistrates believed that the Interim Care Order was an essential aspect of the adjournment procedure. It was therefore decided to evaluate their usefulness. Between 1985 and 1987 a randomly controlled trial was undertaken to compare Interim Care Orders with weekly visits to court. Children whose school attendance was poor after two visits to court on adjournment were randomly assigned either to an 'Interim Care Order' group or 'Four consecutive weekly attendance at court' group whenever their attendance at school dropped below a particular level. This point was usually reached about 2 months after first attending court and starting on regular adjournments. Once again the two procedures were not shown to be significantly different in helping absence from school (Brown *et al*, 1990). It therefore appeared possible to manage severe school attendance problems successfully without Interim Care Orders.

Perhaps the most important outcome of the randomly controlled trials was the effect on delinquency that adjournment appeared to have. There are many studies showing a link between truancy and delinquency (Berg *et al*, 1988). Four of the random trials described indicated that attendance at court under the adjournment system reduced rates of criminal offending.

A survey of the work of the Education Welfare Department in Leeds provided evidence that most children whose school attendance slipped below 70% were visited by an education welfare officer and that the chances of being taken to court were increased exponentially as school attendance worsened. This showed that the system of visiting poor school attenders seemed to be working as it should.

Psychiatric disorders

Attempts have been made to classify disorders affecting children with severe school attendance problems in order to identify groups of individuals who may need particular methods of management. In one study (Bools *et al*, 1990), mothers of 100 children taken to a school attendance committee, prior to instituting legal proceedings, were interviewed. A cluster analysis of responses to a standard scale showed the existence of the following subgroups:

(a) About one in ten were boys who 'truanted' (that is whose parents, at least initially, did not know that their son was not going to school) and who also displayed severely antisocial behaviour.
(b) One in five stayed home refusing to go to school and showed evidence of emotional upset in the form of anxiety and depression either confined to the situation of having to go to school, or more generally. They appeared to be rather typical 'school refusers'.
(c) The remainder often truanted and sometimes manifested problems of conduct but social circumstances appeared more relevant to their problem of not going to school than any antisocial tendencies in the child.

As will be clear from other parts of this book, clinical studies have identified the problem of school refusal as one where the child remains at home and appears emotionally upset at the prospect of having to go to school. Physical symptoms such as abdominal pain, headache, poor appetite, pallor, nausea and excessive use of the toilet often occur on school mornings. Antisocial conduct is exceptional and educational backwardness is not a feature. The problem has been variously interpreted as an irrational fear, that is a phobia, of some aspect of the school situation or as anxiety leaving home or mother, so-called 'separation anxiety'. School refusal may affect otherwise emotionally well-adjusted children or those more generally prone to anxiety, depression and associated social impairment. The condition has been well reviewed (Hersov, 1990; Berg, 1992).

There is a great deal of current interest in classification of child psychiatric disorders. This has led to increasing emphasis being placed on any particular disorder and less interest being taken in school attendance problems *per se*. Truancy is only mentioned as one possible feature of a conduct disorder in the generally accepted systems of classifications: the *Diagnostic and Statistical Manual of Mental Disorders*, third edition, revised (DSM–III–R; American Psychiatric Association, 1987), DSM–IV (American Psychiatric Association, 1994) and the *International Classification of Diseases* (ICD–10; World Health Organization 1992). Likewise, school refusal features in these classifications as a possible feature of separation anxiety disorder. It is also sometimes accorded the status of 'phobic disorder–school' (Last, 1993). Recent textbooks (Tongue *et al*, 1990; Rutter *et al*, 1994) give school attendance problems little prominence.

This process may have gone too far, particularly in the case of school refusal, since this is such a common presentation of anxiety and mood disorders in the clinical setting. There is much to be said for defining both truancy and school refusal without regard to whether there is an associated psychiatric disorder or not. Truancy may be said to exist when a child who stays away from school tries to conceal the fact from the family. School refusal is considered to be the problem when a child remains at home without any attempts at concealment and becomes upset at the prospect of having to go to school. Otherwise failure to go to school may reflect social circumstances, as when a single parent works long hours leaving the child unsupervised or parents who frankly condone or even encourage staying off school, so-called school withdrawal (Kahn & Nursten, 1962).

Clinical investigation of school attendance difficulties have nearly always been undertaken on selected populations, either those referred to psychologists or psychiatrists or those dealt with as disciplinary problems and taken to school attendance committees or court. What has been found has been influenced in no small measure by how the various types of school attendance problems have been defined. Thus school refusal has sometimes been said to exist only when there was an anxiety or mood disorder (Kolvin *et al*, 1984; de Aldaz *et al*, 1987).

The Bradford survey

To avoid problems of selection, four high schools were studied in the city of Bradford looking at children with very severe attendance problems who had no excuse for not going to school (Berg *et al*, 1993). It was not dissimilar from an investigation of severe persistent absentees from school carried out in Sheffield (Galloway, 1985) but the Bradford investigation was designed to provide more detailed information on the nature of any psychiatric disorders found and on social circumstances and any help offered to deal with the problem.

The third and fourth years of four high schools were investigated. Of over 2000 mainly 14 and 15-year-olds, 156 (8%) were off school for more than 40% of the autumn term and 122 of them had no acceptable explanation. It proved possible to study 80. Thirty children selected randomly irrespective of attendance were used as controls. In both groups of children there were slightly more girls than boys. The mean age was 15 years in poor attenders and in controls.

Interviews with the parents and with the child, using a standard scale (Child and Adolescent Psychiatric Assessment (CAPA) of Angold, Rutter and Cox), indicated a significant excess of antisocial problems affecting the absentees when compared with the controls. The conduct difficulties included: lying, stealing, vandalism, running away, fighting, tempers, forgery and contact with the police. Education welfare had records on 56 (70%) of the poor attenders and only three (10%) of the controls. None of the controls had been referred to psychology or psychiatry and none of them had a criminal record. Only one had had contact with social services.

Homes of the absentees were characterised by poor material circumstances in comparison with controls that was striking. Heating, washing facilities, freezers, cars, televisions and the state of the house were all significantly less in evidence where the absentees lived. Fathers were more frequently unemployed and relationships between parents were rated as less satisfactory in the families of those who had poor attendance. Significantly higher A (anxiety) and D (depression) scores on the Leeds Scales (Snaith *et al*, 1976) and GHQ total scores on the General Health Questionnaire (Goldberg & Huxley, 1980) affected mothers of the absentees. Relevant DSM–III–R psychiatric disorders affected about half of the attendance problem group compared to one-tenth of the controls, a significant difference. The Conners Teachers Questionnaire (Conners, 1969) showed that the attendance group had significantly higher scores than controls from the same class in school on three factors: I, conduct problems; II, inattentiveness; and IV, hyperactivity in the case of the boys not the girls.

Considering the school attendance problem group, irrespective of whether the CAPA interviews were carried out with parent or child, only half of the children had a DSM–III–R psychiatric disorder. About one-third of them had a conduct disorder and roughly one-fifth had an anxiety/mood disorder:

four girls and three boys had separation anxiety disorder. Inter-rater reliabilities of diagnoses, undertaken by two psychiatrists listening to recordings of child CAPA interviews, were satisfactory.

Truancy was said to exist when parents were unaware of their child's absence for most of the time: there were 23 children with truancy and no psychiatric disorder and 21 children with truancy accompanied by a conduct disorder. One child had truancy with an associated anxiety disorder. School refusal was said to exist when there was an emotional reaction to the prospect of having to go to school and the child remained at home: 12 children had school refusal without an associated disorder and six children had school refusal with an associated anxiety disorder; one child had a conduct disorder accompanying school refusal. Fourteen children had neither school refusal nor truancy. Overall, equal numbers of boys and girls truanted and twice as many girls as boys were school refusers. In a few instances, school refusal and truancy had affected the same child.

It was found that parents, in almost all instances, knew that they had a responsibility to ensure that their child went to school regularly. They hardly ever sought help from family doctors, but did discuss the problem with education welfare officers, social workers and sometimes the school. About one-quarter of children with a conduct disorder had committed at least one criminal offence about the time of the survey. Referral to clinical services because of school attendance difficulties rarely occurred.

Half the families had the natural father living with the mother. Half the mothers went out to work. The social class grouping was mostly III on the Registrar-General's classification with the remainder below that level.

The Bradford survey just described appears to have overcome some of the sampling and methodological deficiencies of previous attempts to obtain information on the features of severe absentees from school in the normal school population (Robins, 1978; Galloway *et al*, 1985; Bools *et al*, 1990). The findings suggest that the arbitrary criterion of more than 40% of time away from school over a term identifies a group of children aged 13–15 who have a 50:50 chance of suffering from a psychiatric disorder, who are likely to have conduct problems in school when they are there, who tend to break the law and to manifest antisocial behaviour more generally, who have mothers who are more likely to complain of anxiety and depression than would otherwise be the case and who come from materially disadvantaged homes. They also suggest that a significant proportion of these children suffer from school refusal and sometimes have separation anxiety and/or other anxiety disorders. The well-documented distinction between truancy with a conduct disorder and school refusal with an emotional disorder, particularly involving separation anxiety which has often been found in clinical samples (Hersov, 1960; Hersov & Berg, 1980), appears to reflect the situation in the normal school population.

The children who did not have a disorder were just as likely to have homes characterised by social disadvantage. We assumed that where there was no clear pattern of school attendance problem and no psychiatric disorder, the poor social circumstances may have been associated with parental irresponsibility and the condoning of absence from school. The predominance of girls among poor attenders confirmed what has been known for a long time (Hersov & Berg, 1980). It possibly reflects the importance of school refusal and school withdrawal (Kahn & Nursten, 1962), as opposed to truancy with conduct disorder, among persistent absentees at normal schools.

Considering the fact that school refusal associated with anxiety/mood disorders is effectively managed by child and adolescent psychiatric services (Berg, 1985), it was disappointing to find that they were involved so little. The work was undertaken at a time when juvenile courts could still be relied on to improve school attendance particularly when psychiatric disorders were not present, so it seemed unfortunate that this method of dealing with the school attendance problem had hardly ever been employed.

Department for Education survey (DFE, 1994)

The recent DFE survey of children in their last 2 years of compulsory education sampled secondary schools in England: 150 were chosen randomly from 20 education authority areas, giving a group of over 45 000 children. Questionnaires were actually completed by 38 000 of them. Although two forms of truancy, vaguely defined, were looked at (blanket absence and post registration), the two overlapped to a considerable extent. Roughly 8% admitted to absenting themselves from school at least once a week. Boys and girls owned up to truanting to a similar extent. The frequency of truancy increased in the last year of compulsory schooling, particularly in the case of boys. A considerable proportion of those admitting to truancy said that their parents and teachers were aware of it. It was generally considered easy to miss school. There was no evidence that truancy was any less when schools were smaller in size or when there were more teachers. Although truancy was usually a social activity in that only about one in six children did it on their own, the view that peer group pressure is important was denied. Bullying was rarely incriminated as a factor. A small percentage blamed illness, a similar proportion complained of tiredness or depression, apathy affected a small number and 'home problems' were also mentioned by a small percentage.

When the children who did not admit to truancy were looked at, concern that parents and/or teachers might find out was often given as a reason for not wanting to miss school. It was not demonstrated that poor economic circumstances was a major factor associated with truancy.

Compulsory education

School attendance remains compulsory in Britain although legal sanctions have become much less compelling. While the possibility of taking severe and persistent absentees to juvenile court under care proceedings existed, the children dealt with in this way tended to respond well not only by better school attendance but also by reducing offending. The present system of legal sanctions for school attendance problems now requires proper evaluation. Although only a proportion of very severe attendance problems have DSM psychiatric disorders, it is evident that 40% absence from school over a term is a useful indication of a greater number of both conduct and anxiety disorders than would otherwise be expected. It is a pity that the DFE survey was so education based and failed to look at personal factors and social circumstances in sufficient detail. Nevertheless, it was a very substantial study that looked at the views of children themselves and provided some confirmation of previous findings.

References

AMERICAN PSYCHIATRIC ASSOCIATION (1987) *Diagnostic and Statistical Manual of Mental Disorders* (3rd edn, revised) (DSM–III–R). Washington, DC: APA.
—— (1984) *Diagnostic and Statistical Manual of Mental Disorders* (4th edn) (DSM–IV). Washington, DC: APA.
BALL, N. (1973) Elementary school attendance and voluntary effort before 1870. *History of Education*, **2**, 19–34.
BERG, I. (1985) Management of school refusal. *Archives of Disease in Childhood*, **60**, 486–488.
—— (1992) Absence from school and mental health. *British Journal of Psychiatry*, **161**, 154–166.
——, BROWN, I. & HULLIN, R. (1988) *Off School in Court – An Experimental and Psychiatric Investigation of Severe School Attendance Problems*. Heidelberg: Springer.
——, BUTLER, A., FRANKLIN, J., et al (1993) DSM–III–R disorders, social factors and management of school attendance problems in the normal school population. *Journal of Child Psychology and Psychiatry*, **34**, 1187–1203.
BOOLS, C., FOSTER, J., BROWN, I., et al (1990) The identification of psychiatric disorders in children who fail to attend school: a cluster analysis of a non-clinical population. *Psychological Medicine*, **20**, 171–181.
BROWN, I., BERG, I., HULLIN, R., et al (1990) Are interim care orders necessary to improve school attendance in truants taken to juvenile court? *Educational Review*, **42**, 231–245.
CONNORS, K. (1969) A teacher rating scale for use in drug studies with children. *American Journal of Psychiatry*, **126**, 884–888.
CURTIS, S. J. (1967) *The History of Education in Great Britain*. Cambridge: University Tutorial Press.
DE ALDAZ, E. G., FELDMAN, L., VIVAS, E., et al (1987) Characteristics of Venezuelan school refusers toward the development of a high risk profile. *Journal of Nervous and Mental Disease*, **175**, 402–407.
DEBUSSE, J. (1951) *Compulsory Education in France*. Paris: UNESCO.

DFE (1994) *Truancy in English Secondary Schools.* London: HMSO.

FOGELMAN, K., TIBBENHAM, A. & LAMBERT, L. (1980) Absence from school: findings from the National Child Development Study. In *Out of School* (eds L. Hersov & I. Berg), pp. 25–48. Chichester: John Wiley.

GALLOWAY, D. (1985) *Schools and Persistent Absentees.* Oxford: Pergamon Press.

———, MARTIN, R. & WILCOX, B. (1985) Persistent absence from school and exclusion from school: the predictive power of school and community variables. *British Educational Research Journal,* **11,** 51–61.

GOLDBERG, D. & HUXLEY, P. (1980) *Mental Illness in the Community – the Pathway to Psychiatric Care.* London: Tavistock Publications.

HERSOV, L. (1960) 1. Persistent non-attendance at school and 2. Refusal to go to school. *Journal of Child Psychology and psychiatry,* **1,** 130–135 and 136–145.

——— (1990) School refusal: an overview. In *Why Children Reject School* (eds C. Chiland & G. Young). Newhaven: Yale University Press.

——— & BERG, I. (1980) *Out of School. Modern Perspectives in Truancy and School Refusal.* Chichester: John Wiley.

KAHN, K. & NURSTEN, J. (1962) School refusal: a comprehensive view of school phobia and other failures of school attendance. *American Journal of Orthopsychiatry,* **32,** 707–718.

KOLVIN, I., BERNEY, T. & BHATE, S. (1984) Classification and diagnosis of depression in school phobia. *British Journal of Psychiatry,* **145,** 347–357.

LAST, C. (ed.) (1993) *Anxiety Across the Lifespan. A Developmental Perspective.* New York: Springer.

LESTER-SMITH, W. O. (1951) *Compulsory Education in England.* Paris: UNESCO.

NEWELL, P. (1983) Truancy and care. *Where,* **186,** 20–21.

PALLISTER, R. (1969) The determinants of elementary school attendance about 1850. *Durham and Newcastle Research Review,* **5,** 384–398.

ROBINS, L. (1978) Sturdy childhood predictors of adult antisocial behaviour: replications from longitudinal studies. *Psychological Medicine,* **8,** 611–622.

RUTTER, M., TAYLOR, E. & HERSOV, L. (eds) (1994) *Child and Adolescent Psychiatry – Modern Approaches* (3rd edn). Oxford: Blackwell Scientific Publications.

SNAITH, R. P., BRIDGE, G. W. K. & HAMILTON, M. (1976) The Leeds scales for the self-assessment of anxiety and depression. *British Journal of Psychiatry,* **128,** 156–165.

TONGE, B., BURROWS, G. & WERRY, J. (1990) *Handbook of Studies on Child Psychiatry.* Amsterdam: Elsevier.

WORLD HEALTH ORGANIZATION (1992) *The Tenth Revision of the International Classification of Diseases and Related Health Problems* (ICD–10). Geneva: WHO.

7 Early adult sequelae of truancy: the National Child Development Study

KEN FOGELMAN

Regulations introduced by the Department for Education (DFE) in 1991 give renewed emphasis to the importance placed by schools and the wider community on school attendance. The distinction must now be made in school attendance registers between authorised and unauthorised absence; and maintained schools are required to include information on rates of unauthorised absence in their prospectuses and annual reports.

Thus, rates of unauthorised absence will join public examination and National Curriculum assessment results as the information that schools will be required to publish and by which they will be judged.

Schools are likely therefore to be seeking ways in which they can reduce their rates of unauthorised absence, and may look to research findings to assist them in their understanding of the phenomenon and in identifying effective action. There is, of course, a substantial body of relevant research, but this chapter is concerned with just one strand – those studies that have examined the relationship between truancy from school and longer term, post-school sequelae. In this chapter I briefly review such studies, and present in more detail findings from the National Child Development Study.

Such studies are important for a number of reasons. First, they can add to understanding of the kinds of young people who truant and why. As discussed briefly below, there are several competing explanations for truancy and knowledge of the longer term outcomes should help in choosing between them, or at least beginning to judge the relative weights of their contribution. Is it the case that truants subsequently experience more problems in the labour market than their peers, for example greater unemployment or more frequent job changes? Are there indications of difficulties in other aspects of their lives, such as their mental health or the stability of their partnerships or marriages? The answers to such questions should help to determine the levels and nature of intervention or support that may be appropriate to reduce truancy levels or their impact on the young people concerned.

Secondly, if such relationships do exist, then there are questions about the causal processes involved. The DFE (1991) Circular which announced the new regulations refers to the fact that former truants are much more likely to leave school with no examination passes and this will lead to increased "risk of subsequent failure in the job market ...". This does beg the question of whether poor qualifications are a sufficient explanation of any job market problems experienced by former truants. They might, for example, be found to experience more severe, or different, difficulties compared with their peers who do not truant but leave school with equally poor qualifications.

Thirdly, there is the important issue of public attitudes to truancy. It might be thought obvious that truancy is undesirable, but this perspective is not always shared by the general public and the media. Frequently, when truancy hits the headlines or a major study is published, the tabloids bring forward a collection of sporting, pop and media personalities, and the occasional successful industrialist, who talk with nostalgic pride about their own truancy from school. The image that this promotes is of the truant as an attractive and successful rogue who has simply outgrown school, and stays away in order to engage in more adult activities which are at least as likely to lead to subsequent happiness and success as is remaining in school and obtaining better qualifications. Clearly it is important to know if there is any truth in such an image. If there is, that has major implications for our response to truancy. If it is not an accurate portrayal of the typical truant, then schools need the support of parents and public whose attitudes to truancy are based on reality.

Explanations of truancy

This is not the place to attempt a comprehensive review of research on truancy and school attendance. However, it is interesting to note that it is possible to trace a broad pattern of how the predominant explanations of truancy have changed over the last three decades; and that in large part this mirrors parallel debates about the major determinants of children's achievement.

In the 1960s and early 1970s, the emphasis was on the individual and their characteristics. Tyerman (1968), for example, saw truancy as part of a more comprehensive maladjustment. An elaboration of this was Haigh's concept of the "reluctant adolescent", moving away from the values of school and towards those of adulthood (Haigh, 1976).

Subsequently, attention turned to the influence of social background, demonstrating high correlations between truancy and such variables as father's occupation, family size and housing tenure (e.g. Tibbenham, 1977). At the same time, the influence of such factors was seen to be much larger than that of the school variables examined, which at that time tended to be straightforward administrative characteristics of schools such as type and size (e.g. Fogelman *et al*, 1980).

However, other researchers (e.g. Reynolds, 1976) were beginning to identify how schools with similar intakes and administrative characteristics nevertheless had substantial variation in their truancy rates. Thus, in the last decade, research has concentrated on the more subtle characteristics of schools that help to explain such variation.

Such contrasting kinds of explanation need not be seen as mutually exclusive. Individual personality, social background and school character-istics could each play a role in leading to a student's decision to truant. However, depending on which is dominant, they could generate different predictions of the long-term associations with truancy. If it is part of more general maladjustment we might expect subsequent problems in other areas, such as family relationships and mental health. If truants have merely outgrown school and are ready for adult life, then we should not predict particular difficulties in the labour market. If social factors are a sufficient explanation, then there should not be a substantial association between truancy and later outcomes, once social background has been taken into account.

Definitions and measures

Before turning to those studies that have attempted to illuminate such issues, a brief note on definitions may be helpful. In the past, great emphasis tended to be given to the fact that, strictly speaking, truancy is absence without the parents' knowledge or approval (e.g. National Association of Chief Education Welfare Officers, 1974). However, more recently, and particularly since the raising of the school leaving age, attention has increasingly turned to the last year or so of compulsory education, when truancy rates are undoubtedly substantially higher. For this age group, parents' knowledge and approval has come to be seen as less important and, consequently, the terms 'truancy', 'unjustified absenteeism' and 'unauthorised absenteeism' tend to be used interchangeably.

In the majority of the studies discussed below, truants have been identified by teachers' reports. Others have relied upon pupils' own reports. Yet others have used a mix of teachers' reports and actual attendance rates and in one or two studies it is difficult to determine exactly how the final measure has been arrived at. In addition, some studies have been included that are of interest, but which did not set out to distinguish between truancy and general poor attendance.

Hibbett (1987) describes analyses of National Child Development Study data that examine the interrelationships of teachers', pupils' and parents' truancy reports, and also those with actual attendance rates, and reports high correlations among them.

Studies of labour market outcomes

Valid research on the adult outcomes of truancy is relatively rare, since it requires longitudinal data spanning a number of years. In fact, all of the studies cited below either take advantage of existing data collected in the course of a longitudinal study with wider purposes, or have built upon such a study with an extra stage of data collection.

The majority of such studies have focused, at least in part, on labour market outcomes. Cherry (1976), for example, from a follow-up at age 26 of the National Survey of Health and Development sample born in 1946, found that poor school attendance was associated with frequent job changing, but not with low job status or earnings. The relationship with an unstable employment record is confirmed by Farrington (1980) from his study of 411 boys from the Cambridge Study of Delinquent Development interviewed at the age of 18. On the other hand, unlike Cherry, he did find that former truants were in lower status occupations.

A second area of some conflict in findings concerns earnings from employment. American studies have tended to concentrate more on drop-out from high school than on truancy and attendance. An exception to this is Robins & Ratcliffe (1980), who interviewed, at the age of 36, 235 black males born in St Louis between 1930 and 1934. In contrast to Cherry, they found that former truants were earning considerably less on average than their peers, of the order of some $100 per week.

There is greater consistency among those studies that have examined experience of unemployment. Robins & Ratcliffe report unemployment as one of a number of indicators of job problems experienced by their former truants (the others being frequent absence and dismissal). Higher unemployment levels associated with poor school attendance were also found by Gray *et al* (1980) when they followed up, one year out of school, 597 young people who had left school at 16 in one London borough.

The role of qualifications

Two of the above studies also set out to examine the role of school attainment and qualifications in explaining the link between truancy or attendance and employment difficulties. From multivariate analysis, Robins & Ratcliffe (1980) conclude that the lower high-school graduation rates and college attendance of truants do not explain the relationship with lack of occupational success. Truancy, they say, has "substantial" additional effects on earnings and a "significant" effect on adult deviance (i.e. including the indicators of employment problems described above).

In this country this was not borne out by Gray *et al* (1980) (who were writing about absenteeism rather than truancy). They conclude that

> "absenteeism had important consequences for first year employment just be-cause of its connection with low scholastic achievement but (with the possible exception of unemployment) we could detect no influence which operated through other mechanisms."

The National Child Development Study

Further insight into these issues is provided by findings from the National Child Development Study (NCDS), a longitudinal, multidisciplinary study of all the people in Great Britain who were born in the week 3–9 March 1958. Originally studied at birth (Butler & Bonham, 1963), subsequent follow-ups were carried out at the ages of 7, 11, 16 and 23 (and new data are about to be available from interviews at 33). In addition, schools were approached in 1979 for the results of public examinations taken up to that time and there have been a number of special exercises to collect data on specific subgroups. Response has generally been high, at about 90% during the school years and 76% at 23. More detailed descriptions of the study can be found in, for example, Davie *et al* (1972), Fogelman (1983) and Shepherd (1985). Analyses related to truancy and school attendance in the school years are reported in Fogelman & Richardson (1974), Fogelman (1978) and Fogelman *et al* (1980); and comprehensive accounts of the results on adult outcomes are in Hibbett *et al* (1990) and Hibbett & Fogelman (1990).

The starting point of the analyses of adult outcomes was one item from a standard behaviour scale (Rutter *et al*, 1970), completed by teachers for the 16-year follow-up, which indicated whether each child had truanted in the past year. This was reported to be the case for 22.6% of the boys and 17.3% of the girls.

To examine the relationship with subsequent experiences, two kinds of multivariate analysis were carried out: analysis of variance where the outcome variable was continuous, generating results in terms of adjusted mean differences between truants and non-truants; and loglinear analysis where the outcome variable was categorical, giving contrasts in the form of relative odds.

For both kinds of outcome, an identical sequence of analyses was undertaken, in order to assess the contribution of other factors in explaining

TABLE 7.1
Economic status at 23: loglinear analysis of odds relative to being in work, truants v. non-truants

		Adjusted for:		
	Background	Attainment at 11	Attendance at 15	Qualifications at 16+
Men (n=2806)				
Full-time education	0.45	0.55	0.57	0.58	0.59
Unemployed	2.37	2.03	2.04	2.05	2.04
Out of labour force	1.43	1.56	1.60	1.62	1.60
Women (n=2843)				
Full-time education	0.46	0.54	0.52	0.53	0.61
Unemployed	2.76	2.32	2.42	2.42	2.41
Out of labour force	3.29	2.59	2.67	2.68	2.56

the initial contrast. First, the simple contrast between truants and non-truants was produced; the second stage of analysis included social background factors (social class of father's occupation, region of residence and family size) as independent variables, and adjusted the truancy contrast for the relationship with these factors; the third stage additionally incorporated and adjusted for measures of ability and attainment at age 11 (i.e. scores on general ability, reading comprehension and mathematics tests); the fourth stage also included the subject's attendance rate at 15; and the fifth and final stage also included a measure of public examination attainment by the time of leaving school. Results presented here are for England and Wales only, as the differing examination system in Scotland required separate analysis.

Table 7.1 presents the results of this sequence of analysis for economic status at the time of the 23-year interview. Thus, from the first column of the table, it can be seen that, for men at age 23, former truants compared to non-truants had almost half (0.45) the relative odds of being in full-time education rather than in work before any adjustments for other factors; they were more than twice (2.37) as likely to be unemployed; and they were 1.43 times as likely to be out of the labour force. Allowing for social background factors reduces the contrasts in full-time education and unemployment, though not substantially. Differences related to truancy then appear to be unaffected by allowing for further factors, suggesting that the increased likelihood of unemployment for truants is not explained by their poor attendance or poor examination qualifications, once social background has been taken into account.

For women, the pattern is similar, except that the truants' relative odds of being out of the labour force are considerably greater. This will largely reflect their greater likelihood of not working for family or child care reasons, and may include some hidden unemployment.

Table 7.1 provides information only about current unemployment at the time of interview. Other analysis examined the amount of unemployment experienced, taking into account varying time spent in the labour market up

TABLE 7.2
Social class of current job at 23: loglinear analysis of odds relative to unskilled manual, truants v. non-truants

		Adjusted for:			
		Background	Attainment at 11	Attendance at 15	Qualifications at 16+
Men (*n*=2666)					
I+II	0.12	0.18	0.18	0.17	0.17
III+IVNM	0.11	0.15	0.15	0.15	0.16
III+IVM	0.59	0.66	0.65	0.64	0.64
Women (*n*=2776)					
I+II	0.07	0.11	0.13	0.13	0.12
III+IVNM	0.12	0.16	0.16	0.16	0.16
III+IVM	0.51	0.53	0.55	0.54	0.56

to the time of interview. Differences again favoured the non-truants and were not substantially affected by allowing for other factors., However, average differences, although statistically significant, were not large. Male former truants had been unemployed for about 2% more of their economically active time than had non-truants, and the comparable figure for women was about 4%.

Table 7.2 presents the results of similar analysis of the social class of the job held at the time of the 23-year interview (or the most recent job for those not currently working). These are similar for each sex – relative to being in unskilled manual occupations, former truants are about one-tenth as likely to be in professional managerial or intermediate non-manual occupations (social classes I and II), one-fifth to one-quarter as likely to be in skilled or semi-skilled non-manual occupations (III and IVNM), and half to two-thirds as likely to be in skilled or semi-skilled manual occupations (III and IVM). As for economic status, these contrasts are very slightly reduced by allowing for social background but change barely, if at all, as further factors are introduced into the analysis.

The conventional measure of job stability would be the number of jobs held. However, at the relatively early age of 23 this will be severely confounded with the length of time in the labour market – former truants are likely to have left education and entered employment at an earlier age then non-truants and this, rather than more frequent job changing, could explain the greater number of jobs held. Therefore, the analysis reported in Table 7.3 attempts to investigate this issue using a different measure, the average duration (in months) of all jobs held. This is a continuous measure, so analysis of variance was used, and the contrast between truants and non-truants is expressed in terms of the average difference in mean length of time in each job.

As can be seen, truants on average held their jobs for a shorter time. In these analyses, the contrasts with non-truants generally increases as account is taken of further factors, particularly end-of-school examination results. In

TABLE 7.3
Mean length of all jobs held (in months): analysis of variance

		Adjusted for:		
	Background	Attainment at 11	Attendance at 15	Qualifications at 16+
Men (*n*=2666)				
Mean difference non-truants v. truants	4.3	4.9	7.0	5.7	9.0
Women (*n*=2689)				
Mean difference non-truants v. truants	6.9	8.3	10.3	9.4	11.2

other words, former truants are particularly likely to be changing jobs frequently compared with non-truants who also left school with poor examination qualifications. The final difference in average job length, of 9 months for men and 11 months for women, is dramatic given the relatively short-time they can have been in any employment by the age of 23.

The final group of labour market outcomes examined relate to earnings and income. In terms of pay from current employment, average differences between truants and non-truants were extremely small, with truants in fact earning slightly more. However there are several reasons why this comparison may be misleading. First, those unemployed and out of the labour force cannot be included and, as we have seen, this accounts for disproportionate numbers of truants. Secondly, the meaning of a particular income will vary according to circumstances such as whether the individual concerned is single and living with their parents or married, with children and paying for their own home. As will be shown in a later section, the latter was more likely at 23 for those who had played truant. Thirdly, as was indicated in Table 7.2, former truants are more likely to be in unskilled and other manual occupations and at the age of 23 such groups are near the peak of their earnings, whereas the earnings of those occupational groups more typical of non-truants will tend to increase as they grow older.

Assessment of the impact of this third point must await the availability of data at a later age, but the first two can be taken into account by examining 'equivalent net family income'. This measure is based on income to the family from all sources and is then weighted according to the structure and size of the family, using weightings (e.g. for children of different ages) that were incorporated in calculations of Supplementary Benefit at that time (see Shepherd, 1984). Table 7.4 presents the results of this analysis. On this measure former truants are considerably less well off, almost £15 per week on average for men and £27 for women. Allowing for other factors reduces this quite markedly. For men the difference is no longer significant at the 5%

TABLE 7.4
Equivalent net family income per week (in £): analysis of variance

		Adjusted for:			
		Background	Attainment at 11	Attendance at 15	Qualifications at 16+
Men (*n*=2658)					
Mean difference non-truants v. truants	14.8	9.8	7.4	4.3	5.9
Women (*n*=2751)					
Mean difference non-truants v. truants	27.1	19.2	11.3	9.1	16.8

level after adjusting the comparison for social background alone. For women, the contrast remains greater and is still at the borderline of statistical significance once all other factors are taken into account.

Overall, the NCDS findings demonstrate that those young people identified as truanting by their teachers are distinct in terms of their labour market experiences up to the age of 23. They had lower status occupations, less stable career patterns, more unemployment and were considerably less well off once their family situations were taken into account.

For most of these outcomes, social background contributed only marginally to explaining this contrast. Neither were differences usually reduced by adjusting for either actual attendance rate or examination qualifications on leaving school. These results suggest strongly that the labour market experiences of former truants are worse than those of their peers who were absent from school to the same extent but for other reasons, and those who did not truant but left school with equally low qualification levels.

Other outcomes

Previous studies of other outcomes are even less numerous than those of labour market experience. Perhaps the most striking finding is that of Robins (1968). From a follow-up at age 25 of the same St Louis sample subsequently re-interviewed by Robins & Ratcliff (1980), truancy "accounted for" higher mortality rates, principally by homicide but also natural causes.

Less dramatic health-related behaviour is reported by several studies. Farrington (1980) reports heavier smoking among truants, as do Charlton & Blair (1989). On the other hand, Farrington found no relationship with drinking habits, whereas Robins & Ratcliffe did find increased alcohol problems.

TABLE 7.5
Cigarettes smoked per day: loglinear analysis of odds relative to smoking no cigarettes, truants v. non-truants

		Adjusted for:			
		Background	Attainment at 11	Attendance at 15	Qualifications at 16+
Men (*n*=2815)					
Up to 10	2.00	2.18	2.11	2.02	2.05
10–30	3.42	3.11	3.12	3.19	3.28
Over 30	5.79	4.89	4.93	4.94	5.05
Women (*n*=2848)					
Up to 10	1.82	2.06	2.16	2.17	1.83
10–30	4.44	3.85	4.05	4.14	4.34
Over 30	8.89	7.65	8.72	9.47	10.51

More general mental health problems have been found, in terms of high scores on a measure of antisocial tendency (Farrington, 1980) and on an adult deviance scale (Robins & Ratcliffe, 1980), and tendency towards psychological disturbance (Rodgers, 1990). In addition Farrington reports higher levels of convictions as young adults and of self-reported delinquency; and Robins & Ratcliffe found truancy associated with reports of criminality and violence. The latter authors also found a higher incidence of marital problems among former truants.

Other outcomes from NCDS

It is possible to investigate several of the above areas with NCDS data. Like Farrington's study they show little relationship between truancy and drinking habits at 23. Table 7.5, however, confirms the strong association with cigarette smoking. Among former truants of both sexes, even moderate smoking, of up to 10 cigarettes per day, is about twice as likely. The odds of being in the highest smoking category, of more than 30 per day, are more than five times greater for the male truants, and almost nine times greater for the females. There are no consistent effects of introducing further variables into the analysis.

The measure of general mental health available from the NCDS 23-year follow-up is the Malaise Inventory (Rutter *et al*, 1976), a short self-completed questionnaire on which high scores indicate tendency to depression (Table 7.6). For both sexes former truants are nearly three times as likely to obtain scores above the cut-off indicating depression. The effect on this of taking social background into account is small, and of other factors trivial.

TABLE 7.6
Tendency to depression (high malaise scores): loglinear analysis of odds relative to 'normal', truants v. non-truants

			Adjusted for:		
		Background	Attainment at 11	Attendance at 15	Qualifications at 16+
Men (*n*=2813)					
High scores	2.64	2.26	2.24	2.38	2.40
Women (*n*=2842)					
High scores	2.75	2.16	2.26	2.23	2.22

TABLE 7.7
Marital status: loglinear analysis of odds relative to married, truants v. non-truants

			Adjusted for:		
		Background	Attainment at 11	Attendance at 15	Qualifications at 16+
Men (*n*=2815)					
Single	0.58	0.66	0.64	0.64	0.64
Separated/divorced/ widowed	2.19	2.07	1.99	2.00	2.01
Women (*n*=2848)					
Single	0.67	0.78	0.79	0.82	0.78
Separated/divorced/ widowed	3.50	3.57	3.44	3.33	3.40

A number of measures are available related to partnership, marriage and family formation. Marked contrasts associated with former truancy are found on all of these, particularly for females. Truants of both sexes were more likely to be married by 23. Females, but not males, were also more likely to be cohabiting. As Table 7.7 shows, both sexes were more likely to have experienced the breakdown of a marriage by the relatively early age of 23. In addition truants had more children – males were more than three times as likely and female truants more than six times (but reduced to 3.6 by allowing for other factors) as likely to have two or more children by this age. Women who had truanted were as much as 7.5 times more likely to be unmarried with children at 23 (for men the comparable figure was 2.6). With the exception mentioned above, these comparisons were not substantially affected by allowing for the other factors.

Conclusions

The NCDS analyses confirm those from other research, and it is clear that young people who have truanted from school do tend to experience difficulties in their adult lives.

Findings are most consistent in relation to areas other than employment, i.e. health-related behaviour, family formation and mental health; although this may reflect the fact that there are fewer studies of such outcomes and therefore less scope for contradictory results.

Studies of labour market variation do amount to a general picture of greater difficulties for former truants, but there is variation among the findings for specific measures. However, the pattern of these findings does prompt some speculation about what might explain some of this variation. Firstly, it does appear likely that problems increase with age. Generally speaking, the effects appear least where follow-ups have taken place within a year or two of leaving school, increase in the twenties and are at their greatest in the mid-thirties (no studies have yet gone beyond this age).

Secondly, the economic context may well be important. Cherry's subjects, who experienced frequent job changing but were not in lower status jobs at 26, were born in 1946. The late 1960s and early 1970s were a period of relative buoyancy in the labour market and low unemployment. For the 1958-born cohort the relevant period is the late 1970s and early 1980s, when recession and high unemployment were beginning to bite. Similarly, it is likely that the economic circumstances of black men in St Louis, as studied by Robins & Ratcliffe and among whom former truants also had particularly low incomes, were generally disadvantaged.

Moreover, there is a suggestion running through all the NCDS results that the difficulties experienced by female truants, both in the labour market and in other aspects of their lives, are even greater than for their male counterparts. While this may in part reflect the fact that fewer women truanted from school, and therefore a more extreme group is being examined, it may also be a function of their generally greater economic vulnerability. Recent work by Kerckhoff (1993) has demonstrated more generally how there are greater continuities between poor school performance and labour market difficulties for women than for men.

What is clear is that the typical truant is not someone who has simply outgrown school and is ready to settle successfully into adult life. On the contrary, there are sad continuities between their disadvantaged status at school and in society subsequently. Furthermore, their disadvantages and difficulties are greater than would be predicted from their social background. The balance of evidence is that they are also greater than would be explained by their low levels of school achievement and qualifications. In terms of the difficulties they are likely to encounter in employment and in their personal lives, truants are a group distinct from others with poor attendance and low achievements.

Although schools can be effective in improving their attendance rates, the impact will inevitably be limited on young people whose difficulties also reside in their personal characteristics and social circumstances. Action that has as its main purpose the reduction of unauthorised absence as a performance indicator is not likely to affect more fundamental employment and personal life skills, even less the social context in which these operate. To tackle and change these continuities in the lives of school truants implies levels of counselling, support and resources that are unlikely to be available in the present climate.

References

BUTLER, N. R. & BONHAM, D. G. (1963) *Perinatal Mortality.* Edinburgh: Livingstone.

CHARLTON, A. & BLAIR, B. (1989) Absence from school related to children's and parental smoking habits. *British Medical Journal,* **298,** 90–92.

CHERRY, N. (1976) Persistent job changing – is it a problem? *Journal of Occupational Psychology,* **49,** 203–221.

DAVIE, R., BUTLER, N. R. & GOLDSTEIN, H. (1972) *From Birth to Seven.* London: Longman.

DFE (1991) *The Education (Pupils' Attendance Records) Regulations 1991.* Circular no. 11/91, 11 July 1991.

FARRINGTON, D. (1980) Truancy, delinquency, home and the school. In *Out of School* (eds L. Hersov & I. Berg), pp. 49–63. Chichester: John Wiley.

FOGELMAN, K. (1978) School attendance, attainment and behaviour. *British Journal of Educational Psychology,* **48,** 148–158.

—— (ed.) (1983) *Growing Up in Great Britain.* London: Macmillan.

—— & RICHARDSON, K. (1974) School attendance: some findings from the National Child Development Study. In *Truancy* (ed. B. Turner), pp. 29–51. London: Ward Lock Educational.

——, TIBBENHAM, A. & LAMBERT, L. (1980) Absence from school: findings from the National Child Development Study. In *Out of School* (eds L. Hersov & I. Berg), pp. 25–48. Chichester: John Wiley.

GRAY, G., SMITH, A., RUTTER, M. (1980) School attendance and the first year of employment. In *Out of School* (eds L. Hersov & I. Berg), pp. 343–370. Chichester: John Wiley.

HAIGH, G. (1976) *The Reluctant Adolescent.* London: Temple Smith.

HIBBETT, A. (1987). *Early Adult Outcomes of Truancy.* NCDS User Support Group Working Paper no. 24. Social Statistics Research Unit, City University.

—— & FOGELMAN, K. (1990) Future lives of truants: family formation and health related behaviour. *British Journal of Educational Psychology,* **60,** 171–179.

——, —— & MANOR, O. (1990) Occupational outcomes of truancy. *British Journal of Educational Psychology,* **60,** 23–36.

KERCKHOFF, A (1993) *Diverging Pathway: Social Structure and Career Deflections.* Cambridge: Cambridge University Press.

NATIONAL ASSOCIATION OF CHIEF EDUCATION WELFARE OFFICERS (1974) *These We Serve.* London: NACEWO.

REYNOLDS, D. (1976) Schools do make a difference. *New Society,* **37,** 223–225.

ROBINS, L. (1968) Negro homicide victims – who will they be? *Trans-action,* **5,** 15–19.

—— & RATCLIFFE, R. (1980) The long-term outcomes of truancy. In *Out of School* (eds L. Hersov & I. Berg), pp. 65–83. Chichester: John Wiley.

RODGERS, B. (1990) Behaviour and personality in childhood as predictors of adult psychiatric disorder. *Journal of Child Psychology and Psychiatry,* **31,** 393–414.

RUTTER, M., TIZARD, J. & WHITMORE, K. (1970) *Education, Health and Behaviour.* London: Longman.

——, ——, YULE, W., *et al* (1976) Isle of Wight studies: 1964–1974. *Psychological Medicine,* **6,** 313–332.

SHEPHERD, P. (1984) *Earnings, Income and Other Aspects of the Financial Circumstances of the NCDS Cohort at 23.* NCDS Working Paper 19, Social Statistical Research Unit, City University.

—— (1985) *The National Child Development Study: an Introduction to the Origins of the Study and the Methods of Data Collection.* NCDS User Support Group Working Paper 1, Social Statistics Research Unit, City University.

TIBBENHAM, A. (1977) Housing and truancy. *New Society,* **39,** 501–502.

TYERMAN, M. (1968) *Truancy.* London: University of London Press.

8 Later life outcomes of truants in the Cambridge Study

DAVID FARRINGTON

Children who fail to attend school without good reason are often divided into truants and school refusers (Kahn *et al*, 1981; Bools *et al*, 1990; Berg *et al*, 1993). The difference between these categories is that truants skip school without parental consent or knowledge, whereas school refusers are too afraid to attend school and stay at home with parental consent. The antisocial and disruptive truants are often contrasted with the neurotic school refusers. In the present research, however, it was not possible to distinguish between these two categories, and both are included as 'truants'.

A great deal is known about the individual characteristics and family backgrounds of truants (Carroll, 1977; Coventry *et al*, 1984; Sommer, 1985; Berg, 1992). Truants are disproportionally drawn from lower-class families (Belson, 1975; May, 1975; Kavanagh & Carroll, 1977; Tibbenham, 1977; Fogelman *et al*, 1980), although Rutter *et al* (1970) did not find this. Truants tend to come from low-income families (Hodges, 1968), with unemployed parents (Galloway, 1982, 1985), and from large-sized families (Hodges, 1968; Rutter *et al*, 1970; May, 1975; Fogelman *et al*, 1980). Truants tend to have suffered inconsistent home discipline (Hersov, 1960), nervous mothers (Galloway, 1982, 1985), parental absence (Hersov, 1960; Hodges, 1968), and their parents show little interest in their education (Douglas & Ross, 1965; Stott, 1966; Fogelman & Richardson, 1974).

Not surprisingly, truants do not like school (Stott, 1966; Mitchell & Shepherd, 1967; Belson, 1975; Kavanagh & Carroll, 1977; University of North London Truancy Unit, 1993). They tend to have low intelligence and attainment (Hersov, 1960; Cooper, 1966; Douglas *et al*, 1968; Rutter *et al*, 1970; Fogelman & Richardson, 1974; May, 1975; Fogelman, 1978; Galloway, 1982, 1985) and poor concentration (Reid, 1984). They tend to be described by teachers as aggressive (Douglas *et al*, 1968), disobedient (Reid, 1984), lazy (Douglas & Ross, 1965), liars (Hersov, 1960; May, 1975; Reid, 1984) and thieves (Galloway, 1982; Reid, 1984). Many researchers have reported a link between truancy and delinquency (Ferguson, 1952; Hersov, 1960; Stott, 1966;

Douglas *et al*, 1968; Tennent, 1971; May, 1975), although it is not clear why they are associated. Truants are described as relatively small (Cooper, 1966), neurotic or nervous (Douglas *et al*, 1968; Kavanagh & Carroll, 1977), solitary and unhappy (Tyerman, 1968; May, 1975; Reid, 1984), and unpopular (Croft & Grygier, 1956; Reid, 1984).

While a great deal is known about prior and concurrent features of truants, far less is known about their later life histories. In two longitudinal studies in St Louis, Robins & Ratcliff (1980) found that elementary school truancy predicted high school truancy, dropping-out of high school, leaving home early and getting married early. Male elementary school truants tended to marry female elementary school truants and tended to have children who truanted, showing the intergenerational transmission of truancy. High school truancy predicted crime, low pay, employment problems, alcohol problems, violence, drug use, depression, anxiety and psychiatric treatment when the men were in their thirties. Similarly, Kandel *et al* (1984) in a New York State longitudinal study showed that school absentees at age 15–16 were more likely to leave school early, had a more unstable employment record, were more likely to be divorced or separated, had more illness, more delinquency and more smoking, but not more drinking and only marginally more drug use, up to age 24–25.

Turning to British studies, Cherry (1976) in the National Survey of Health and Development discovered that poor attendance predicted an unstable job record, unemployment, divorce and separation, and psychiatric disorder up to age 26. In inner London, Gray *et al* (1980) reported that poor attendance in the final year at school predicted early school leaving and unemployment, but not job status in the year after leaving school.

The aim of this chapter is to report new results from the Cambridge Study in Delinquent Development on the characteristics of secondary school truants from childhood (age 8) to adulthood (age 32), and to compare truants with juvenile delinquents.

The Cambridge Study in Delinquent Development

The present research uses data collected in the Cambridge Study in Delinquent Development, which is a prospective longitudinal survey of the development of offending and antisocial behaviour in 411 London males. At the time they were first contacted in 1961–62, these males were all living in a working-class area of south London. The sample was chosen by taking all the boys who were then aged 8–9 and on the registers of six state primary schools within a 1-mile radius of a research office that had been established. Hence, the most common year of birth of these males was 1953. In nearly all cases (94%), their family breadwinner at that time (usually the father) had a working-class occupation (skilled, semi-skilled or unskilled manual worker).

Most of the males were white in racial appearance and of British origin. The study was originally directed by Donald J. West, and it has been directed since 1982 by David P. Farrington, who has worked on it since 1969. The major results are described in four books (West, 1969, 1982; West & Farrington, 1973, 1977), and in more than 60 papers listed by Farrington & West (1990).

A major aim in this survey was to measure as many factors as possible that were alleged to be causes or correlates of offending. The males were interviewed and tested in their schools when they were aged about 8–9, 10–11, and 14–15, by male or female psychologists. For simplicity, these tests are referred to as the tests at ages 8, 10 and 14. They were interviewed in a research office at about 16, 18 and 21, and in their homes at about 25 and 32, by young male social science graduates. At all ages except 21 and 25, the aim was to interview the whole sample, and it was always possible to trace and interview a high proportion: 389 out of 410 still alive at age 18 (95%) and 378 out of 403 still alive at age 32 (94%), for example. The tests in schools measured individual characteristics such as intelligence, attainment, personality and psychomotor impulsivity, while information was collected in the interviews about such topics as living circumstances, employment histories, relationships with females, leisure activities such as drinking and fighting, and offending behaviour.

In addition to interviews and tests with the males, interviews with their parents were carried out by female social workers who visited their homes. These took place about once a year from when the male was about 8 until he was aged 14–15 and was in his last year of compulsory education. The primary informant was the mother, although many fathers were also seen. The parents provided details about such matters as family income, family size, their employment histories, their child-rearing practices (including attitudes, discipline and parental disharmony), their closeness of supervision of the boy and his temporary or permanent separations from them. Also, when the boy was aged 12, the parents completed questionnaires about their child-rearing attitudes and about his leisure activities.

The teachers completed questionnaires when the males were aged about 8, 10, 12 and 14. These furnished data about their troublesome and aggressive school behaviour, their attention deficits, their school attainments and their truancy. Ratings were also obtained from the boys' peers when they were in the primary schools, about such topics as their daring, dishonesty, troublesomeness and popularity.

Searches were also carried out in the central Criminal Record Office in London to try to locate findings of guilt of the males, of their parents, of their brothers and sisters, and (in recent years) of their wives and cohabitees. The minimum age of criminal responsibility in England is 10. The Criminal Record Office contains records of all relatively serious offences committed in Great Britain or Ireland. In the case of 18 males who had emigrated outside Great Britain and Ireland by age 32, applications were made to search their criminal records in the eight countries where they had settled; searches were actually carried out in four countries. Since most males did not emigrate until their twenties, and since the emigrants had rarely been convicted in England, it is likely that the criminal records are quite complete.

Convictions were only counted if they were for offences normally recorded in the Criminal Record Office, thereby excluding minor crimes such as common assault, traffic infractions and drunkenness. The most common offences included were thefts, burglaries and unauthorised takings of vehicles, although there were also quite a few offences of violence, vandalism, fraud and drug abuse. In order not to rely on official records for information about offending, self-reports of offending were obtained from the males at every age from 14 onwards (Farrington, 1989a).

Many data reduction exercises were carried out to reduce the large number of measured variables to a small number of key variables, each measuring one underlying theoretical construct (Farrington & West, 1981). For the present analyses, each variable at each age was dichotomised, as far as possible, into the 'worst' quarter of males (e.g. the quarter with lowest income or lowest intelligence) versus the remainder. This was done in order to compare the importance of different variables and also to permit a 'risk factor' approach. Because most variables were originally classified into a small number of categories, and because fine distinctions between categories could not be made very accurately, this dichotomising did not usually involve a great loss of information. The one-quarter/three-quarters split was chosen to match the prior expectation that about one-quarter of the sample would be convicted as juveniles. Variables were not included in the analyses if more than about 10% of the sample were not known on them. (For more information about all the variables discussed here, see the books on the study listed above.)

In summary, the Cambridge Study in Delinquent Development has a unique combination of features. Eight face-to-face interviews have been completed with the males over a period of 24 years, between ages 8 and 32. The attrition rate is unusually low for such a long-term survey. The main focus of interest is on crime and delinquency, but the survey also provides information about alcohol and drug abuse, educational difficulties, poverty and poor housing, unemployment, sexual behaviour and other social problems. The sample size of about 400 is large enough for many statistical analyses, but small enough to permit detailed case histories of the males and their families. Information has been obtained from multiple sources, including the subjects themselves, their parents, teachers, peers and official records. Generally, the information came from parents, teachers, peers or tests completed by the males between ages 8 and 14, but primarily from interviews with the males between ages 16 and 32. Data have been collected about a wide variety of theoretical constructs at different ages, including biological (e.g. pulse rate), psychological (e.g. intelligence), family (e.g. parental discipline) and social (e.g. socio-economic status) factors.

Prior research on truancy in the Cambridge Study

The most extensive research on truancy in the Cambridge Study was reported by Farrington (1980). Information about truancy was obtained from the teachers' questionnaires completed when the boys were aged 8, 10, 12 and 14, and from the self-reports at age 14. Only 24 boys (6%) were identified by teachers as primary school truants (age 8–10), but 73 (18%) were either identified by teachers as "frequent truants" at their secondary schools (age 12–14) or had poor attendance (less than 90%) attributed to truancy. Half of the primary school truants became secondary school truants, showing the continuity in truancy over time. A total of 72 boys (18% of 405 interviewed) admitted frequent truancy in the self-reports at age 14. The teacher-rated and self-reported frequent truants overlapped significantly: 40% of teacher-rated truants were self-reported truants, compared with only 13% of teacher-rated non-truants (χ^2=28.5, 1 d.f., P<0.0001, one-tailed; odds ratio or OR=4.5). Consequently, characteristics of teacher-rated truants were similar to characteristics of self-reported truants.

The teachers said that the secondary school truants tended to be lazy, lacking in concentration, frequently restless, frequently disobedient, quarrelsome and aggressive, persistently late and frequent liars. They tended to be poor readers and to have a low position in class. Also, they tended to be anxious, gloomy and sad, frequently day-dreaming, tired and washed out, ignored by other children and unable to make friends.

At age 8–10, the secondary school truants tended to come from low-income, low social class families; large families; and tended to be living in slum housing. They were likely to have convicted parents and delinquent older siblings by their tenth birthday. Their parents used poor child-rearing techniques characterised by harsh or erratic discipline, parental disharmony and poor supervision. The parents tended to be uninterested in the boy's education and truants were likely to have been separated from a parent (usually the father) for reasons other than death or hospitalisation (usually parental disharmony). Truants tended to have low non-verbal and verbal IQ scores and low junior school attainment. They tended to be relatively small in height, but troublesome and daring.

At age 18, secondary school truants tended to have low status (unskilled manual) jobs and an unstable job record. They tended to be heavy gamblers, heavy smokers and sexually promiscuous. They spent a lot of time hanging about on the streets and were involved in antisocial groups who committed violence or vandalism. Truants also tended to be in conflict with their parents and to be tattooed.

There was a significant overlap between truancy and juvenile delinquency: 48% of secondary school truants were convicted, compared with 14% of non-truants (χ^2=39.3, P<0.0001, OR=5.4). Every variable that was significantly related to delinquency was also significantly related to truancy, and every variable that was significantly related to truancy was also significantly related to delinquency except for a low social class family at age 8–10. In light of all these results, Farrington (1980) concluded that truancy and delinquency were two symptoms of an underlying antisocial personality.

In this chapter, the previous results are extended in a number of ways. First, whereas in the previous analyses characteristics of teacher-rated and self-reported truants were considered separately, this chapter uses a combined measure of truancy. Second, the characteristics of truants and delinquents at ages 8–10, 12–14 and 18 are reported, including a wider range of variables than before. Third, an attempt has been made to disentangle truancy and delinquency by studying characteristics of non-delinquent truants, delinquent non-truants, delinquent truants and non-delinquent non-truants. Fourth, regression techniques are used to establish the independent predictors at age 8–10 of truancy and delinquency. Fifth, the characteristics of truants and delinquents much later in life, at age 32, are reported. Sixth, the extent to which truancy predicts adult criminality and adult social dysfunction independently of other variables is investigated.

Childhood and adolescent features of truants and delinquents

Table 8.1 shows characteristics of secondary school truants and convicted juvenile delinquents at ages 8–10 and 12–14. The truants were those identified as frequent truants by either teachers or self-reports (116 boys, or 28% of the sample), on the assumption that a combined measure is more valid than either measure alone. (Similarly, variables measured at ages 8 and 10 were often combined, and variables measured at ages 12 and 14). The average school attendance in the previous year was 66% for the 116 truants and 85% for the 295 non-truants; each boy was scored according to the lower of his two attendances at 12 and 14. The juvenile delinquents convicted between ages 10 and 16 totalled 85 (21% of the sample), rather than the 84 reported by West & Farrington (1973), because one more case was discovered in the 1980s. There were 52 delinquent truants, 64 non-delinquent truants, 33 delinquent non-truants and 262 non-delinquent non-truants.

The OR is used in Table 8.1 as the main measure of strength of association. Measures of strength are often more meaningful than measures of statistical significance. The OR basically measures increases in risk associated with a risk factor. An OR of 2 or greater indicates a doubling of the risk and hence a strong relationship. For example, 45% of boys from low-income families at age 8 became secondary school truants, compared with 23% of the remainder, a significant difference ($\chi^2 = 16.0$, $P < 0.0001$, OR=2.7; one-tailed tests are used throughout in light of the directional predictions). Similarly, 34% of boys

TABLE 8.1
Childhood and adolescent features of truants and delinquents

	T (116)	D (85)	Odds ratios ND, T (64)	D, NT (33)	D, T (52)
Age 8–10					
Low family income	2.7**	2.6**	2.2*	2.0	4.2**
Poor housing	2.4**	1.7*	2.5**	1.5	2.5*
Low social class	2.2*	1.5	1.7	0.7	2.5*
Large family size	2.5**	2.5**	2.1*	2.0	3.7**
Convicted parent	2.8**	3.4**	2.0*	2.3*	5.5**
Delinquent sibling	3.6**	3.2**	2.7*	2.0	5.8**
Behaviour-problem sibling	2.7**	2.7**	2.6**	2.7*	3.7**
Poor child-rearing	2.0*	2.8**	1.7	3.1*	3.1**
Authoritarian parents	1.1	2.1*	1.1	3.7*	1.5
Poor supervision	3.3**	2.2*	3.0**	1.5	4.0**
Separated from parent	2.6**	2.4**	1.8*	1.4	4.0**
Father not interested	2.5*	2.1	2.3*	1.6	3.1*
Nervous father	2.3**	1.3	2.3*	0.8	2.2*
Nervous mother	1.6*	1.6*	1.4	1.3	2.0*
Uninterested in education	3.4**	2.2*	3.2**	1.5	4.1**
Catholic family	2.1*	2.0*	1.7	1.4	2.9*
Delinquent school	2.3*	2.6**	2.7*	3.8**	3.0*
Low non-verbal IQ	2.9**	2.3**	2.6*	1.7	3.9**
Low attainment	3.0**	2.6**	2.9**	2.3*	4.2**
Unpopular	1.7*	1.7*	1.4	1.2	2.2*
Small	2.0*	2.1*	2.2*	2.6*	2.5*
Lacks concentration	2.1*	2.3*	1.7	1.8	3.2**
Psychomotor impulsivity	1.9*	2.3**	1.4	1.7	3.1**
Daring	2.5**	4.2**	1.5	3.1*	5.9**
Troublesome	3.6**	5.0**	1.9*	2.7*	9.3**
Dishonest	2.1*	3.8**	1.4	3.3*	4.7**
Vulnerable	4.1**	5.7**	2.5*	3.9*	10.4**
Antisocial	3.5**	5.0**	2.1*	3.4*	8.7**
Age 12–14					
Poor housing	2.6**	1.4	3.1**	1.4	2.2*
Unemployed father	3.2**	4.2**	2.3	3.5*	6.4**

TABLE 8.1
Continued

	T (116)	D (85)	Odds ratios ND,T (64)	D,NT (33)	D,T (52)
Large family size	2.3**	2.2*	2.3*	2.3*	2.9**
Poor child-rearing	2.2*	2.1*	2.0*	1.8	2.8**
Father not involved	2.0*	1.9*	1.7	1.4	2.5*
Low non-verbal IQ	2.4**	2.2*	1.8*	1.3	3.6**
Low verbal IQ	2.8**	2.3**	2.8**	2.1	3.6**
Early school leaving	5.6**	4.2**	5.3**	3.4*	8.4**
Unpopular	2.5**	1.8*	1.7	0.4	3.4**
High nervousness	2.7**	1.2	3.1**	0.8	2.1*
Lacks con-centration	6.4**	4.8**	3.5**	1.6	16.0**
Daring	2.0*	4.9**	0.5	2.7*	5.7**
Frequent liar	5.0**	5.0**	2.4*	1.6	16.2**
Regular smoker	2.6**	1.9*	2.3*	1.3	3.2**
Had sex	3.6**	3.6**	2.8**	2.6*	6.7**
Aggressive	4.2**	3.4**	2.9**	1.8	7.9**
Hostile to police	3.3**	2.8**	2.8**	2.0	4.8**
Delinquent friends	4.6**	4.8**	3.3**	3.2*	9.9**
High SR offending	5.9**	6.9**	3.8**	4.3**	16.9**

*$P < 0.05$; **$P < 0.001$ (one tailed).
SR, self-reported; T, truants; D, delinquents; ND, non-delinquents; NT, non-truants.

from low-income families became delinquents, compared with 17% of the remainder ($\chi^2 = 12.7$, $P = 0.0002$, OR = 2.6).

The strongest predictors at age 8–10 of secondary school truancy were troublesomeness (rated by peers and teachers), a delinquent sibling, parents uninterested in the boy's education, poor parental supervision, low junior school attainment (according to the school's own tests), low non-verbal IQ (on the Progressive Matrices), a convicted parent, low family income, a behaviour-problem sibling and separation from a parent (usually the father) for reasons other than death or hospitalisation (usually disharmony). The strongest predictors at age 8–10 of delinquency were troublesomeness, daring (rated by peers and parents), dishonesty (rated by peers), a convicted parent, a delinquent sibling, poor parental child-rearing behaviour (harsh or erratic discipline, parental conflict), a behaviour-problem sibling, low family income, a high delinquency-rate school and low junior school attainment.

Primary school truancy is not shown as a predictor in Table 8.1 because there were only 24 primary school truants (6% of the sample). As mentioned earlier, variables were dichotomised as far as possible into the 'worst' quarter versus the remainder, and variables with extreme splits were excluded from the analyses. However, 15 of the primary school truants became frequent truants in the secondary school (according to this combined measure based on teachers and self-reports) and 14 of them were convicted as juveniles.

It can be seen that six of the ten strongest predictors of truancy were also among the ten strongest predictors of delinquency. However, this may reflect the significant overlap between truancy and delinquency. It is conceivable that these variables predict delinquency rather than truancy and hence that they are characteristic of delinquent truants but not of non-delinquent truants. In an attempt to disentangle truancy and delinquency, delinquent-truants were studied separately from non-delinquent truants and from delinquent non-truants.

The three right-hand columns of Table 8.1 show comparisons of these categories with the reference category of non-delinquent non-truants. For example, 16% of non-delinquent non-truants were from low-income families, compared with 30% of non-delinquent truants, 27% of delinquent non-truants and 44% of delinquent truants. Comparing 16% of non-delinquent non-truants with 30% of non-delinquent truants, $\chi^2=5.44$, $P=0.010$, OR$=2.2$. Comparing 16% of non-delinquent non-truants with 27% of delinquent non-truants, $\chi^2=1.86$, $P=0.086$, OR$=2.0$. Comparing 16% of non-delinquent non-truants with 44% of delinquent truants, $\chi^2=19.3$, $P<0.0001$, OR$=4.2$.

The OR for non-delinquent truants indicates the strength of the relationship of a variable with truancy in the absence of delinquency, while the OR for delinquent non-truants indicates the strength of the relationship of a variable with delinquency in the absence of truancy. The OR for delinquent truants indicates how far relationships with truancy and delinquency reflect characteristics of the overlapping delinquent truant group. In the case of family income, the ORs show that low income was related to both truancy and delinquency, but that it was especially a feature of the delinquent truant group.

Of the age 8–10 variables, truancy and delinquency were approximately equally (and strongly) related to low family income, large family size, a convicted parent, a delinquent sibling, a behaviour-problem sibling, low junior school attainment, small height and troublesomeness. They were approximately equally (but weakly) related to separation from a parent, coming from a Roman Catholic family (which often reflected Irish origin), a nervous mother (based on ratings by psychiatric social workers, a health questionnaire completed by mothers and psychiatric treatment), unpopularity (rated by peers), poor concentration or restlessness (rated by teachers) and impulsivity on psychomotor tests. The relationships between these latter variables and truancy and delinquency were primarily driven by the delinquent truant group. For example, the percentage lacking in concentration was 15% of non-delinquent non-truants, 23% of non-delinquent truants, 24% of delinquent non-truants, and 37% of delinquent truants.

Truancy was more strongly related than delinquency to poor housing, a low social class family, poor parental supervision, the father not interested in the boy, a nervous father (based on ratings by psychiatric social workers and psychiatric treatment), a lack of interest in education by the parents and low non-verbal IQ (on the Progressive Matrices). Delinquency was more strongly related than truancy to poor parental child-rearing behaviour, authoritarian child-rearing attitudes of parents, going to a school with a high delinquency rate, daring and dishonesty. Delinquency was also more closely related to a combined measure of background vulnerability based on low family income, large family size, a convicted parent, low non-verbal IQ and poor child-rearing (West & Farrington, 1973, p. 131), and to a combined measure of antisocial personality based on ten types of bad behaviour (Farrington, 1991).

The variables measured at age 12–14 were more contemporaneous with truancy (also measured at age 12–14) and juvenile delinquency (covering ages 10–16). The measure of antisocial personality at age 14 included truancy and delinquency and so is not shown in Table 8.1. The strongest correlates of truancy were poor concentration or restlessness (rated by teachers), high self-reported offending, early school leaving (at age 15), frequent lying (rated by teachers), delinquent friends, aggressive behaviour (rated by teachers), having sexual intercourse by age 15, a hostile attitude to the police (on a questionnaire), an unemployed father and low verbal IQ (on the Mill Hill Vocabulary test). Nine of these ten variables were also among the ten strongest correlates at age 12–14 of delinquency. The only difference was that low verbal IQ for truancy was replaced by daring for delinquency.

Of the age 12–14 variables, truancy and delinquency were approximately equally (and strongly) related to large family size, poor child-rearing, low verbal IQ, having sexual intercourse, delinquent friends and high self-reported offending. They were approximately equally (but weakly) related to the father not joining in the boy's leisure activities. Truancy was more strongly related to poor housing, low non-verbal IQ, early school leaving, unpopularity, nervousness (rated by psychiatric social workers), poor concentration or restlessness, frequent lying, regular smoking, aggressive behaviour and a hostile attitude to the police. Interestingly, unpopularity and nervousness were negatively related to delinquency. Delinquency was more strongly related to an unemployed father and daring.

Most variables that were significantly related to truancy were also significantly related to delinquency, and vice versa. Therefore, it is still plausible to argue that most categories of variables – socio-economic deprivation, family criminality, poor parenting, poor school performance and impulsivity – foster the development of an antisocial personality, and that truancy and delinquency are two behavioural symptoms of this. However, there were indications that truancy was more related to nervousness and unpopularity, and truants were more likely to have nervous fathers. Therefore, it may be that nervousness causes truancy but not

TABLE 8.2
Predicting truants and delinquents

	OLS regression		Logistic regression	
	F *change*	P	*LRCS change*	P
Truants				
Troublesome	24.68	0.0001	17.30	0.0001
Behaviour-problem sibling	17.19	0.0001	22.31	0.0001
Nervous father	12.28	0.0003	13.46	0.0001
Low non-verbal IQ	9.27	0.001	3.75	0.026
Separated from parent	5.51	0.010	6.25	0.006
Uninterested in education	6.40	0.006	6.23	0.006
Low attainment	3.71	0.027	—	—
Daring	3.73	0.027	3.52	0.030
Delinquents				
Troublesome	34.67	0.0001	26.23	0.0001
Daring	12.22	0.0003	13.05	0.0002
Behaviour-problem sibling	11.97	0.0003	5.40	0.010
Dishonest	10.30	0.0008	5.60	0.009
Convicted parent	5.60	0.009	16.35	0.0001
Poor child-rearing	2.57	0.055	—	—
Non-delinquent truants				
Uninterested in education	11.94	0.0003	—	—
Nervous father	7.46	0.003	8.73	0.002
Behaviour-problem sibling	6.69	0.005	13.64	0.0001
Low attainment	5.10	0.012	6.23	0.006
Poor housing	4.06	0.022	4.07	0.022
Low non-verbal IQ	2.45	0.059	—	—
Poor supervision	—	—	3.39	0.033
Delinquent non-truants				
Delinquent school	9.68	0.001	3.21	0.037
Authoritarian parents	6.29	0.006	—	—
Daring	5.71	0.009	3.83	0.025
Dishonest	3.08	0.040	10.15	0.0007
Behaviour-problem sibling	3.45	0.032	5.94	0.007
Delinquent truants				
Troublesome	55.95	0.0001	38.35	0.0001
Convicted parent	19.09	0.0001	20.14	0.0001
Delinquent sibling	16.24	0.0001	—	—
Daring	10.33	0.0008	9.08	0.001
Behaviour-problem sibling	8.24	0.002	11.23	0.0004
Nervous father	6.17	0.007	—	—

TABLE 8.2
Continued

	OLS regression		Logistic regression	
	F change	*P*	*LRCS change*	*P*
Dishonest	5.47	0.010	3.61	0.029
Separated from parent	5.17	0.012	4.15	0.021
Low non-verbal IQ	4.61	0.016	—	—
Low attainment	2.75	0.049	3.93	0.024
Catholic family	2.70	0.051	—	—

P values one-tailed.
OLS, ordinary least squares; LRCS, likelihood ratio chi-squared.

delinquency, or alternatively that, for a minority of children, truancy is a behavioural symptom of a nervous–withdrawn temperament rather than of an antisocial personality. Also having parents who are uninterested in education may be specifically conducive to truancy rather than to delinquency.

Predicting truancy and delinquency

Regression analyses were carried out to investigate how far each variable at age 8–10 predicted the various measures of truancy and delinquency independently of each other variable. The combined variables of vulnerability and antisociality were not included in these analyses. In order to avoid problems of multicollinearity, highly correlated risk factors were removed from the analyses. Specifically, when two factors had a ϕ correlation of 0.5 or greater, one of them was removed. For example, at age 8–10 low family income was retained in the analysis in preference to an erratic job record of the father, poor parental supervision in preference to physical neglect of the boy, low junior school attainment in preference to low verbal IQ, and height in preference to weight. Excluded variables are not shown in Table 8.1.

Two methods of investigating independent predictors were used, namely ordinary least squares (OLS) regression and logistic regression. In practice, the two methods tend to produce similar results with dichotomous data (e.g. Cleary & Angel, 1984). The main differences between them follow from the fact that missing cases can be deleted variable by variable in OLS regression (thereby using as much of the data as possible), whereas in logistic regression a case that is missing on any one variable has to be deleted from the whole analysis, causing a considerable loss of data. The most reliable predictors are

TABLE 8.3
Teenage and adult features of truants and delinquents

	Odds ratios				
	T (116)	D (85)	ND,T (64)	D,NT (33)	D,T (52)
Age 18					
Unskilled manual job	6.0**	4.1**	4.5**	2.3	10.7**
Unstable job record	3.8**	3.7**	3.0**	2.7*	6.8**
Poor relation with parents	2.2*	2.9**	1.3	1.9	4.1**
No exams taken	4.6**	5.6**	3.3**	3.8**	12.8**
Has girlfriend	2.1*	2.6**	1.5	1.8	3.9**
Sexually promiscuous	3.2**	2.8**	3.0**	2.5*	4.6**
Hospital treatment	1.7	2.1*	1.7	2.4	2.3*
Heavy gambler	2.1*	2.5**	2.2*	3.2*	2.9*
Heavy smoker	3.3**	2.3**	2.3*	0.9	5.0**
Taken marijuana	2.4**	2.9**	1.6	1.9	4.4**
Hangs about	2.3*	2.7**	2.4*	3.4*	3.3**
Antisocial group	3.0**	3.7**	2.2*	2.9*	5.7**
Heavy drinker	3.0**	3.2**	2.4*	2.6*	5.2**
Fights after drinking	2.7**	2.3**	2.1*	1.4	4.0**
Drunk driver	2.3**	4.3**	1.4	3.5*	5.6**
Motoring conviction	1.9*	3.5**	1.6	4.2**	3.7**
Small	1.3	2.0*	1.0	1.9	2.0*
Anti-establishment	2.0*	2.1*	2.1*	2.5*	2.5*
High impulsivity	1.9*	1.9*	1.7	1.6	2.5*
Tattooed	5.7**	5.4**	4.5*	4.2*	12.3**
High SR violence	3.9**	4.7**	2.2*	2.5*	9.1**
High SR offending	3.1**	7.2**	1.6	5.1**	10.6**
Antisocial	5.8**	14.9**	2.9*	9.4**	34.7**
Age 32					
Not home owner	1.7*	2.7**	1.4	3.5*	2.7*
Lives in London	1.5	2.2*	1.2	2.2*	2.2*
Problems with area	1.6	1.8*	1.6	2.0	1.9
Unstable job record	2.4**	2.3*	1.9*	1.5	3.6**
Poor relation with mother	2.5*	1.1	2.7*	0.4	2.0
Poor relation with father	1.9*	1.1	2.2*	1.0	1.5
Rows with wife	1.7*	1.6	1.2	0.8	2.3*
Has hit wife	1.4	3.2**	0.5	2.0	3.3*
Divorced or separated	2.0*	2.0*	1.9*	2.0	2.5*
Child elsewhere	2.7**	3.6**	3.0*	6.9**	4.2**
Hospital treatment	2.2*	1.3	2.7*	1.5	1.9
Heavy gambler	1.1	1.8*	1.0	2.3*	1.6
Heavy smoker	1.4	1.9*	1.2	2.2*	1.9*
Taken marijuana	2.9**	3.6**	1.3	1.1	6.3**
Taken other drug	2.2*	3.4**	0.7	1.0	4.8**
Frequently out	1.2	2.7**	0.6	2.5*	2.4*
Heavy drinker	2.3*	2.9**	1.6	2.2	3.9**
Alcoholism (CageTest)	2.0*	2.0*	1.3	0.9	3.2**
Drunk driver	1.3	2.1*	1.1	2.4*	2.0*
Involved in fights	2.5**	3.4**	1.7	2.3*	5.2**
Anti-establishment	2.3**	3.4**	2.4*	5.0**	3.7**

TABLE 8.3
Continued

	Odds ratios				
	T (116)	D (85)	ND,T (64)	D,NT (33)	D,T (52)
High-impulsivity	2.2*	2.0*	2.2*	2.1	2.6*
Tattooed	4.1**	4.0**	3.3**	3.2*	7.3**
High SR offending	1.8*	2.6**	1.6	3.3*	2.6*
Convicted 21–32	4.0**	10.1**	2.4*	8.7**	16.4**
Antisocial	4.8**	6.4**	3.3**	4.7**	12.5**
Social dysfunction	2.3**	4.3**	1.5	3.8**	5.2**

*P<0.05; **P<0.001 (one-tailed).
SR, self-reported; T, truants; D, delinquents; ND, non-delinquents; NT, non-truants.

those identified by both methods. The OLS regression analyses were carried out first, beginning with all significant predictors. Because they were computationally more intensive, the logistic regression analyses were then carried out second with all independent predictors identified in the OLS regression, together with the next predictors that would have entered the OLS equation.

Table 8.2 shows the results of the regression analyses. The best independent predictors of truancy were troublesomeness, a behaviour-problem sibling, a nervous father, low non-verbal IQ, separation from a parent, parents uninterested in education and daring. The best independent predictors of delinquency were troublesomeness, daring, a behaviour-problem sibling, dishonesty and a convicted parent.

The best independent predictors of non-delinquent truants (compared with non-delinquent non-truants) were a nervous father, a behaviour-problem sibling, low junior school attainment and poor housing. These variables predict truancy in the absence of delinquency. The best independent predictors of delinquent non-truants (compared with non-delinquent non-truants) were attending a high delinquency-rate school, daring, dishonesty and a behaviour-problem sibling. These variables predict delinquency in the absence of truancy. The best independent predictors of delinquent truants (compared with non-delinquent non-truants) were troublesomeness, a convicted parent, daring, a behaviour-problem sibling, dishonesty, separation from a parent and low junior school attainment. These variables are most predictive of the overlapping group of delinquent truants.

Previous regression analyses have been carried out in the Cambridge Study to study the predictors of convictions (Farrington, 1990a; Farrington & Hawkins, 1991), chronic offending (Farrington & West, 1993), bullying (Farrington, 1993a), teenage and adult violence (Farrington 1989b), soccer violence and spouse assault (Farrington, 1994), antisocial personality (Farrington, 1995) and adult social dysfunction (Farrington, 1993b). Most of these have focused on possibly explanatory variables as predictors, rather than all variables; for example, truancy was not studied as a predictor of antisocial personality, since it was regarded as a symptom of antisocial personality.

Teenage and adult features of truants and delinquents

Table 8.3 shows features of truants and delinquents at ages 18 and 32. At age 18, the most characteristic features of past truants were that they had unskilled manual jobs, were tattooed, had taken no examinations, had high self-reported violence, had an unstable job record (marked by many short-term jobs, periods of unemployment and getting sacked), were heavy smokers (20 cigarettes per day or more), were sexually promiscuous (having intercourse with two or more girls in the previous 6 months), had high self-reported offending, were heavy drinkers (40 units of alcohol per week or more) and were members of antisocial groups that committed vandalism or violence.

Generally, the same features were characteristic of delinquents at age 18; eight of the ten strongest correlates of truancy were among the ten strongest correlates of delinquency. The difference was that drunk driving (driving after consuming 10 units of alcohol or more) and motoring convictions were among the strongest correlates of delinquency, replacing heavy smoking and sexual promiscuity for truancy.

The ORs for non-delinquent truants compared with delinquent non-truants show that having an unskilled manual job, heavy smoking and fighting after drinking were more related to truancy than to delinquency. In contrast, drunk driving, motoring convictions and self-reported offending were more related to delinquency.

The combined measure of antisocial personality at age 18 (based on 14 types of antisocial behaviour; see Farrington, 1991) was more closely related to delinquency. Two-thirds of the delinquents (65%) and half of the truants (46%) were among the most antisocial quarter of the males at age 18. Only 9% of non-delinquent non-truants were antisocial at age 18, compared with 21% of non-delinquent truants, 47% of delinquent non-truants and 76% of delinquent truants.

At age 32, the most characteristic features of past truants were that they were tattooed, had taken marijuana in the previous 5 years, had a child living elsewhere (for those with children), were involved in fights in the previous 5 years, did not get on well with their mothers, had an unstable job record, were heavy drinkers, had anti-establishment attitudes on a questionnaire (negative to police, school, rich people and civil servants), had received hospital treatment in the previous 5 years, had taken some drug other than marijuana in the previous 5 years and had high impulsivity on a questionnaire.

Generally, the same features were characteristic of delinquents at age 32; seven of the eleven strongest correlates of truancy were among the eleven strongest correlates of delinquency. The difference was that delinquents were more likely to have hit their wife or cohabitee, to rent rather than own their homes, to be frequently out (four or more evenings out per week) and to be high on self-reported offending. In contrast, a poor relationship with mothers and fathers, hospital treatment and high impulsivity were more characteristic of past truants.

The ORs for non-delinquent truants compared with delinquent non-truants show that not getting on well with mothers and fathers and hospital treatment were more related to truancy than to delinquency. In contrast, renting as opposed to home ownership, living in London, having a child living elsewhere, heavy gambling, heavy smoking, frequently out, drunk driving, involvement in fights, anti-establishment attitudes and high self-reported offending were more related to delinquency.

Truancy significantly predicted convictions between ages 21 and 32; 41% of truants were convicted, compared with 15% of non-truants (χ^2=31.0, $P<0.0001$, OR=4.0). Not surprisingly, juvenile delinquency was a more significant predictor of later adult convictions; 59% of delinquents were convicted, compared with 13% of non-delinquents (χ^2=80.0, $P<0.0001$, OR=10.1). The continuity between juvenile delinquency and adult crime has been documented by Farrington (1992). Only 10% of non-delinquent non-truants were convicted between ages 21 and 32, compared with 22% of non-delinquent truants, 50% of delinquent non-truants and 65% of delinquent truants.

The combined measure of antisociality at age 32 (based on 12 types of antisocial behaviour) was predicted by both truancy and delinquency. Over half of the delinquents (56%) and almost half of the truants (47%) were among the most antisocial quarter of the males at age 32. Only 13% of non-delinquent non-truants were antisocial at age 32, compared with 32% of non-delinquent truants, 41% of delinquent non-truants and 65% of delinquent truants.

At age 32, Farrington *et al* (1988a, b) developed a combined measure of adult social dysfunction based on poor accommodation, poor employment history, poor cohabitation history, problems with children, a high score on the General Health Questionnaire (which detected anxiety–depressive types of psychiatric illness), involvement in fights, substance abuse, self-reported offending and convictions in the previous 5 years. Table 8.3 shows that secondary school truants were significantly likely to be dysfunctional at age 32; 36% of truants were dysfunctional, compared with 20% of non-truants (χ^2=10.4, P=0.0006, OR=2.3). However, delinquency was more strongly predictive of adult social dysfunction; 49% of delinquents were dysfunctional, compared with 18% of non-delinquents (χ^2=29.2, $P<0.0001$, OR=4.3). The group of non-delinquent truants were not significantly likely to show adult social dysfunction; 24% of them were dysfunctional, compared with 17% of non-delinquent non-truants ($\chi^2=0.94$, NS, OR=1.5). In contrast, 44% of delinquent non-truants and 52% of delinquent truants showed adult social dysfunction.

The number of key variables investigated in these analyses was 29 at age 8–10, 23 at age 12–14, 28 at age 18 and 37 at age 32. The most important results are shown in Tables 8.1 and 8.3, and it can be seen that the number of significant results is far greater than the chance expectation of six per analysis.

Some of the non-significant results are of interest. While truants were rated as significantly nervous at age 14 (based on parent information), they were not rated as significantly nervous at age 8 (based on parent information), and they did not obtain significantly high neuroticism scores on the New Junior Maudsley Inventory at either age 10 or 14. While truants were rated as significantly unpopular at age 8–10 (by peers) and at age 12–14 (by teachers), they were not rated as having few or no friends at age 8 (based on parent information). Truants were significantly small and from lower class families at age 8–10 but not at age 14.

Truants were not significantly likely to have high debts either at age 18 or at 32. While they had a significantly poor relationship with their parents at age 18, they were not particularly likely to be living away from home. At age 18, they did not tend to have significantly low pulse rates, unlike violent and chronic offenders (Farrington, 1987). While truants were significantly likely to have low status jobs at age 18, this was not true at age 32. At age 32, truants were not specially likely to be living alone as opposed to with a wife or cohabitee, to have moved house frequently (three or more times in the previous 5 years) or to have a high score on the General Health Questionnaire, measuring anxiety–depressive psychiatric illness.

The final question that was investigated (in regression analyses) was whether secondary school truancy was an independent predictor of antisocial personality at ages 18 and 32, convictions between age 21 and 32, and adult social dysfunction at age 32. If truancy predicted undesirable life outcomes independently of all other variables, this might suggest that truancy had some causal effect on undesirable life outcomes. On the other hand, if truancy was not an independent predictor, this would suggest that truancy predicted undesirable life outcomes primarily because it was a symptom of an underlying antisocial personality that persisted from childhood to adulthood.

In the interests of brevity, the results are not presented in detail here. Briefly, truancy was not an independent predictor of any of these undesirable life outcomes. The most important independent predictors of antisociality at age 18 were juvenile delinquency, self-reported offending at age 14, a convicted parent by age 10, the father not joining in the boy's leisure activities at age 12, having sexual intercourse by age 15, high neuroticism (on the New Junior Maudsley Inventory) at age 10, poor concentration or restlessness at age

TABLE 8.4
Most characteristic features of truants at different ages

	Truants (%)	Non-truants (%)	χ^2	P	Odds ratio
Age 8–10					
Troublesome	40	16	26.4	0.0001	3.6
Delinquent sibling	22	7	16.0	0.0001	3.6
Uninterested in education	30	11	19.0	0.0001	3.4
Poor supervision	34	14	19.6	0.0001	3.3
Low attainment	39	17	19.1	0.0001	3.0
Low non-verbal IQ	41	19	19.4	0.0001	2.9
Convicted parent	41	19	18.7	0.0001	2.8
Low family income	36	17	16.0	0.0001	2.7
Behaviour-problem sibling	55	31	16.9	0.0001	2.7
Separated from parent	34	17	14.0	0.0001	2.6
Age 12–14					
Lacks concentration	53	15	61.1	0.0001	6.4
High SR offending	48	13	52.7	0.0001	5.9
Early school leaving	85	51	40.0	0.0001	5.6
Frequent liar	55	20	48.6	0.0001	5.0
Delinquent friends	47	16	40.0	0.0001	4.6
Aggressive	56	23	38.9	0.0001	4.2
Had sex	49	21	28.8	0.0001	3.6
Hostile to police	44	20	24.4	0.0001	3.3
Unemployed father	21	8	10.8	0.0005	3.2
Low verbal IQ	43	24	13.2	0.0001	2.8
Age 18					
Unskilled manual job	35	8	40.5	0.0001	6.0
Tattooed	21	4	23.6	0.0001	5.7
No exams taken	76	41	38.3	0.0001	4.6
High SR violence	38	13	27.3	0.0001	3.9
Unstable job record	42	16	28.4	0.0001	3.8
Heavy smoker	45	20	24.3	0.0001	3.3
Sexually promiscuous	47	22	23.7	0.0001	3.2
High SR offending	41	18	20.7	0.0001	3.1
Heavy drinker	41	19	19.9	0.0001	3.0
Antisocial group	29	12	14.7	0.0001	3.0
Age 32					
Tattooed	31	10	23.5	0.0001	4.1
Taken marijuana	31	13	14.9	0.0001	2.9
Child elsewhere	35	17	9.5	0.001	2.7
Involved in fights	53	31	14.6	0.0001	2.5
Poor relation with mother	25	12	6.9	0.004	2.5
Unstable job record	37	20	11.5	0.0004	2.4
Heavy drinker	32	17	8.9	0.001	2.3
Anti-establishment	42	24	11.8	0.0003	2.3
Hospital treatment	27	15	7.4	0.003	2.2
Taken other drug	15	7	4.4	0.018	2.2
High impulsivity	32	18	8.1	0.002	2.2

P values one-tailed.
SR, self-reported.

12–14, regular smoking at age 14 and having a nervous or psychiatrically treated mother at age 10.

The most important independent predictors of convictions between ages 21 and 32 were a conviction between ages 10 and 20, low junior school attainment, separation from a parent by age 10, heavy drinking at age 18, a motoring conviction by age 18, high self-reported offending at age 18 and frequent lying at age 12–14. The most important independent predictors of antisociality at age 32 were a conviction between ages 10 and 20, tattooed at age 18, no examinations taken by age 18, an unstable job record at age 18, delinquent friends at age 14, an anti-establishment attitude at age 18, a convicted parent by age 10 and high self-reported offending at age 18. The most important predictors of adult social dysfunction at age 32 were a conviction between ages 10 and 20, a poor relationship with parents at age 18, an unstable job record at age 18, high dishonesty at age 10 and an unskilled manual job at age 18.

Conclusions

When they were in their primary schools, male secondary school truants tended to be rated as troublesome by peers and teachers, to have delinquent siblings, to have parents who were uninterested in their education and to be poorly supervised by their parents. Also, they tended to have low intelligence and low attainment, a convicted parent and a behaviour-problem sibling. In addition, they tended to come from low-income families and to have been separated from a parent (usually the father). Table 8.4 summarises the variables that were most strongly related to truancy at all ages. For example, it shows that 40% of truants were troublesome in their primary schools, compared with 16% of non-truants, a significant difference ($\chi^2=26.4$, $P<0.0001$, OR=3.6).

At age 12–14, concurrently with their truancy, truants were lacking in concentration or restless in class, had high self-reported offending, left school at the earliest possible age of 15 (in 85% of cases) and were rated as frequent liars. Also, they had relatively many delinquent friends, were aggressive in behaviour, had had sexual intercourse by age 15, were hostile to the police, had low verbal intelligence and tended to have unemployed fathers. No doubt because they were contemporaneous, variables measured at age 12–14 were more strongly related to truancy than variables measured at any other age.

At age 18, not long after leaving school, truants tended to have unskilled manual jobs, to be tattooed, to have taken no examinations (in 76% of cases), to have high self-reported violence and an unstable job record. They tended to be heavy smokers, sexually promiscuous, high self-reported offenders, heavy drinkers and members of antisocial groups.

Many years later, at age 32, truants were characterised by tattoos, taking marijuana, separation from their children, involvement in fights and not getting on well with their mothers. Also, they tended to have an unstable job record, were heavy drinkers, had anti-establishment attitudes, had had hospital treatment, had taken drugs other than marijuana and had high impulsivity. It should be noted that the variables were not dichotomised in exactly the same way at all ages, but consistently to identify the 'worst' quarter of males. For example, the quarter with an unstable job record at age 32 were generally more stable than the quarter with an unstable job record at age 18 (see Farrington, 1990*b*).

There was an overlap between truancy and delinquency – truants and delinquents were similar in many respects. However, truants were more likely than delinquents to be living in slum housing at ages 8–10 and 14, they were more likely to be poorly supervised by their parents at age 8, their fathers were more likely to be nervous and uninterested in the boy at age 8–10 and the parents of truants were more likely to be uninterested in their education. Truants were more likely than delinquents to have low non-verbal IQ at ages 8–10 and 14, and to be unpopular, nervous, lacking in concentration or restless, frequent liars and regular smokers at age 12–14. Truants were more likely to have an unskilled manual job and to be heavy smokers at age 18, and to have had hospital treatment and a poor relationship with their mothers and fathers at age 32.

The major conclusion from these analyses is that truancy and delinquency are two behavioural symptoms of an underlying antisocial personality that arises in childhood and persists into adulthood. Therefore, explanations of truancy and delinquency should focus on theories of the development of antisocial personality and conduct disorder in childhood.

For example, my theory (Farrington, 1993*c*) focuses on motivating and inhibiting processes. Briefly, it suggests that the major motivating factors are desires for material goods, status and excitement, and that children from poor families, who tend to fail in school, are likely to try to achieve these desires by antisocial means. It suggests that the major inhibiting factor is the conscience, which is built up in a learning process, depending on parental attitudes, family models, rewards and punishment. It also suggests that committing an antisocial act essentially involves a cost–benefit decision and that more impulsive people are more likely to commit antisocial acts because they give more weight to immediate benefits as opposed to longer term negative outcomes. This theory is designed to explain why the most important predictors of antisocial behaviour and delinquency are socio-economic deprivation, poor child-rearing, family criminality, poor school performance and impulsivity.

While the results overwhelmingly demonstrate similarities between truants and delinquents from childhood to adulthood, there are also some differences.

The most important difference was that truancy, but not delinquency, was related to nervousness. Therefore, it may be that, for a minority of children, truancy is a behavioural symptom of a nervous–withdrawn temperament rather than of an antisocial personality. A review by Parker & Asher (1987) distinguished between aggressive children, who are later involved in delinquency and crime, and shy children, who later have mental health problems. It may be that there are two pathways to truancy and two types of truants – aggressive and nervous – who need to be distinguished.

References

BELSON, W. A. (1975) *Juvenile Theft: the Causal Factors.* London: Harper and Row.
BERG, I. (1992) Absence from school and mental health. *British Journal of Psychiatry,* **161**, 154–166.
––––––, BUTLER, A., FRANKLIN, J., *et al* (1993) DSM–III–R disorders, social factors and management of school attendance problems in the normal population. *Journal of Child Psychology and Psychiatry,* **34**, 1187–1203.
BOOLS, C., FOSTER, J., BROWN, I., *et al* (1990) The identification of psychiatric disorders in children who fail to attend school: a cluster analysis of a non-clinical population. *Psychological Medicine,* **20**, 171–181.
CARROLL, H. C. M. (1977) The problem of absenteeism: research studies, past and present. In *Absenteeism in South Wales* (ed. H. C. M. Carroll), pp. 4–29. Swansea: Faculty of Education, University College of Swansea.
CHERRY, N. (1976) Persistent job changing – is it a problem? *Journal of Occupational Psychology,* **49**, 203–221.
CLEARY, P. D. & ANGEL, R. (1984) The analysis of relationships involving dichotomous dependent variables. *Journal of Health and Social Behaviour,* **25**, 334–348.
COOPER, M. G. (1966) School refusal: an enquiry into the part played by school and home. *Educational Research,* **8**, 223–229.
COVENTRY, G., CORNISH, G., COOKE, R., *et al* (1984) *Skipping School: An Examination of Truancy in Victorian Secondary Schools.* Melbourne: Victorian Insitute of Secondary Education.
CROFT, I. J. & GRYGIER, T. G. (1956) Social relationships of truants and juvenile delinquents. *Human Relations,* **9**, 439–466.
DOUGLAS, J. W. B. & ROSS, J. M. (1965) The effects of absence on primary school performance. *British Journal of Educational Psychology,* **35**, 28–40.
––––––, –––––– & SIMPSON, H. R. (1968) *All Our Future,* London: Peter Davies.
FARRINGTON, D. P. (1980) Truancy, delinquency, the home and the school. In *Out of School,* (eds L. Hersov & I. Berg), pp. 49–63. Chichester: John Wiley.
–––––– (1987) Implications of biological findings for criminological research. In *The Causes of Crime: New Biological Approaches,* (eds S. A. Medrick, T. E. Moffitt & S. A. Stack), pp. 42–64. Cambridge: Cambridge University Press.
–––––– (1989*a*) Self-reported and official offending from adolescence to adulthood. In *Cross-National Research in Self-reported Crime and Delinquency,* (ed. M. W. Klein), pp. 399–423. Dordrecht, Netherlands: Kluwer.
–––––– (1989*b*) Early predictors of adolescent aggression and adult violence. *Violence and Victims,* **4**, 79–100.
–––––– (1990*a*) Implications of criminal career research for the prevention of offending. *Journal of Adolescence,* **13**, 93–113.
–––––– (1990*b*) Age, period, cohort, and offending. In *Policy and Theory in Criminal Justice: Contributions in Honour of Leslie T. Wilkins* (eds D. M. Gottfredson & R. V. Clarke), pp. 51–75. Aldershot: Gower.
–––––– (1991) Antisocial personality from childhood to adulthood. *Psychologist,* **4**, 389–394.

——— (1992) Criminal career research in the United Kingdom. *British Journal of Criminology*, **32**, 521–536.

——— (1993a) Understanding and preventing bullying. In *Crime and Justice* (ed. M. Tonry) vol. 17, pp. 381–458. Chicago: University of Chicago Press.

——— (1993b) Childhood origins of teenage antisocial behaviour and adult social dysfunction. *Journal of the Royal Society of Medicine*, **86**, 13–17.

——— (1993c) Motivations for conduct disorder and delinquency. *Development and Psychopathology*, **5**, 225–241.

——— (1994) Childhood, adolescent and adult features of violent males. In *Aggressive Behaviour: Current Perspectives* (ed. L. R. Huesmann), pp. 215–240. New York: Plenum.

——— (1995) Psychosocial influences on the development of antisocial personality. In *Psychology, Law and Criminal Justice: International Developments in Research and Practice* (eds G. Davies, S. Lloyd-Bostock, M. McMurran & C. Wilson). Berlin: De Gruyter, in press.

——— & WEST, D. J. (1981) The Cambridge Study in Delinquent Development. In *Prospective Longitudinal Research: An Empirical Basis for the Primary Prevention of Psychosocial Disorders* (eds S. A. Mednick & A. E. Baert), pp. 137–145, Oxford: Oxford University Press.

———, GALLAGHER, B., MORLEY, L., *et al* (1988a) A 24-year follow-up of men from vulnerable backgrounds. In *The Abandonment of Delinquent Behaviour: Promoting the Turnaround* (eds R. L. Jenkins & W. K. Brown), pp. 155–173. New York: Praeger.

———, ———, ———, *et al* (1988b) Are there any successful men from criminogenic backgrounds? *Psychiatry*, **51**, 166–130.

——— & WEST, D. J. (1990) The Cambridge Study in Delinquent Development: a long-term follow-up of 411 London males. In *Kriminalitat: Personlichkeit, Lebensgeschichte und Verhalten (Criminality: Personality, Behaviour and Life History)* (eds H. J. Kerner & G. Kaiser), pp. 115–138.

——— & HAWKINS, J. D. (1991) Predicting participation, early onset, and later persistence in officially recorded offending. *Criminal Behaviour and Mental Health*, **1**, 1–33.

——— & WEST, D. J. (1993) Criminal, penal and life histories of chronic offenders: risk and protective factors and early identification. *Criminal Behaviour and Mental Heatlh*, **3**, 492–523.

FERGUSON, T. (1952) *The Young Delinquent in his Social Setting*. London: Oxford University Press.

FOGELMAN, K. (1978) School attendance, attainment and behaviour. *British Journal of Educational Psychology*, **48**, 148–158.

——— & RICHARDSON, K. (1974) School attendance: some results from the National Child Development Study, In *Truancy* (ed. B. Turner), pp. 29–51. London: Ward Lock Educational.

———, TIBBENHAM, A. & LAMBERT, L. (1980) Absence from school: findings from the National Child Development Study. In *Out of School* (eds L. Hersov & I. Berg), pp. 25–48. Chichester: John Wiley.

GALLOWAY, D. (1982) A study of persistent absentees and their families. *British Journal of Educational Psychology*, **52**, 317–330.

——— (1985) *Schools and Persistent Absentees*. Oxford: Pergamon.

GRAY, G., SMITH, A. & RUTTER, M. (1980) School attendance and the first year of employment. In *Out of School* (eds L. Hersov & I. Berg), pp. 343–370. Chichester: John Wiley.

HERSOV, L. A. (1960) Persistent non-attendance at school. *Journal of Child Psychology and Psychiatry*, **1**, 130–136.

HODGES, V. (1968) Non-attendance at school. *Educational Research*, **11**, 58–61.

KAHN, J. H., NURSTEN, J. P. & CARROLL, H. C. M. (1981) *Unwillingly to School* (3rd edn). Oxford: Pergamon.

KANDEL, D. B., RAVEIS, V. H. & KANDEL, P. I. (1984) Continuities and discontinuities: adjustment in young adulthood of former school absentees. *Youth and Society*, **15**, 325–352.

KAVANAGH, A & CARROLL, H. C. M. (1977) Pupil attendance at three comprehensive schools: a study of the pupils and their families. In *Absenteeism in South Wales* (ed. H. C. M. Carroll), pp. 40–50. Swansea: Faculty of Education, University College of Swansea.

MAY, D. (1975) Truancy, school absenteeism, and delinquency. *Scottish Educational Studies*, **7**, 97–107.

MITCHELL, S. & SHEPHERD, M. (1967) The child who dislikes going to school. *British Journal of Educational Psychology*, **37**, 32–40.

PARKER, J. G. & ASHER, S. R. (1987) Peer relations and later personal adjustment: are low-accepted children at risk? *Psychological Bulletin*, **102**, 357–389.

REID, K. (1984) The behaviour of persistent school absentees. *British Journal of Educational Psychology,* **54,** 320–330.

ROBINS, L. N. & RATCLIFF, K. S. (1980) The long-term outcome of truancy. In *Out of School* (eds L. Hersov & I. Berg), pp. 65–83. Chichester: John Wiley.

RUTTER, M., TIZARD, J. & WHITMORE, K. (1970) *Education, Health, and Behaviour.* London: Longman.

SOMMER, B. (1985) Truancy in early adolescence. *Journal of Early Adolescence,* **5,** 145–160.

STOTT, D. H. (1966) *Studies of Troublesome Children.* London: Tavistock.

TENNENT, T. G. (1971) School non-attendance and delinquency. *Educational Research,* **13,** 185–190.

TIBBENHAM, A. (1977) Housing and truancy. *New Society,* **39,** 501–502.

TYERMAN, M. (1968) *Truancy.* London: University of London Press.

UNIVERSITY OF NORTH LONDON TRUANCY UNIT (1993) *Truancy in English Secondary Schools.* London: Department for Education.

WEST, D. J. (1969) *Present Conduct and Future Delinquency.* London: Heinemann.

—— (1982) *Delinquency: Its Roots, Careers and Prospects.* London: Heinemann.

—— & FARRINGTON, D. P. (1973) *Who Becomes Delinquent?* London: Heinemann.

—— & —— (1977) *The Delinquent Way of Life.* London: Heinemann.

9 Truancy and later psychiatric disorder

LEE N. ROBINS and JUDITH ROBERTSON

In a previous volume devoted to the effects of truancy (Robins & Ratcliff, 1980) we reported that truancy from elementary school and high school by black St Louis schoolboys predicted their chances of completing high school, entering college and finishing college. We tested the possibility that truancy's predictive power was due only to its serving as a marker for a variety of deviant juvenile behaviours but found that it was associated with poor school outcomes even among those without other deviance. That study also showed truancy to predict many psychiatric symptoms in adult life, including hallucinations, depression, anxiety, alcohol and drug problems, and antisocial behaviour.

That study was small, restricted to a single city, to black males only and to a single age cohort born in the early 1930s. We now have available a sample from the Epidemiologic Catchment Area (ECA) study. This study was carried out by five universities in the USA between 1980 and 1985 and covered inner city, suburban and rural areas. It provides interviews with a very large random sample of the population 18 years of age and older, of both sexes and all races. Blacks, hispanics, the elderly and institutionalised persons were overrepresented. The subjects were carefully assessed for the presence of the major adult psychiatric disorders as described in the *Diagnostic and Statistical Manual of Mental Disorders*, third edition (DSM–III; American Psychiatric Association, 1980) by means of the Diagnostic Interview Schedule, Version III (Robins *et al*, 1981). Despite these assets, the ECA has one major flaw for our purposes: while the earlier study calculated truancy from school attendance records, the ECA relies on recall about truancy during an adult interview. This both raises questions about the information's accuracy and limits our options with respect to categorising truancy. We are able to define it at only two levels: (a) a broad definition – skipping school at least twice in one year; and (b) a strict definition – skipping school at least five times a year in two or more school years. The broad definition is roughly comparable to our definition of mild truancy in the previous study, i.e. one or more quarters in elementary school or one semester in high school in which 10 days of absence occurred, and the strict definition corresponds roughly to the 'often truant' group in the previous study, i.e. three or more elementary school quarters or two or more high school semesters in which 10 days of absence occurred.

In the earlier study, we found that most youngsters who would meet criteria as truants displayed excess absences in their very first year of school (ages 6–7). In the current study, we do not have year-by-year data, but we can date age at first truancy. Only 5% of the truants report beginning before age 8; the median age of first truancy is 14 years 4 months for the broad definition and 13 years 11 months for the strict definition. (The strict definition's earlier age of onset is probably explained by the fact that it takes longer to accumulate the higher level of truancy.) The later age of onset in the current study may be attributable to forgetting early absences or not defining them as truancy, or to the fact that the sample is more diverse in place of rearing, age and ethnic background.

Since truancy begins in childhood, it will generally have predated the first symptoms of the disorders associated with it. Because we are interested in this prediction of adult disorder by truancy, not the prevalence of truancy itself, we present the results unweighted. Diagnoses are based on positive criteria only, omitting the pre-emptions by other diagnoses suggested in DSM–III, and are considered positive if the criteria were met at any time in the respondent's lifetime. Previous reports from this study (Robins & Regier, 1991) have shown that younger persons qualify for more disorders than do older persons, even though they have had fewer years at risk. For this reason, we test the significance of all relationships between truancy and disorder by logistic regression, using age as a control variable.

Results

Frequency of truancy

Truancy was very commonly recollected by this random sample of adults. Broadly defined, it was reported by 43% of the men and 22% of the women. More strictly defined, it was reported by 21% of the men and 8% of the women.

Truancy and adult disorder

Because truancy is a cardinal symptom of conduct disorder, which has been shown to be an excellent predictor of antisocial personality, alcohol abuse and drug abuse, we would expect its strongest relationships among men to be with these three disorders. Expectations for women are not so clear, because truancy's relationship to conduct disorder in girls has not had much attention.

We found that the relationships expected for males held not only for them, but for women as well (Table 9.1). For both sexes, rates of antisocial personality and substance abuse were greatly elevated in those who had been truant, whether a broad or strict definition of truancy was used, but rates were particularly high when the stricter definition of truancy was used. We found that one-quarter of all seriously truant boys would grow into men with antisocial personality, half (48%) would have a diagnosable alcohol problem and more than one-quarter (29%) would have drug abuse; these rates are 12.5 times, 2.5 times and 6 times respectively the rates for men who did not truant. Comparable figures for highly truant girls are one in nine (11%) with antisocial personality, one in six (17%) with a diagnosable alcohol problem and one in four (25%) with drug abuse; these rates are 37, 6 and 12.5 times respectively the rates for women who did not truant.

For all other common disorders explored except dementia, a weaker but positive relationship with truancy was found for both sexes, with more severe truancy associated with the higher rate. Those who reported truancy were *less* often demented, as shown by fewer failing the Mini-Mental State Examination. Perhaps those with dementia could no longer remember their truancy or it may be that we see the effect of their having had fewer years of education in which to have been truant, since low educational level is associated with dementia.

We assessed the strength of truancy as a factor used to predict later psychiatric disorder by separate logistic regressions for each of the two measures of truancy versus one disorder at a time, controlling for age (Table 9.2). We omitted dementia, because truancy did not predict it, and the rare

TABLE 9.1
Two measures of truancy and the occurrence of adult disorders

	Males (%)			Females (%)		
	Strict	Broad	None	Strict	Broad	None
Lifetime disorders	*(1290)*	*(2608)*	*(3463)*	*(628)*	*(1804)*	*(6290)*
Antisocial personality	24.7	15.3	1.8	10.8	4.7	0.3
Alcohol abuse	47.8	40.2	18.7	17.4	11.2	3.3
Drug abuse	28.5	20.6	4.1	24.7	14.2	1.8
Phobia	18.3	14.9	11.5	31.7	26.3	21.0
Depression	6.4	4.9	2.8	12.4	10.7	5.0
Dysthymia	3.8	2.9	2.0	7.2	5.9	4.1
Obsessive–compulsive	5.7	4.1	2.2	6.7	4.7	2.7
Panic	2.0	1.8	0.7	4.5	3.2	1.6
Schizophrenia	2.6	1.9	0.8	2.1	2.0	0.9
Mania	0.5	0.5	0.4	1.8	1.2	0.3
Somatisation	0.3	0.2	0.1	1.0	0.6	0.5
Anorexia	0.2	0.1	0.0	0.2	0.2	0.0
Dementia	6.1	5.3	12.5	2.9	3.3	12.2

Broad, 2+ days truant in any school year; Strict, 5+ days truant in at least two school years.

TABLE 9.2
Effect of truancy on the occurrence of adult disorders, controlling for age (logistic regression)

	Males			Females		
		Truancy (OR)			Truancy (OR)	
Lifetime disorders	No. with disorder	Broad (2608)	Strict (1290)	No. with disorder	Broad (1804)	Strict (628)
Antisocial personality	458	7.5****	8.7****	101	12.4****	17.6****
Alcohol	1709	3.0****	3.1****	411	3.1****	3.9****
Drug	677	3.8****	3.8****	366	4.6****	5.5****
Phobia	801	1.3***	1.7****	1811	1.4****	1.7****
Depression	225	1.4*	1.9****	509	1.7****	1.7***
Dysthymia	147	NS	1.7**	369	1.4*	1.6**
Obsessive–compulsive	185	1.6**	2.2****	259	1.6**	2.2****
Panic	70	2.1**	1.9*	160	1.7**	2.1***
Schizophrenia	79	1.8*	2.2**	95	NS	NS

Broad, 2+ days truant in any school year; Strict, 5+ days truant in at least two school years; OR, odds ratio.
Significant increase in the disorder if truant: *$P < 0.05$; **$P < 0.01$; ***$P < 0.001$; ****$P < 0.0001$.

disorders, mania, somatisation and anorexia, whose rarity makes the differences insignificant once age is controlled.

A significant relationship was found between truancy and every one of the more common disorders for both sexes. While, as expected, the relationships were strongest with the 'externalising' disorders (antisocial personality, alcohol abuse and drug abuse) known to be predicted by conduct disorder, there were also highly significant associations with phobia, depression and obsessive–compulsive disorder for both men and women. Schizophrenia in men and panic disorder in both sexes had equally substantial odds ratios, but less statistical significance because of the small number of cases.

In all instances, except for panic disorder in men and depression in women, the prediction of disorder was as strong or stronger when the stricter definition of truancy was used.

While truancy was expected to be related to the 'externalising' disorders, because it is a symptom of conduct disorder, it is not obvious why it should be related to disorders like depression or panic or schizophrenia. However, every adult disorder in the ECA has been noted to be associated with an increased frequency of other disorders (Robins & Regier, 1991). This overlap between disorders could be an artefact of a differential willingness to report that affects symptoms and risk factors alike, but it could also be true comorbidity. Comorbidity could be explained either by one disorder increasing the predisposition to another or by disorders sharing risk factors. If the explanation was either one disorder causing another or an artefact of reporting style, one would still find an association between disorders and risk factors, by purely mathematical necessity.

Ruling out willingness to report and secondary disorders

One way to test the proposition that these non-externalising disorders share truancy as a risk factor, rather than simply being secondary to antisocial personality or substance abuse, is to hold constant the presence of antisocial personality and substance abuse and see whether the relationship between truancy and other disorders disappears. This strategy effectively holds constant the tendency to report symptoms as well, because those who report symptoms more readily will be more likely to report symptoms of antisocial personality and substance abuse.

To hold the presence of externalising disorders constant, we repeated the logistic regressions of truancy, controlling for age, on the non-externalising disorders for men and women, but this time separately for those with and without antisocial personality or substance abuse. If the impact of truancy were only through the acting out disorders or differential willingness to report symptoms, we should now expect to find no relationship between truancy and these other disorders.

Controlling for externalising disorders reduced the association between truancy and other disorders, indicating that the association was in part a secondary effect of truancy leading to the externalising disorders or an artefact (Table 9.3), but the associations did not disappear. There were interesting differences between the sexes, however. Strictly defined truancy predicted all the other disorders in men with externalising disorders, although splitting the sample and the smaller odds ratios reduced some below statistical significance, while truancy, however defined, predicted other disorders in women *free* of externalising disorders (again with a reduction in the number statistically significant). Men without externalising disorders and women *with* them showed relatively little impact of truancy on later non-externalising disorder.

Truancy and remission

It is of interest to know whether in addition to increasing the likelihood of disorder, truancy plays a role in its chronicity. To test this possibility, we looked at persons who had a disorder at some time in their lives and asked whether it was more likely to be still active during the year before interview if it was preceded by truancy. The answer is that only one disorder, depression, was found to be significantly more recent and only in men, a result no greater than chance when nine disorders were evaluated in two sexes (Table 9.4). However, it may not be correct to discount this association as explained by chance because there was a trend in the same direction for women. Drug abuse too appeared somewhat more persistent in both men and women if preceded by truancy, but the relationships were not statistically significant. It

TABLE 9.3

Effect of truancy on internalising disorders, controlling for externalising disorders, and age (logistic regression)

| | Males | | | | | | Females | | | | | |
| | No. extern. (2036) | No. not extern. (4147) | Extern. (OR) | | Not extern. (OR) | | No. extern. (688) | No. not extern (7589) | Extern. (OR) | | Not extern. (OR) | |
Diagnoses			Broad	Strict	Broad	Strict			Broad	Strict	Broad	Strict
Phobia	(385)	(416)	<1.1	1.3**	1.2	1.4**	(253)	(1557)	<1.1	<1.1	1.2***	1.7****
Depression	(144)	(81)	<1.1	1.3*	<1.1	1.3	(140)	(368)	<1.1	<1.1	1.5***	1.4
Dysthymia	(96)	(51)	<1.1	1.2	<1.1	<1.1	(78)	(290)	<1.1	<1.1	1.2	1.2
Obsessive–compulsive	(122)	(63)	1.2	1.8***	<1.1	<1.1	(62)	(196)	1.2	1.7*	1.3	1.5
Panic	(49)	(—)	2.4**	1.5	—	—	(52)	(108)	1.1	<1.1	1.2	1.7
Schizophrenia	(58)	(—)	1.4	1.5	—	—	(38)	(57)	<1.1	<1.1	1.1	<1.1

Externalising disorders: antisocial personality, alcohol dependence/abuse, drug dependence/abuse.
Broad, 2+ days truant in any school year; Strict, 5+ days truant in at least two school years; OR, odds ratio.
Significant increase in the disorder if truant: *$P < 0.1$; **$P < 0.05$; ***$P < 0.01$; ****$P < 0.0001$.
—, Less than 35 persons affected.

may be noteworthy, in addition, that highly truant females tended to have more persistent disorders overall. If real, these effects are modest at best.

Early versus late truancy

Truancy is typically one of the first conduct problems to appear (Robins & Wish, 1977), but some youngsters do not start truanting until adolescence. Truancy in adolescents, despite previous good behaviour, is often linked to the onset of substance use and sexual activity and may be followed by the full panoply of symptoms of conduct disorder. These findings have led to speculation as to whether late-onset conduct disorder is a different disorder as opposed to early-onset disorder, or perhaps not a disorder at all but only conformity with deviant peers. Knowing whether the adult consequences of early truancy differ from the consequences of late-onset truancy may help to resolve these debates.

To learn whether age of onset of truancy matters in predicting adult disorder, we limited the sample to truants and asked whether truancy before 14 is a better predictor of adult disorder than is truancy of later onset. Early truancy greatly increased the likelihood of antisocial personality for both sexes, as compared with later truancy (Table 9.5). However, this is somewhat circular, because the diagnosis in DSM–III and DSM–III–R requires three behaviour problems before age 15; having early truancy guarantees that there will be at least one. A more interesting result was that, for men, early truancy was a better predictor than later truancy of alcohol and drug disorders, obsessive–compulsive disorder and schizophrenia. While none of these relationships reached statistical significance for women, a trend in the same direction can be seen. It is interesting that an early onset of truancy matters less for women, given the fact that it is less 'normative' for them. In male truants onset was before age 14 in half (51%), but in only one-third (36%) of female truants.

Discussion

This study in a large representative population of all ages continues our efforts to link childhood behaviour problems to adult psychiatric disorder. As in our earlier studies of black men born in the early 1930s (Robins & Ratcliff, 1980) and male child guidance clinic patients seen in the 1920s (Robins, 1966), we found truancy to be a powerful predictor of a variety of adult psychiatric disorders. We have found only one other study linking truancy to adult disorder (Rodgers, 1990). This follow-up of a British 1945 birth cohort looked at links between early behaviour and later psychiatric disorder assessed with the Present State Examination (PSE), an instrument limited to non-externalising

TABLE 9.4

Effect of truancy on persistence of adult disorders into current year, controlling for age (logistic regression)

Lifetime diagnoses	Males (OR)			Females (OR)		
	n	Broad	Strict	n	Broad	Strict
Antisocial personality	458	< 1.1	< 1.1	101	< 1.1	< 1.1
Alcohol	1709	1.1	< 1.1	411	< 1.1	< 1.1
Drug	677	1.4	1.1	366	1.3	1.4
Phobia	801	< 1.1	1.1	1811	< 1.1	1.3
Depression	225	1.9**	2.2**	509	1.2	1.3
Dysthymia	147	< 1.1	1.9	369	< 1.1	1.5
Obsessive–compulsive	185	1.5	2.1*	259	< 1.1	1.4
Panic	70	< 1.1	< 1.1	160	< 1.1	1.1
Schizophrenia	79	< 1.1	< 1.1	95	< 1.1	1.2

Broad, 2+ days truant in any school year; Strict, 5+ days truant in at least two school years; OR, odds ratio. Disorder significantly more likely to be active if truant: *$P < 0.10$; **$P < 0.05$.

syndromes occurring in the current month. Boys who reported truancy when surveyed at age 15 as adults had significantly higher total scores on the PSE, but no specific disorder was associated with truancy. Truancy in girls was not found to predict disorder.

In the current study, truants not only showed the increase in antisocial personality and substance abuse that would be expected because truancy is a symptom of conduct disorder, but were more often depressed, phobic, obsessive and psychotic. The increase in this variety of later disorders was similar for males and females. This suggests that greater attention should be paid to truancy in girls, in whom school absence is more often viewed as school refusal than truancy (Berg *et al*, 1993). While half as many women as men recalled having been truant, truancy was a frequent event for both sexes and had similar outcomes. For both, the main effect was a large increase in the frequency of antisocial personality, a smaller but very substantial increase in substance abuse and modest increases in most other disorders. For males, the effect of truancy on the non-externalising disorders was greater among those who also had antisocial personality or substance abuse. For females, the impact of truancy was greater among those without those externalising disorders.

Other childhood behaviour problems could probably also successfully predict adult psychiatric disorders, but truancy is of special interest as an indicator because it is so common, can be readily detected in primary school attendance records, without a need for special screening instruments, and appears early enough to allow interventions that might forestall incipient conduct disorder. Frick *et al* (1993) in a meta-analysis found the median age of the child when parents and teachers reported truancy to be 8.5 years, but assessment via school records would probably disclose it even earlier. The study reported here found truancy to be of special importance when it occurs

TABLE 9.5
Effect of early v. late-onset truancy on adult disorders, controlling for age (logistic regression)

Diagnoses	Truant males (OR)		Truant females (OR)	
	Broad (2189)	Strict (1272)	Broad (1386)	Strict (622)
Antisocial personality	3.2****	3.4****	3.9****	3.5****
Alcohol	1.5****	1.6****	1.4*	1.3
Drug	1.6****	1.5***	1.3*	1.1
Phobia	1.2	1.1	< 1.1	1.3
Depression	1.2	1.3	< 1.1	< 1.1
Dysthymia	1.6*	1.4	< 1.1	< 1.1
Obsessive–compulsive	2.1***	2.3***	1.5*	1.7
Panic	1.3	—	1.8*	—
Schizophrenia	2.1**	2.3**	—	—

Early-onset truancy, first truant below age 14; Broad, 2+ days truant in any school year; Strict, 5+ days truant in at least two school years; OR, odds ratio.
Significant increase if truant early: *$P < 0.10$; **$P < 0.05$; ***$P < 0.01$; ****$P < 0.0001$.
—, ≤30 persons.

early in the school history, not only for its chief consequences – antisocial personality and substance abuse – but also for obsessive–compulsive disorder and schizophrenia.

Thus truancy is an indicator that avoids the selection biases associated with treatment because it is available in records routinely maintained for all children. It even avoids selection biases associated with early school termination because truancy prior to the age at which drop-out begins to occur identifies the population at greater risk. Truancy's use as a screen to select children who need intervention is unobtrusive and not stigmatising.

Using a stricter definition of truancy produces stronger predictions, in general, than does a broader definition. However, it also takes youngsters longer to meet the stricter criteria, and waiting for that threshold to be crossed would postpone intervention. If an effective intervention with low monetary and psychological costs were available, it might be wise to use a broader definition in order to intervene early, before the other types of behaviour that would predict disorder have appeared.

The fact that truancy predicts adult disorders does not, of course, necessarily mean that the intervention of choice would be simply stopping the truancy. There may be precursors of truancy that are the true culprits, and only when those are controlled will prevention of disorder be achieved. Indeed, it seems unlikely that truancy alone could have so powerful and long-lasting an effect on psychiatric health. Still, it would make sense to experiment with a direct effort to improve school attendance by persuasion or providing attendance rewards to learn whether such simple procedures would change the risk for the occurrence of conduct disorder and the later appearance of adult psychiatric disorders. If this approach is not successful, it may be necessary to treat other symptoms of conduct disorder as well and to learn what other childhood syndromes truancy is linked to, and treat these syndromes.

While we found truancy to have substantial power to predict the occurrence of adult disorders, it had little power to predict the course of an adult disorder. Males with psychiatric disorder had approximately equal chances of remission and relapse whether or not they had been truant. While severe truancy did seem to predict having more persistent disorders for females, the size of the impact was minimal. This contrast between the power of truancy in predicting disorder and its inability to predict that disorder's duration underscores an important, more general epidemiological observation – the causes of first occurrence of disorder are often quite different from the forces that maintain a disorder once it begins. This is the reason that it is important to study incidence rather than prevalence of disorder when searching for causes. Studies of prevalence confound predictors of occurrence with predictors of duration. While longitudinal studies are ideal for the study of incidence, cross-sectional studies can also be useful if they attend to lifetime occurrence and control on current age to correct for the fact that the period at risk of incident disorders depends on the individual's age at interview.

References

AMERICAN PSYCHIATRIC ASSOCIATION (1980) *Diagnostic and Statistical Manual of Mental Disorders* (3rd edn) (DSM–III). Washington DC: PA.

BERG, I., BUTLER, A., FRANKLIN, J., *et al* (1993) DSM–III–R disorders, social factors and management of school attendance problems in the normal population. *Journal of Child Psychology and Psychiatry and Allied Disciplines*, **34**, 1187–1203.

FRICK, P. J., LAHEY, B. B., LOEBER, R., *et al* (1993) Oppositional defiant disorder and conduct disorder: a meta-analytic review of factor analyses and cross-validation in a clinic sample. *Clinical Psychology Review*, **13**, 319–340.

ROBINS, L. (1966) *Deviant Children Grown Up: A Sociological and Psychiatric Study of Sociopathic Personality*. Baltimore: Williams & Wilkins.

——— & WISH, E. (1977) Childhood deviance as a developmental process: a study of 223 urban black men from birth to 18. *Social Forces*, **56**, 448–473.

——— & RATCLIFF, K. S. (1980) The long-term outcome of truancy. In *Out of School: Modern Perspectives in Truancy and School Refusal* (eds L. Hersov & I. Berg), pp. 65–83.

———, HELZER, J. E., CROUGHAN, J. L., *et al* (1981) The NIMH Diagnostic Interview Schedule, Version III. Public Health Service (HSS) ADM-T-42-3 (5-81, 8-81), Washington, DC.

——— & REGIER, D. A. (eds) (1991) *Psychiatric Disorders in America*. New York: The Free Press.

RODGERS, B. (1990) Behaviour and personality in childhood as predictors of adult psychiatric disorder. *Journal of Child Psychology and Psychiatry and Allied Disciplines*, **31**, 393–414.

10 The role of the child and adolescent psychiatrist

MARGARET MURPHY and
STEPHEN WOLKIND

School plays an important part in the life of most children in the developed world. In addition to the provision of a formal education, school also has a major role in promoting the child's social development by providing opportunities to "extend relationships from within the family to relationships with the community" (Kahn & Nursten, 1962). The importance of school for child development is recognised in law and in Britain, as in most countries in the developed world, school attendance is compulsory.

As one might imagine, prolonged or recurrent absence from school is a cause of concern not only because of the immediate consequence of interference with learning but also because of the long-term implications. There is good evidence from a number of studies that poor school attendance is linked to poorer educational attainment. The National Child Development Study, which followed a cohort of children born in one week in 1958, found that at age 16 school non-attendance and attainment were negatively correlated even after allowing for relevant factors such as social background (Fogelman et al, 1980). Similar findings are reported from other studies suggesting that school absence itself limits educational achievement (Farrington, 1980; Gray et al, 1980). The findings with respect to the long-term implications are more complex and many studies differentiate between the long-term outcomes of school absence due to truancy and school refusal. Nevertheless studies of the outcome of persistent absence from school suggest that in both groups excessive absence is associated with subsequent problems in employment, personal relationships and general adjustment (Cherry, 1976; Robins, 1978; Flakierska et al, 1988; Fogelman, 1992).

Until about 60 years ago all forms of persistent absence from school were labelled as truancy and considered to be due to 'naughtiness'. The offending children were dealt with, in the main, by 'truant officers', officials appointed to ensure regular attendance and were, in some cases, sent to residential correctional schools commonly known as 'truant schools' (Hersov, 1985). Psychiatrists, who were at the time largely asylum based and concerned mainly with adults, played little part in the management of such problems. In 1932, Broadwin published the first account of what we would now consider to be school refusal (Broadwin, 1932). This study was followed by others differentiating between school attendance problems thought to be neurotic in origin and the more common 'antisocial' variant (Partridge, 1939; Johnson *et al*, 1941; Warren, 1948; Hersov, 1960). The recognition of the links between school attendance problems and psychiatric disorder coupled with the emergence of child psychiatry as a discipline led to the greater interest and involvement of psychiatrists.

Definition

Most authorities would now divide school attendance problems into three main types: truancy, school refusal and school withdrawal. School refusal is said to occur when the child is upset at the prospect of going to school and stays at home with the knowledge but not approval of the parents (Hersov & Berg, 1980). School withdrawal is used to describe the situation where the parents deliberately withhold the child from school or encourage non-attendance (Kahn & Nursten, 1962). Truancy is more difficult to define and there are several different definitions in use: the term is sometimes restricted to those cases where the child attempts to conceal his or her not going to school from the parents; alternatively the term can be used more loosely to refer to absence from school without an acceptable reason whether or not the parents know or approve (Hersov & Berg, 1980).

There are a number of children whose absence from school does not fall into any of the above categories, for example children who have been excluded because of behavioural problems. An unknown number of children are kept at home because of a lack of appropriate clothing, often school uniform or shoes (Galloway, 1980). The latter are in Britain regarded as illegal absences and parents may be liable for prosecution.

Clinical features

School refusal and truancy – the distinction

The clinical distinction between truancy and school refusal made by Broadwin has been further clarified by a number of studies, such as that by Hersov (1960) who systematically compared 50 truants and 50 school refusers with an equal number of controls, all of whom were Maudsley Hospital patients. The findings showed that the children referred for school refusal demonstrated a higher standard of work and behaviour at school, were more likely to be passive, dependent and over-protected, and had less experience of maternal absence during early childhood. There was also a higher rate of neurotic illness among other family members. School refusal by these children was most often one manifestation of a neurotic disorder in which anxiety and depressive affect were prominent features. The truants, in contrast, had poor school histories characterised by frequent changes of school and a poor standard of work. They were more likely to come from larger families and had experienced inconsistent parenting and paternal absence. Their truancy was generally one indication of a wider conduct disorder.

This distinction has been criticised and an alternative hypothesis put forward that school refusal and truancy are not discrete entities but lie on a continuum of reasons for absence (Tyerman, 1968). While there is some support for this argument in that some of the factors associated with school refusal may also be found in association with truancy, for example in the Cambridge Study of Delinquent Development, truancy occurring in secondary school was found to be associated with anxiety, sadness and isolation from other children (Farrington, 1980), the distinction between truancy and school refusal has generally been upheld.

School refusal

School refusal has thus come to be regarded as persistent absence from school characterised by disturbances of emotion and mood. Studies of the prevalence have shown a particular pattern with peaks of onset at about age 5–7 around the time of school entry, at age 11 associated with the transfer to secondary school and a further peak at age 14 (Hersov, 1985). Historically, school refusal has been seen primarily as a consequence of separation anxiety (Johnson *et al*, 1941; Eisenberg, 1958) with some researchers reporting very high rates of the order of 75–80% (Waldron *et al*, 1975; Gittelman-Klein & Klein, 1980), while in other studies it has been found in only a minority of cases (Smith, 1970; Hoshino *et al*, 1987). The issue is further complicated by the different conceptual schemes in use. Some authors consider that separation anxiety can arise at any time during childhood whereas others regard it as a phenomenon or disorder of early childhood, a view reflected in ICD-10 (World Health Organization, 1992), which stipulates an onset prior to age 6. However as conceptualised in most studies, anxiety has been found to be a prominent feature of the psychopathology of school refusal.

As with most psychiatric disorders in childhood the presentation may vary with age. An acute onset is more often seen in younger children whereas in older children and adolescents the development is more insidious (Hersov, 1985). In some cases the anxiety appears to be particularly related to leaving home, which in its most severe form may mean that the child not only stays off school but also withdraws from other outside activities. The anxiety may primarily be related to separation from the family and home or be due to a severe wariness of strangers. In older children particularly, the problem of school refusal may resemble that of agoraphobia seen in adult life and, in some cases, may represent an early onset of this disorder (Berg *et al*, 1974). It has been reported that in some children the anxiety is not so much of leaving home but of some specific aspect of the school situation (Last *et al*, 1987) such as performing in class, games or bullying. The anxiety may be manifest as fearfulness, clinging, crying and, in some cases, irritability. Physical symptoms may occur such as nausea, vomiting, diarrhoea, abdominal pains, frequent micturition and headaches. Typically these symptoms are present in the mornings and resolve once the time for school has past. In more severe cases symptoms persist and may be present throughout the day; there may also be sleep disturbance. Occasionally the physical symptoms may predominate as in the so-called 'masquerade syndrome' where the child typically presents initially to a GP or paediatrician (Waller & Eisenberg, 1980).

Depressed mood has often been reported in school refusal. In some studies the rates have been relatively low, for example in a study of 50 cases of school refusal referred to the Maudsley, depressed mood was considered to be present in 20% (Hersov, 1960). However, in other series the rates have been much higher, for example Davidson reported it in 77% of a series of 30 cases (Davidson, 1960) and more recently a study of early adolescent chronic school refusers found that 69% met DSM–III (American Psychiatric Association, 1980) diagnostic criteria for depressive disorders (Bernstein & Garfinkel, 1986). In this study there were more subjects with depressive disorders (69%) than anxiety disorders (62%) although a significant number of subjects exhibited both (50%). It has been argued that in children, as in adults, depressive and anxiety symptoms may often coexist (Kolvin *et al*, 1984; Bernstein & Garfinkel, 1986). In the past school refusal has been considered by some to be a form of 'masked depression' (Frommer, 1967). However, there is little evidence to support this view. Gittelman-Klein & Klein (1980) make the distinction between the demoralised, depressed look of school refusers when seen in clinics, pointing out that when no demands to return to school are made these children are said to be capable of engaging in a variety of activities which they enjoy in contrast to the more pervasive low mood associated with true depression. Depression is more likely in older children, particularly adolescents presenting with school refusal for the first time. It is particularly important to consider the possibility of depression in the assessment of school refusal as illustrated by Schaffer's study of completed suicide in children and young adolescents where four of the 30 subjects had a history of school refusal (Schaffer, 1974).

Premorbidly, children exhibiting school refusal are said to have good school records in contrast to children who truant (Broadwin, 1932; Hersov, 1960). A comparison of 100 children with severe school refusal and the same number of control cases (with a similar level of disturbance but without school refusal) indicated no excess of learning difficulties or problems in achievement in the school refusers (Berg *et al*, 1975). However, the possibility that school refusal and learning difficulties can coexist should not be discounted. In a study by Chazan (1962) it was found that children of poorer ability exhibiting school refusal had an excess of school work difficulties.

As one might imagine school refusal is not a homogeneous condition and no single premorbid personality type has been identified. School refusal has mainly been studied in clinic populations and the findings have probably been influenced by referral bias as it may be that children with more severe problems and accompanying emotional disturbance are more likely to be referred to clinics. Much attention has been paid to excessive dependence on parents. It is difficult to separate out the situation which arises due to the disorder itself from that which existed premorbidly. Several studies have shown that children who exhibit school refusal tend to be unduly reliant on their parents, particularly their mothers, and to remain at home to an unusual extent (Berg & McGuire, 1971; Berg, 1974) and that this is to some extent fostered by their parents (Berg, 1974; De Aldez *et al*, 1987). However, a study of adolescent school refusers who all had associated neurotic disorders failed to find any significant differences from other psychiatric cases (non-school refusers) or normal controls on a number of family life variables such as contact with relatives and friends, activities outside the home, work and patterns of managing domestic affairs (Berg *et al*, 1981). While it would appear to be true that many children who develop school refusal are dependent and over-reliant on their families, this is by no means universal and a proportion have had a relatively normal pattern of activities and friendships premorbidly. Coolidge *et al* (1957) differentiated between what they termed Type I or "neurotic crisis" school refusers and Type II or "way of life" school refusers. Kennedy (1965, 1971) originally postulated that the two groups differed in response to treatment; however, this distinction has been criticised by subsequent authors (Rines, 1973). Clinical experience would suggest that the prognosis is poorer for long-established cases where parental cooperation is lacking.

The family background and social circumstances of school refusers have also been widely studied, although as with other aspects of the disorder most of the studies have been carried out in selected, clinic populations. In contrast with truancy it has not been found to be particularly associated with multiple adversity (Berg, 1992). However, in a study in Leeds of a non-clinical population approximately half of the school refusers identified had experienced parental separation and a significant number came from socially disadvantaged backgrounds (Bools *et al*, 1990). It was notable in this study that the parents of school refusers as compared with other poor attenders had higher rates of chronic physical illness and other handicaps, and that significantly more of them had received psychiatric treatment, mainly for anxiety and depression. The findings on the rates of parental psychiatric disorder are in keeping with the findings from clinical samples (Hersov, 1960; Berg *et al*, 1974) which also identified higher rates of parental mental illness, particularly affective disorders among the parents of school refusers. Family size, social class and being an only child are not related to the occurrence of school refusal (Berg, 1992).

Although there is interest in the families of school refusers there has been little research into the family dynamics. Bowlby (1973) suggested that the majority of cases of school refusal could be understood as the products of one or more of four patterns of family interaction:

(a) mother, or more rarely father, suffers from chronic anxiety regarding attachment figures and retains the child at home to be a companion;
(b) the child fears something dreadful may happen to the parents while he or she is at school and so remains at home to prevent it happening;
(c) the child fears that something dreadful will happen at school and so stays at home;
(d) mother, or more rarely father, fears something dreadful will happen to the child while at school and so keeps the child at home.

Although there is some clinical and empirical support for this hypothesis (i.e. the high incidence of psychiatric disorders and physical illness among the parents and the child's fears that something may happen to the parents), Bowlby did not present detailed evidence on the different patterns of family interaction and tended to disregard the evidence from other studies (Hersov, 1960; Chazan, 1962) that events or situations in school could have any role in causing school refusal. Skynner (1974) emphasised the passive role played by the fathers of school refusers and the overly close relationship between the child and the mother, who he described as frequently anxious or depressed. While the situations described by both Bowlby and Skynner may well occur in the families of school refusers, at the present time there is no way of knowing how commonly these patterns occur nor how they relate to other variables such as family size, socio-economic status, psychopathology in the child, etc. (Lask reviews more fully the role of family factors in Chapter 17.)

Although a number of studies have identified events or situations in school as being important in the development of school refusal, the role of the school has not been studied as widely as is the case for truancy. As already noted, several authors have noted the importance of school factors such as bullying (Hersov, 1960; Last *et al*, 1987) and clinical experience suggests that children may find particular aspects of school life aversive, such as a particular teacher, performing in class, physical education, etc.

The role of life events in the development of school refusal has not been widely researched, although it is often reported that precipitating factors such as a minor accident, illness, a change of teacher, moving house, etc. precede the onset of the disorder. Hersov (1985) described these as "events which appear to represent a threat to the individual child, arousing anxiety that he cannot control".

Truancy

Studies on the epidemiology of truancy suggest that many children truant occasionally; however, much less is known about them than about persistent truants, the group with which we are mainly concerned. Historically, truancy has been considered to be one of a group of antisocial types of behaviour, a view reflected in the current classifications of child psychiatric disorder where truancy is just one criterion towards a diagnosis of conduct disorder (ICD–10 and DSM–IV). There is considerable empirical support for this view: most clinical studies have found high rates of other patterns of antisocial behaviour among truants (Hersov, 1985) and this would appear to be true for truancy at primary as well as secondary school level, although there are fewer studies into the former. The association between truancy and other patterns of antisocial behaviour has also been found in studies of the general population. Thus in the Cambridge Study of Delinquent Development (Farrington, 1980) children who truanted at secondary school were described by their teachers as rebellious, lazy, aggressive and uncaring to a greater extent than were non-truants. Similar comments on the behaviour of both primary and secondary school children who had a history of truancy were reported in the National Child Development Study (Douglas & Ross, 1965; Douglas *et al*, 1968). Many researchers have found links between truancy and juvenile delinquency (Hersov, 1960; Tennent, 1971; West & Farrington, 1973; Belson, 1975).

Although there is compelling evidence to suggest that in many children truancy is just one manifestation of a wider conduct disorder, there is evidence that a number of children who truant show few features of conduct disorder and indeed in some cases truancy may occur as an isolated symptom. The investigation of the Leeds sample of 100 persistent absentees from school who were referred to a school attendance committee identified a group of children who truanted but did not fulfil criteria for ICD–9 conduct disorder (Bools *et al*, 1990). This may have reflected underreporting of other types of antisocial behaviour but may also be evidence of the existence of a different variety of truancy. A study in Bradford of poor school attenders aged 13–15 also identified a group of children who were considered to be truants but who did not reach criteria for a diagnosis of conduct disorder, this time using DSM–III–R criteria (Berg *et al*, 1993).

While it is clear that in many cases truancy coexists with conduct disorder it is not yet known what kind or kinds of conduct disorder are involved. In the past attempts have been made to categorise/subclassify conduct disorder so that in DSM–III, for example, four different types of conduct disorder were recognised, the differentiating factors being the presence of aggression and the quality of social relationships. There continues to be considerable debate as to the existence of these subcategories and in general there is little empirical support for them; at the present time only the socialised/unsocialised distinction is recognised in ICD–10 and DSM–IV. Clinical experience would suggest that a whole variety of antisocial behaviour can occur in association with truancy and that both unsocialised and socialised conduct disorder is found.

We have already commented on the relationship between truancy and delinquency. It is often assumed that one causes the other, for example by being out of school the child is more likely to commit offences perhaps because of more time to do so. The available research does not support this idea. Instead of a causal relationship existing between the two it would appear that truancy and delinquency are two symptoms of the same underlying problems. Thus many of the findings on family background, etc. quoted in relation to truancy are mirrored by those published in relation to delinquency (Farrington, 1980). In general truancy precedes convictions, few factors have been found that differentiate between delinquent and non-delinquent truants and it would appear that the two groups differ in degree not in kind (i.e. the factors found that predict both truancy and delinquency are present to a more severe degree in the delinquent truants).

Given the level of public concern regarding adolescent drug and alcohol abuse there is surprisingly little research and interest in this area among child and adolescent psychiatrists. Studies on the adult outcomes of truancy have found an association with later drug and alcohol use (Robins & Price, 1991). There are less available data on young misusers. Swadi (1992) in a community study of adolescent drug use among 15–16-year-olds found that truancy was one of several predictors of drug use. In a separate study of 1232 adolescents aged 11–17 years (Swadi, 1989) truancy was strongly associated with daily smoking and the use of solvents and illegal drugs, but only weakly associated with alcohol use. The pattern of substance use was found to differ between the sexes, with truant boys being more involved in drug taking and truant girls in alcohol use. Similar findings with respect to the increased risk of drug misuse and under-age drinking associated with truancy are reported from a study of fourth and fifth year pupils in three mainstream comprehensive schools (Pritchard *et al*, 1987).

While emotional symptoms are not generally considered to be a characteristic feature of the psychopathology of truants, several studies have found truancy to be associated with anxiety, sadness and isolation from other pupils (Tennent, 1971; Berg *et al*, 1978; Farrington, 1980). Several studies have also identified a group of children who show features of both school refusal and truancy (Tennent, 1971; Bools *et al*, 1990; Berg *et al*, 1993). Where a psychiatric disorder is present this is usually found to be a mixed disorder of conduct and emotions.

Many researchers have commented on the poor school histories of children who truant both in terms of troublesome classroom behaviour (Hersov, 1960; Farrington, 1980) and poor educational attainment (Hersov, 1960; Cooper, 1966; Douglas *et al*, 1968; Fogelman & Richardson, 1974; Farrington, 1980). The links between conduct disorder, low verbal intelligence and specific reading retardation are well established (Sturge, 1982; Huesmann *et al*, 1984; Walsh *et al*, 1987) and while not specifically addressed in most studies on truancy it is likely that specific reading retardation is similarly associated with truancy (Galloway, 1983). As is the case for conduct disorder in general, the exact nature of the relationship between truancy and low intelligence is not clear. It may be that antisocial behaviour itself causes school under-achievement. An alternative hypothesis is that cognitive deficits in language and low intelligence itself might cause children to respond to their inadequate school achievement with antisocial behaviour, including truancy. Finally, it may be that both the lower intelligence and antisocial behaviour are caused by some additional background factor or factors. Recent findings from the Collaborative Perinatal Study in the USA support the existence of the third hypothesis, suggesting that in the case of conduct disorder in general it is likely that a social or cultural factor, most probably the family environment, forecasts both the low verbal intelligence scores and conduct disorder (Schonfield *et al*, 1988). Whether lower intelligence and truancy go on to have some additional role, perhaps in serving to perpetuate the school problems, has not been clarified although intuitively this would seem to be possible.

The relationship between truancy and particular temperamental characteristics has not been widely researched. Studies such as the National Child Development Study and the Cambridge Study in Delinquent Development have reported teachers' comments or descriptions of children who truant but the question of whether particular temperamental characteristics are a risk for truancy has not been specifically addressed. The relationship between temperamental characteristics and conduct disorder in general has been studied although as yet it is not possible to draw any firm conclusions, partly because of differing models of the nature of temperament (Earls, 1993) and the difficulty in measuring certain very relevant temperamental characteristics such as impulsivity (Buss & Plomin, 1984).

Attention deficit disorder is known to be often accompanied by conduct problems, including truancy (Taylor *et al*, 1986). In Britain, where the diagnosis is based upon ICD–10 criteria, the disorder is said to be present where the child shows an enduring disposition to behave in a restless, inattentive, distractible and disorganised fashion that may or may not be accompanied by increased motor activity. Attention deficit disorder is one of the routes into conduct disorder; in most cases where there is comorbidity it precedes the development of conduct disorder (Barkley *et al*, 1990). Children who exhibit comorbidity respond to stimulant medication (Taylor *et al*, 1987) although the response is less satisfactory than for children with attention deficit disorder alone.

Truancy is more likely to occur in children from adverse family backgrounds. Tyerman (1968) investigated the causes of truancy and found it to be associated with excessive parental control (particularly by corporal punishment), dirty homes, uninterested parents, keeping the child at home in the past without good cause and homes in a working-class area. In many studies truancy has been found to be associated with lower social class; however, it is noteworthy that this was not the case in the Isle of Wight study (Rutter *et al*, 1970). Factors such as poor parenting, unemployment, low income, an absent parent, parental criminality and harsh inconsistent parenting have also emerged as significant (Hodges, 1968; Belson, 1975; May, 1975; Tibbenham, 1977; Farrington, 1980). Thus truancy has been found to be associated with multiple adversity. There is rather less information available on the quality of relationships in the families of truants; however, it is likely that the patterns of relationships identified for conduct disorder in general apply in many cases of truancy. Patterson and others have described an escalating cycle of coercive interactions involving both the parents and the child that leads to patterns of maladaptive behaviour in both and which these authors believe is central to the development of conduct disorder (Patterson *et al*, 1989; Reid & Patterson, 1989).

School factors have been found to be important in the aetiology of truancy. Attendance rates are known to differ between schools even after allowing for differences in intake, i.e. according to ability and previously disturbed behaviour (Rutter *et al*, 1979). Factors such as the extent to which parents are involved in the school and a less authoritarian approach to enforcing rules have been found to be associated with improved attendance (Reynolds *et al*, 1980). However, although school factors are known to play some role in the aetiology of truancy it has been suggested by more recent research that the school itself is not a major determinant (Reynolds & Cuttance, 1991) but exerts its effects in conjunction with the individual and family factors already identified.

Management: the role of the child psychiatrist

Given the prevalence of school attendance problems and the relatively small number of child psychiatrists, approximately 387 consultants (*Health Trends*, 1994), it would not be feasible for each child to be referred to a child psychiatrist nor would it necessarily be desirable. In Britain there are a large number of other professionals involved in the management of such children: education social workers, education psychologists and teachers. It has been argued that the problem of persistent absence from school is largely educational or sociological in origin and is the product of the inconsistent and conflicting demands upon the individual child both in school and society at large (Gutfreund, 1975; Reynolds & Murgatroyd, 1977) and that clinical interventions are only of peripheral relevance (Galloway, 1986). This model implies a need for changes in the child's family, school or social situation to improve attendance, which may be better achieved by school-based agencies than referral to a child psychiatrist. An alternative view is that persistent absence from school represents a psychiatric disturbance in the child resulting either from individual vulnerability or family factors, implying a need for treatment. The most popular view among clinicians, educators and policy makers is that to a certain extent both models are valid, that in the minority of cases there is evidence of a psychiatric disorder but that most cases reflect an "irresponsible or indifferent" attitude towards education (Galloway, 1980).

This view favours a system whereby the school-based team of education social workers, teachers and psychologists carry out the initial assessment and interventions, referring on to more specialist agencies, including child psychiatrists, as necessary. Unfortunately, this process often breaks down. The decision to refer on to a specialist agency is often taken in a rather arbitrary fashion (Gath *et al*, 1972) and there continues to be a lack of understanding among potential referrers about when it is appropriate to refer and what a child psychiatric service can offer (Oke & Mayer, 1991). In a recent study of school absentees in Bradford very few of those children exhibiting school refusal with evidence of anxiety or mood disturbance had been referred to child psychiatric services despite evidence that such problems can be very effectively managed by child psychiatrists (Berg *et al*, 1993).

There is unfortunately a dearth of research on routes to child psychiatric care and the factors influencing the referral process in general. The situation is further complicated by the fact that the organisation of both health and education services and the relationships between them vary from one region to another. Similarly, child psychiatric practice also varies from clinic to clinic according to the orientation and interests of the psychiatrists and availability of professionals from other disciplines. Given these factors it is perhaps not surprising that the referral process is so haphazard.

Although practice among child psychiatrists may vary, by virtue of their training child psychiatrists should all possess the same core skills and it may be useful for professionals from other disciplines to know what these skills are to enable them to decide when referral is appropriate. Child psychiatrists are medical practitioners who after postgraduate experience in various non-psychiatric medical specialities and further training in general psychiatry undertake a higher training in child and adolescent psychiatry. In addition to skills in the assessment and treatment of physical disorders in both children and adults, child psychiatrists also gain knowledge, experience and clinical skills relevant to the assessment and treatment of the full spectrum of mental disorder in adults, children and adolescents. The Royal College of Psychiatrists (1990) recommend that this combination of skills is essential when emotional, behavioural and developmental disorder in children and adolescents is:

(a) associated with a physical disorder in the child or those with whom they live
(b) associated with mental disorders among those with whom they live, especially parents
(c) is such that the administration of drugs needs to be considered
(d) is thought to be due to the ingestion of drugs, either prescribed or non-prescribed
(e) is of a severe degree or when the presentation of a problem is complex or unusual or where a wide range of aetiological factors are present
(f) is associated with a threat to the life of the child or other person with whom they are associated
(g) might require admission to hospital
(h) where detailed coordination and decision making with respect to the case is required.

In addition to the special skills of the child psychiatrist, traditionally referral to a child psychiatric service also enables access to a wider range of skills than those of the psychiatrist alone because the psychiatrist usually works within a multidisciplinary team. Although the team may vary in composition from one clinic to another, psychologists, social workers, nurses and, less often, child psychotherapists and family therapists may be represented. In recent years the multidisciplinary team has been under threat as being unnecessarily expensive. In many areas social workers have been withdrawn and there is an increased trend towards unidisciplinary working. Nevertheless, even when a child is seen by a professional working alone there is usually the opportunity for supervision and consultation with professionals of other disciplines so that some sharing of skills still occurs.

In the absence of any guidelines on who should be referred to a child psychiatric team we would like to put forward some of our own, which are based on a knowledge of the clinical features and factors associated with poor school attendance together with a consideration of the core skills possessed by a child psychiatric team.

Firstly, we would recommend referral to a child psychiatrist in cases where the school attendance problems are associated with any disorder in which a psychiatric assessment is necessary and where there may be a need for treatment that can best or only be provided by a specialist child psychiatric team. We would consider depression to come into this category and recommend that a child psychiatrist assess any child or adolescent who shows some evidence of depression, such as low mood, lack of interest and enjoyment in usual activities, social withdrawal, poor concentration, irritability, perhaps accompanied by sleep and appetite disturbance and suicidal feelings.

It is our view that anxiety states would also fulfil criteria for referral to a child psychiatric clinic. Anxiety is a feature of most cases of school refusal and we would suggest that in all but mild uncomplicated cases of recent onset, referral to a child psychiatric team be considered as there is considerable evidence that such problems can be managed effectively by child psychiatrists.

Other disorders such as obsessive–compulsive disorder (where the child or adolescent experiences repetitive worries or thoughts that may be associated with compulsive actions or rituals), eating disorders (manifest principally by disturbance of body image and weight loss) and psychotic disorders (which usually present with unusual or bizarre behaviour coupled with abnormal experiences such as auditory hallucinations and abnormal beliefs) all require referral to a child psychiatrist because of the need for a psychiatric assessment and specific psychiatric treatments.

Attention deficit disorder is often accompanied by conduct problems including truancy and there is considerable evidence that children with attention deficit disorder respond to treatment with stimulant medication (Taylor, 1993). We would suggest that in cases where there is a history of impaired attention and concentration, which may be accompanied by impulsivity and motor overactivity, referral to a child psychiatrist be considered.

Drug and alcohol misuse may be associated with truancy. Although in the young dependence is thought to be rare (Farrell & Taylor, 1993) substance misuse at a level of anything other than occasional, experimental use is often associated with other behavioural and family problems. There are very few services specifically for young misusers and it is recommended that most generic workers coming into contact with young people seeking help for such problems should possess sufficient skills to assess and manage an alcohol or drug problem (Farrell & Taylor, 1993). In practice, therefore, because of the complexity of such problems, and in some cases the associated medical risk, referral to a child psychiatrist is necessary.

In cases where physical symptoms are a prominent feature of the presentation involvement of a child psychiatrist is usually necessary.

Parental mental illness is often associated with both truancy and school refusal. We would suggest that where this is a feature a child psychiatrist should be involved.

Finally in cases where intervention by other agencies has failed or which are particularly complex because of a combination of difficulties a child psychiatry opinion should be obtained.

Assessment

We have alluded to the fact that one of the reasons for referral to a child psychiatric service is the need for a comprehensive, multidimensional assessment. The purpose of such an assessment is to attempt to answer a number of questions (Cantwell, 1988).

(a) Does the child have any form of psychiatric disorder and, if so, what is the nature of this disorder?

(b) What are the various roots of that disorder in terms of intrapsychic, family, socio-cultural and biological factors, and what are the relative contributions of each of these in the aetiology of the disorder in this particular patient?

(c) What is the likely outcome if no intervention or treatment is offered and is the intervention necessary?

(d) What type of intervention is most likely to be effective?

In child and adolescent psychiatry it is also necessary to consider the context of the referral and the patient–referrer system. This is particularly important in the assessment of a child presenting with school attendance problems because by the time the child is seen there are usually a number of other professionals involved. Two further questions can therefore be added to the previous list.

(e) Who is most worried about the problem? Families are often sent to child psychiatrists but may themselves not see a need for intervention.

(f) What has precipitated this referral? It may be the child's symptoms; alternatively it could be that support services are being withdrawn from the school or the parents are being threatened with legal action.

The assessment process may vary from one clinic to another and even from one case to another, as it is important to adapt the assessment to the type of problem, age and developmental level of the child and circumstances of the clinic. While it is important not to be prescriptive in recommending any particular method of assessment there are some important general principles. Firstly, while some practitioners may not wish to take a formal history it is essential to have some system which ensures that all the necessary information is obtained so that important factors are not overlooked.

Secondly, it is vital that practitioners are flexible in their approach and avoid attempting to deal with all problems in the same way. For example, although family therapy and assessment may be the preferred treatment in a particular clinic, there will be occasions when an individual interview with a family member is necessary. This leads on to the third point, that certain types of assessment are crucial for particular problems, for example an individual interview with a family member who is thought to be psychotic or depressed. Fourthly, there is considerable evidence that children's behaviour may vary according to the situation and that informants may give differing accounts and have different views on the child's problems. Thus in order to gain a complete picture it is usually necessary to gather information from various sources such as schools, playgroups, etc. Parental consent is generally needed in order to approach outside agencies and it is often preferable to meet with the family and gain their trust before contacting these. Finally, if a particular mode of therapy is envisaged it is usually necessary to conduct at least part of the assessment in that mode, for example a family interview if family therapy is proposed.

Thus in the assessment of a child or adolescent presenting with school attendance problems we would recommend carrying out a 'screening assessment' initially to determine the type of problem, the nature of any underlying child psychiatric disorder and to reach some understanding of the aetiology in that particular child in order to formulate an appropriate management plan. It is our practice to interview the child individually in addition to seeing the family as a whole. Many children, particularly older children and adolescents, may prefer to discuss their worries, feelings, etc. in the absence of their parents and as we have already indicated an individual interview is essential if there are any concerns about the child's mental state or any suspicion of abuse. We would usually attempt to obtain information on the following areas during the course of the assessment.

(a) The nature of the presenting problem(s), its duration and severity. Whether there are any provoking or ameliorating factors and any precipitants or stresses thought to be important by the child, family or school. What interventions, if any, have already been tried.
(b) The child's anxiety level in general, any specific fears or worries. The child's mood, energy level, interest in activities and the presence of depressive or suicidal feelings. Whether there is any evidence of antisocial behaviour such as aggression, defiance, stealing, etc. and in the case of adolescents any suspicion of drug or alcohol abuse. The child's activity level, concentration and attention span. The presence of other symptoms such as obsessional thoughts or worries, bizarre beliefs, etc., which may rarely be associated with school non-attendance.

(c) The child's general health and whether there is any history of physical symptoms such as headaches or stomach pains, sleep or appetite disturbance, and problems with elimination (enuresis/encopresis).

(d) The child's educational history, in particular whether there have been any previous problems in attendance, how the child has coped with previous transitions (e.g. from infants to juniors), whether there is any evidence of learning difficulties and the child and family's attitudes to education.

(e) The child's pattern and quality of relationships with parents, siblings, peers and other adults.

(f) Whether the child has had any significant illness or injuries, behavioural or developmental problems including perinatal problems. The child's temperament, the quality of early parent–child relationships and the child's care history (i.e. who have been the child's principal carers, details of any significant separations, the nature of substitute care, if any).

(g) The family structure and the quality of family relationships. Whether there is any history of physical or psychiatric disorder in other family members.

Observation of the child and family provides useful information on the child's behaviour, development and emotional state and the quality of family interactions and relationships. If there is a suspicion that the child may have learning difficulties including specific reading retardation then a psychometric assessment is important. A more detailed behavioural, family or individual assessment can be added if treatment in any of these modalities is planned.

Treatment

The distinction between assessment and treatment is often artificial in that the assessment process itself may alter the perceptions, feelings and attitudes of both the child and family (Cox, 1993) and is an opportunity to engage the family. While some therapists may not differentiate between school refusers and truants, for example, many family and individual therapists may not make this distinction, so for the purpose of discussion we will deal with each problem separately.

School refusal

The principal aims in managing cases of school refusal are to bring about a return to school and ensure regular attendance at school as soon as possible and to treat any underlying psychiatric disorder. There is now abundant evidence that in most cases the aim should be an early return to school. Requests for home tuition to avoid subjecting the child to the stress of having to return to school should be resisted (Berg, 1992) because of the risks of further educational, social and psychiatric problems (Kahn & Nursten, 1962; Berg *et al*, 1969).

The parents will often need to be convinced of the wisdom of this course of action particularly as they may have already attempted to insist that the child attend school only to be confronted by extreme distress and resistance on the part of the child. In those cases where physical complaints such as headache, abdominal pains, etc. are present both parents and child will need reassuring that no physical illness is present and this will often need to be coupled with an explanation of the cause of the symptoms, which in many cases are somatic expressions of anxiety. In some cases the physical symptoms are due to some underlying somatic illness that is not in itself sufficient reason to keep the child off school. The paediatricians as well as the family will often need to be convinced that a return to school is in the child's best interests; the parents will need reassurance that a return to school will not put the child's health at risk or cut short the evaluation and follow-up of the child's physical symptoms; parents and school officials will need to be supported by the paediatrician and or psychiatrist to encourage school attendance (Waller & Eisenberg, 1980).

Parents may often blame the school and suggest that a change of school might help. Experience suggests that where this happens the same difficulties usually re-emerge at the new school. Nevertheless it is important to recognise that the complaints about the school situation may be justified and, for example, action to eliminate bullying and help for any learning difficulties should be sought as part of the overall management plan.

The re-entry to school itself needs careful discussion with both parents and school officials, with advice on how best to prepare the child and deal with any emotional crises. As for whom should accompany the child to school, it is preferable to try and mobilise any strengths within the family (Hersov, 1985) so that the father, for example, may be encouraged to rearrange his hours of work to enable him to support the mother in dealing with the child's temper tantrums and distress, or an elder sibling in the same school may be involved in visiting the child at break-time. Occasionally the parents may be too anxious and uncertain to accompany the child to school. In such cases a member of the clinical team or representative of the school or support services must be involved, the aim being to start the process and share responsibility with the parents initially, eventually withdrawing and passing over total responsibility to the parents.

Individual sessions with the child, particularly in the case of older children and adolescents, may also be useful, the aim being to explore the child's worries and offer support. It is sometimes helpful to give the child some say in just when return to school is attempted and how it will be done (Berg, 1985).

In some cases, particularly milder cases of recent onset, counselling of parents and the child without further specific treatment is sufficient to bring about regular attendance. In many cases, however, additional measures are needed. A variety of therapeutic approaches have been advocated for the treatment of school refusal: individual psychotherapy, behavioural treatments, family therapy, milieu day and in-patient therapy and finally pharmacotherapy. Behavioural treatments have been the most widely evaluated; however the other treatment modalities are relatively unresearched and there are few comparative studies to guide treatment choice. Blagg & Yule (1984) compared the outcome of 30 children treated behaviourally compared with 16 children admitted to an in-patient facility and 20 cases who received home tuition. The assignment was not random but based on geographical areas served and successful treatment was defined as the child returning to full-time education: 93% of the behaviourally treated group, 38% of the hospital group and 10% of the home tuition group were successful.

Behavioural treatments are widely used, particularly in cases where the child has a true phobia about some aspect of the school situation or there is evidence of separation anxiety. The general principle underlying most behavioural treatments for disorders in which anxiety plays a major role is that exposure to the feared situation or stimulus leads to a rise in the anxiety levels which in turn leads to avoidance. The behavioural therapist's aim is to bring about a reduction in the patient's anxiety on exposure to the stimulus thereby preventing the avoidance reaction. Habituation or a reduction in anxiety levels on exposure to the stimulus occurs naturally in most cases if the period of exposure is long enough. Although flooding, a sudden massive exposure to the feared stimulus, is sometimes used in cases of relatively recent onset where the anxiety is not severe, in most cases graded exposure, where the child is encouraged to face the feared situation in pre-planned steps of increasing difficulty, is the preferred option. The exposure can occur either in imagination or in reality and in practice both techniques are often combined. Desensitisation is often used in the treatment of childhood phobias and school refusal. Here graded exposure occurs while the subject is being relaxed, the aim being to reciprocally inhibit the feared response by keeping the child relaxed (i.e. to aid habituation). A variety of techniques are used and several authors have described the use of muscular relaxation (Ule *et al*, 1980). One of the earliest accounts of treatment of school refusal described the treatment of a 9-year-old girl, where the school refusal was thought to be due to separation anxiety. The girl was given relaxation training and asked to imagine being separated from her mother while relaxing, the periods of separation gradually lengthening (Lazarus, 1960).

Although there are no definitive studies clinical experience suggests that while relaxation training may be successful in older children, it is more difficult with young children (Rosenstiel & Scott, 1977). Emotive imagery, in which the child is asked to conjure up images that arouse feelings of self-assertion, pride, affection, mirth and similar anxiety-inhibiting responses, can be used instead of relaxation training (Lazarus & Abramowitz, 1962). This is illustrated by the description of the treatment of an 8-year-old girl who was said to be 'school phobic'. She was asked to imagine her favourite fictional hero, Noddy, as someone who was fearful of going to school and encouraged to protect him by active reassurance (Lazarus & Abramowitz, 1962). Children can be asked to imagine that they have joined forces with a favourite hero such as Batman and that they are tackling the feared situations together. Verbal self-instruction training has also been described in the treatment of anxiety-based conditions (Kanfer *et al*, 1975). Here children are asked to rehearse active control or competence-mediating statements (e.g. "I am a brave boy and I can handle school") or statements aimed at reducing the aversive quality of the stimulus itself (e.g. "school is not so bad"). This technique is again combined with exposure to the feared situation.

Children's behavioural problems are often caused or maintained by the responses of others around them; for this reason operant conditioning techniques are frequently employed. Here responses are increased or strengthened (and thus shaped) by having consequences that are rewarding (positive reinforcement) or that lead to the avoidance of, or escape from punishment (negative reinforcement) (Herbert, 1993). This may involve the removal of pay-offs (positive reinforces) that generally follow a maladaptive response and/or the provision of positive reinforces or penalities following the display of desirable or undesirable actions, respectively. Thus Allyon *et al* (1970) described the treatment of an 8-year-old girl who was 'school phobic'. The girl was taken to school towards the end of the school day by an assistant who remained with her until school was dismissed. Each successive day she was taken to school a little earlier; for each step of the programme she completed she was positively reinforced by her mother and the assistant. A number of other authors have described a contingency contracting approach employing a variety of reinforces, of which material and peer social reinforces (Morgan, 1975) and the school making direct contact with the parents and showing approval or disapproval at their child's absence (Parker & McCoy, 1977) emerged as the most effective.

As already mentioned the exposure may occur *in vivo* or in imagination. Both situations have been described in the literature and there is little guidance as to which approach to adopt in a particular situation. Some authors have described moving from imaginal desensitisation to *in vivo* desensitisation, while others have carried out both at the same time or used *in vivo* exposure alone. In cases where the child finds it difficult to imagine the feared situation, *in vivo* exposure is likely to be more successful; this is reported to be the case in younger children (Yule, 1985). Where imaginal desensitisation has been attempted and failed, it is recommended by some authors that *in vivo* exposure be attempted (Yule *et al*, 1980; Yule, 1985).

Similarly a variety of desensitisation techniques have been described (i.e. relaxation, emotive imagery, verbal self-instruction) and again there is little guidance on the indications for each technique and when to switch to a different approach. There is also continuing debate on the value of the different elements of the treatment approaches described. In adults systematic desensitisation is now rarely used, exposure by itself having been found to be effective (Marks, 1986) although the situation as regards childhood fears and anxieties is less clear cut (Herbert, 1993).

We have already highlighted the role of family factors in the aetiology and maintenance of school refusal. As already described for any treatment to be successful the parents must be involved. However, in some cases in addition to the parental counselling and involvement of parents in the behavioural management, more formal family therapy is needed. Again, as with most aspects of the treatment of school refusal, there is little empirical research to guide the choice of treatment. However, where it is thought that the family system or dynamics are important in this particular case then family therapy should be considered and can be combined with other treatment modalities such as behavioural treatment.

Counselling of the child and supportive psychotherapy have already been described and are often combined with behavioural and family approaches. More formal psychotherapy, usually along psychodynamic lines, is less often employed in the treatment of school refusal. While there is no empirical work to support the choice of treatment, as with most of the other treatment approaches, most authorities would probably recommend individual psychotherapy for severe chronic disorders that have not been particularly responsive to changes in the child's environment, particularly the family environment. In almost all cases the individual psychotherapy would be combined with work with the family and or school.

Pharmacotherapy has little place in the treatment of school refusal. There are a number of anecdotal accounts of the use of medication in school refusal (Frommer, 1967; Skynner, 1974; Abe, 1975) but few controlled trials. A controlled trial of imipramine in a dose of 100–200 mg daily found it to be superior to placebo in children and adolescents with school phobia (Gittelman-Klein & Klein, 1971). However, in two more recent studies imipramine in similar doses to those used by Gittelman-Klein & Klein was not found to be superior to placebo in the treatment of children with school refusal and symptoms of anxiety and depression (Gittelman-Klein & Koplewicz, 1986; Bernstein *et al*, 1990). Another study investigated the efficacy of clomipramine in school phobia and found no advantage over placebo at doses of 40–75 mg daily (Berney *et al*, 1981). Thus the evidence on the efficacy of antidepressant use in school refusal is conflictual and at the present time, given the availability of safer psychological therapies, antidepressant treatment is not generally recommended. Some authors suggest short-term use of an anxiolytic such as a benzodiazepine, to facilitate the initial re-entry into school. There is very little research available on the efficacy of benzodiazepines in reducing anxiety in children. Although clinical experience suggests that there may be some short-term benefit there are few controlled trials, and those studies that do exist have found conflicting results (Lucas & Pasley, 1969; Simeon *et al*, 1992). Given the concerns regarding the problems of tolerance and dependence on benzodiazepines their use is not generally recommended.

Occasionally out-patient treatment of school refusal using the techniques described previously is unsuccessful; in these cases the option of day attendance at a special unit should be considered. These may be provided either by education authorities or be attached to psychiatric units for children and adolescents. Those units run by education authorities are generally centres in which education is provided to small groups of children, which may be more acceptable to school refusers (Berg, 1985) and act as a stepping stone to reintegration into mainstream schooling. Day-patient hospital units share some of the characteristics of these units but their function overlaps more with that of the in-patient unit, in that psychiatric assessment and a variety of treatments can be offered. Day-patient attendance at a hospital may be preferred to in-patient admission where it is thought separation of the child from his or her family is not appropriate or to allow the opportunity to test out whether change can be achieved with the child at home.

Where out-patient and possibly day placement have been tried and failed admission to an in-patient psychiatric unit for children and adolescents should be considered (Berg, 1985). This is often necessary if the child becomes increasingly anxious or depressed, or is able to manipulate and control his or her parents so that they are unable to exert effective control on behaviour in general and school attendance, or where the parents may be too psychiatrically ill to act in accord with a treatment plan (Hersov, 1985).

In the past, in-patient units were used to provide long-term placement for children with behavioural problems in a neutral setting to offset negative family influences while the child received psychotherapy and there was a tendency for all children to be subjected to the same kind of regime or treatment programme. Nowadays, in-patient admission is generally just one phase of an overall treatment plan, the aim being to provide specialised assessment and treatment. Such units generally provide a 24-hour service and 5–7 day a week placement. Although decisions regarding admission, diagnosis and treatment are ultimately the responsibility of the psychiatric staff, the units are staffed by a multidisciplinary team and there is usually a school on the premises.

In practice, in-patient admission usually affords the opportunity for a more detailed and specialised assessment than is possible on an out-patient basis. In particular the period in hospital will often provide some guide as to whether relapse will occur if the child returns home, in which case an alternative provision such as boarding school will need to be considered. The same range of treatment options as has already been described in the out-patient management of school refusal is also available on an in-patient basis. However, it is often easier to offer a combination of approaches and more intensive treatment as an in-patient and, in addition, the social group and therapeutic milieu of the unit itself play an important role in treatment. The term 'therapeutic milieu' is usually used to denote "those aspects of in-patient ward structure, organisation and setting that can help to reduce the emotional and behavioural disorders of children" (Hersov, 1993). The social group in the ward is particularly helpful in the treatment of children who have difficulties in social relationships or who have missed social experiences because of long-standing school absence (Hersov, 1974). While there are often good reasons for considering admission to an in-patient unit there are also dangers. In situations where the disturbed child has become the family scapegoat or is the target of parental hostility there is a risk that he or she may be later permanently excluded from the family unless determined efforts are made to prevent this. Admission under such circumstances can also lead to strong feelings of anger and rejection on the part of the child (Mandelbaum, 1977). There is also a chance that in-patient admission will be requested because of the lack of other suitable care or educational provision.

Truancy

There is much less work on management of truancy than school refusal. While many psychiatrists and educators would agree that psychiatrists have a definite role in the treatment of school refusal, there is much less information on the value of psychiatric interventions for truancy and it has been argued that improved social conditions and change in the school environment are more important (Galloway, 1986). The aims of treatment are nevertheless similar to those in school refusal, namely the restoration of regular attendance and treatment of any associated psychiatric disorder.

Where there is evidence of learning difficulties remedial education should be obtained. If there is evidence of ADDH (Attention Deficit Disruptive Disorder) specific treatment including the use of stimulant medication should be considered. If there is associated drug or alcohol abuse specific treatment may be required, although in children and adolescents this is often the management of the associated family and behaviour problems (Farrell & Taylor, 1993). Given that truancy is now regarded as a symptom of conduct disorder, the treatment is generally that of conduct disorder although there is very little published on the effect of the treatment techniques employed in conduct disorder on school attendance.

Treatment approaches may target the individual child or adolescent, parents, family as a whole or involve the wider community in which the child lives (Earls, 1993). In general, in the treatment of conduct disorder therapeutic techniques that target the individual child are insufficient, for example individual counselling, and attention should be given to the influence of family and peers, school factors and the social and economic circumstances (Wells *et al*, 1980; Lipsey, 1992). It is particularly important that the psychiatric team work in conjunction with other agencies such as school and social work.

A variety of school and community-based interventions have been developed and these are described elsewhere. In terms of psychological or psychiatric treatments available, behavioural and family therapy are the most widely used. Thus 'reinforcement' and 'contingency contracts' have been described in the management of children with truancy (Galloway, 1980; Yule *et al*, 1980). Parent management training, where parents are trained to use positive reinforcement for pro-social behaviour and mild non-violent punishments (e.g. time out) for infractions such as temper outbursts, have been found to be effective for pre-adolescents although the efficacy in the parents of adolescents (who are more likely to truant) is not established. Cognitive–behavioural approaches with the individual child aimed at improving the child's social reasoning, problem-solving and capacity to deal with conflict situations have been described for use in the treatment of children and adolescents with conduct disorder and oppositional behaviour (Kendall & Braswell, 1985). Family therapy is also widely used and is described more fully in Chapter 17. Individual counselling or psychotherapy may be of value in cases where there are prominent emotional symptoms and the young person is able to use this technique, although in almost all cases this would need to be combined with other approaches, e.g. family work.

Day-patient and hospital admission should not have much of a role in the management of truancy although conduct disorder remains a common reason for the use of such a facility (Kashani & Cantwell, 1983). As is the case for school refusal such a facility can be used if there is a need for a specialised assessment and for a multifaceted intervention with a higher degreee of control than is possible on an out-patient basis. In practice residential treatment is usually reserved for very disturbed children and adolescents where truancy is only one aspect of the problem.

Legal aspects

It is important to remember that both school refusal and truancy, as well as school withdrawal, can occur in the context of child abuse and neglect. In such cases the psychiatrist should be aware of the need to involve social services and education social work as appropriate. The situation may arise where the psychiatrist discovers during the course of working with the family that the child is being abused or neglected. Alternatively it may be the family's refusal to seek help or co-operate with treatment that is putting the child at risk of significant harm.

Future directions

One is aware when reading an account of the features and management of school attendance problems of the many gaps in the knowledge. There is a need for more research on the characteristics of those children who truant but show few features of conduct disorder. A greater understanding of the patterns of family relationships in both truancy and school refusal is needed. The need for good evaluative treatment studies is particularly pressing.

References

ABE, K. (1975) Sulpiride in school phobia. *Psychiatria Clinica*, **8**, 95–98.
ALLYON, T., SMITH, D. & ROGERS, M. (1970) Behavioural management of school phobia. *Journal of Behaviour Therapy and Experimental Psychiatry*, **1**, 125–138.
AMERICAN PSYCHIATRIC ASSOCIATION (1980) *Diagnostic and Statistical Manual of Mental Disorders* (3rd edn) (DSM–III). Washington: APA.
—— (1987) *Diagnostic and Statistical Manual of Mental Disorders* (3rd edn, revised) (DSM–III–R). Washington, DC: APA.
—— (1994) *Diagnostic and Statistical Manual of Mental Disorders* (4th edn) (DSM–IV). Washington: APA.
BARKLEY, R. A., McMURRAY, M. B., EDELBROCK, C. S., *et al* (1990) The adolescent outcome of hyperactive children diagnosed by research criteria: I. An 8 year prospective follow-up study. *Journal of the American Academy of Child and Adolescent Psychiatry*, **29**, 546–557.
BELSON, W. A. (1975) *Juvenile Theft: The Causal Factors*. London: Harper and Row.
BERG, I. (1974) A self-administered dependency questionnaire (SADQ) for use with mothers of school children. *British Journal of Psychiatry*, **124**, 1–9.
—— (1985) Management of school refusal. *Archives of Disease in Childhood*, **60**, 486–488.
—— (1985) The management of truancy. *Journal of Child Psychiatry and Psychology*, **26**, 325–331.
—— (1992) Absence from school and mental health. *British Journal of Psychiatry*, **161**, 154–166.
——, NICOLS, K. & PRITCHARD, C. (1969) School phobia – its classification and relationship to dependency. *Journal of Child Psychiatry and Psychology*, **10**, 123–141.
——, MARKS, I., McGUIRE, R., *et al* (1974) School phobia and agoraphobia. *Psychological Medicine*, **4**, 428–434.
—— & McGUIRE, R. (1971) Are school phobic adolescents overdependent? *British Journal of Psychiatry*, **199**, 167–168.
—— & —— (1974) Are mothers of school phobic adolescents overprotective? *British Journal of Psychiatry*, **124**, 10–13.
——, COLLINS, T., McGUIRE, R., *et al* (1975) Educational attainment in adolescent school phobia. *British Journal of Psychiatry*, **125**, 435–438.
——, BUTLER, A., HULLIN, R., *et al* (1978) Features of children taken to Juvenile Court for failure to attend school. *Psychological Medicine*, **8**, 447–453.
——, ——, FAIRBURN, I., *et al* (1981) The parents of school phobic adolescents – a preliminary investigation of family life variables. *Psychological Medicine*, **11**, 79–84.

———, ———, FRANKLIN, J., *et al* (1993) DSM–III–R disorders, social factors and management of school attendance problems in the normal population. *Journal of Child Psychology and Psychiatry*, **34**, 1187–1203.

BERNEY, T., KOLVIN, I., BHATE, S. R., et al (1981) School phobia: a therapeutic trial with clomipramine and short-term outcome. *British Journal of Psychiatry*, **138**, 110–118.

BERNSTEIN, G. A. & GARFINKEL, B. D. (1986) School phobia: the overlap of affective and anxiety disorders. *Journal of the American Academy of Child and Adolescent Psychiatry*, **25**, 235–241.

——— & BORCHHARDT, C. M. (1990) Comparative studies of pharmacotherapy for school refusal. *Journal of the American Academy of Child and Adolescent Psychiatry*, **29**, 773–781.

BLAGG, N. & YULE, W. (1984) The behavioural treatment of school refusal: a comparative study. *Behavioural Research and Therapy*, **22**, 119–127.

BOOLS, C., FOSTER, J., BROWN, I. *et al* (1990) The identification of psychiatric disorders in children who fail to attend school: a cluster analysis of a non-clinical population. *Psychological Medicine*, **20**, 171–181.

BOWLBY, J. (1973) *Attachment and Loss, Volume 2: Separation, Anxiety and Anger.* London: Hogarth Press.

BROADWIN, I. T. (1932) A contribution to the study of truancy. *American Journal of Orthopsychiatry*, **2**, 253–259.

BUSS, A. H. & PLOMIN, R. (1984) *Temperament: Early Developing Personality Traits.* Hillsdale, NJ: Lawrence Erlbaum.

CANTWELL, D. P. (1988) DSM–III studies. In *Assessment and Diagnosis in Child Psychopathology* (eds M. Rutter, A. H. Tuma & I. S. Lann). London: Fullon.

CHAZAN, M. (1962) School phobia. *British Journal of Educational Psychology*, **32**, 200–217.

CHERRY, B. (1976) Persistent job changing – is it a problem? *Journal of Occupational Psychology*, **49**, 203–221.

COOLIDGE, J. C., HAHN, P. B. & PECH, A. L. (1957) School phobia: neurotic crisis or way of life. *American Journal of Orthopsychiatry*, **27**, 296–306.

COOPER, M. G. (1966) School refusal: an enquiry into the part played by school and home. *Educational Research*, **8**, 223–229.

COX, A. (1993) Diagnostic appraisal. In *Child and Adolescent Psychiatry. Modern Approaches* (eds M. Rutter, E. Taylor & L. Hersov), pp. 22–33. London: Blackwell.

DAVIDSON, S. (1960) School phobia as a manifestation of family disturbance. Its structure and treatment. *Journal of Child Psychology and Psychiatry*, **1**, 270–287.

DE ALDEZ, E. G., GRANNELL, E., FIELDMAN, L., *et al* (1987) Characteristics of Venezuelan school refusers. *Journal of Nervous and Mental Disease*, **175**, 402–407.

DOUGLAS, J. W. B. & ROSS, J. M. (1965) The effects of absence on primary school performance. *British Journal of Educational Psychology*, **35**, 28–40.

———, ——— & SIMPSON, H. R. (1968) *All Our Future.* London: Peter Davies.

EARLS, F. (1993) Oppositional deficit and conduct disorders. In *Child and Adolescent Psychiatry. Modern Approaches* (eds M. Rutter, E. Taylor & L. Hersov), pp. 308–329. London: Blackwell.

EISENBERG, L. (1958) School phobia – a study in the communication of anxiety. *American Journal of Orthopsychiatry*, **114**, 712–718.

FARRELL, M. & TAYLOR, E. (1993) Drug and alcohol use and misuse. In *Child and Adolescent Psychiatry. Modern Approaches* (eds M. Rutter, E. Taylor and L. Hersov), pp. 529–545. London: Blackwell.

FARRINGTON, D. (1980) Truancy, delinquency and the home. In *Out of School – Modern Perspectives in Truancy and School Refusal* (eds L. Hersov & I. Berg), pp. 49–64. Chichester: John Wiley.

FLAKIERSKA, N., LINDSTRÖM, M. & GILLBERG, C. (1988) School refusal: a 15–20 year follow-up of 35 Swedish urban children. *British Journal of Psychiatry*, **152**, 834–837.

FOGELMAN, K. (1992) The long-term effects of truancy. *Association of Child Psychology and Psychiatry Newsletter*, **14**, 57–61.

——— & RICHARDSON, K. (1974) School attendance: some findings from the National Child Development Study. In *Truancy* (ed B. Turner), pp. 29–51. London: Ward Lock-Educational.

———, TIBBENHAM, A. & LAMBERT, L. (1980) Absence from school: findings from the National Child Development Study. In *Out of School – Modern Perspectives in Truancy and School Refusal* (eds L. Hersov & I. Berg), pp. 25–48. Chichester: John Wiley.

FROMMER, E. A. (1967) Treatment of childhood depression with antidepressant drugs. *British Medical Journal*, **1**, 729–732.

GALLOWAY, D. (1980) Problems in the assessment and management of persistent absenteeism from school. In *Out of School – Modern Perspectives in Truancy and School Refusal* (eds L. Hersov & I. Berg), pp. 149–169. Chichester: John Wiley.

—— (1983) Research note: truants and other absentees. *Journal of Child Psychology and Psychiatry*, **24**, 607–611.

—— (1986) School truants be treated. *Maladjustment and Therapeutic Education*, **4**, 18–24.

GATH, D., COOPER, B. & GATTONI, F. (1972) Child guidance and delinquency in a London borough. *Psychological Medicine*, **2**, 185–191.

GITTELMAN-KLEIN, R. & KLEIN, D. F. (1971) Controlled imipramine treatment of school phobia. *Archives of General Psychiatry*, **25**, 204–207.

—— & KOPELWICZ, H. S. (1986) Pharmacotherapy of childhood anxiety disorders. In *Anxiety Disorders of Childhood* (ed. R. Gittelman), pp. 188–203. New York: Guilford.

GRAY, G., SMITH, A. & RUTTER, M. (1980) School attendance and the first year of employment. In *Out of School – Modern Perspectives in Truancy and School Refusal* (eds L. Hersov & I. Berg), pp. 343–370. Chichester: John Wiley.

GUTFREUND, R. (1975) Resolving the problem. *Youth in Society*, May/June, 12–15.

HEALTH TRENDS (1994) Merit Awards. *Health Trends*, **25**, 11.

HERBERT, M. (1993) Behavioural methods. In *Child and Adolescent Psychiatry. Modern Approaches* (eds M. Rutter, E. Taylor & L. Hersov), pp. 858–879. London: Blackwell.

HERSOV, L. A. (1960) Persistent non-attendance at school. II. Refusal to go to school. *Journal of Child Psychology and Psychiatry*, **1**, 130–136, 136–145.

—— (1974) Neurotic disorders with special reference to school refusal. In *The Residential Psychiatric Treatment of Children* (ed. P. Barker). London: Crosby.

—— (1985) School refusal. In *Child and Adolescent Psychiatry. Modern Approaches* (eds M. Rutter & L. Hersov) pp. 382–399. London: Blackwell.

—— (1993) In-patient and day-hospital units. In *Child and Adolescent Psychiatry. Modern Approaches* (eds M. Rutter, E. Taylor & L. Hersov), pp. 983–995. London: Blackwell.

—— & BERG, I. (eds) (1980) *Out of School – Modern Perspectives in Truancy and School Refusal*. Chichester: John Wiley.

HODGES, V. (1968) Non-attendance at school. *Educational Research*, **11**, 58–61.

HOSHINO, Y., NIKKUNI, S., KANEKO, M., *et al* (1987) The application of DSM–III diagnostic criteria to school refusal. *Japanese Journal of Psychiatry and Neurology*, **41**, 1–7.

HUESMAN, L. R., ERON, L. D., LEFKOWITZ, M. M., *et al* (1984) Stability of aggression over time and generations. *Developmental Psychology*, **20**, 1120–1134.

JOHNSON, A. M., FALSTEIN, E. I., SZUREK, S. A., *et al* (1941) School phobia. *American Journal of Orthopsychiatry*, **11**, 702–711.

KAHN, J. & NURSTEN, J. P. (1962) School refusal: a comprehensive view of school phobia and other failures of school attendance. *American Journal of Orthopsychiatry*, **32**, 707–718.

KANFER, F. H., KAROLY, P. & NEWMAN, A. (1975) Reduction of children's fear of the dark by competence-related and situational threat-related verbal cues. *Journal of Consulting and Clinical Psychology*, **43**, 251–258.

KASHANI, J. H. & CANTWELL, D. P. (1983) Characteristics of children admitted to in-patient community mental health centre. *Archives of General Psychiatry*, **40**, 397–400.

KENDALL, P. C. & BRASWELL, L. (1985) *Cognitive–Behavioural Therapy for Impulsive Children*. New York: Guilford.

KENNEDY, W. A. (1965) School phobia: rapid treatment of 50 cases. *Journal of Abnormal Psychology*, **70**, 285–289.

—— (1971) A behaviouristic community-oriented approach to school phobia and other disorders. In *Behavioural Intervention in Human Problems* (ed. H. C. Richards). Oxford: Pergamon.

KOLVIN, I., BERNEY, T. P. & BHATE, S. R. (1984) Classification and diagnosis of depression in school phobia. *British Journal of Psychiatry*, **145**, 347–357.

LAST, C. G., FRANCIS, G., HERSEN, M., *et al* (1987) Separation anxiety and school phobia: a comparison using DSM–III criteria. *American Journal of Psychiatry*, **144**, 653–657.

LAZARUS, A. A. (1960) The elimination of children's phobias by deconditioning. In *Behavioural Therapy and the Neuroses* (ed. H. J. Eysenck), pp. 114–122. Oxford: Pergamon.

—— & ABRAMOWITZ, A. (1962) The use of "emotive imagery" in the treatment of children's phobias. *Journal of Mental Science*, **108**, 191–195.

LIPSEY, M. W. (1992) Juvenile delinquency treatment: a meta-analytic inquiry into the variability of effects. In *Meta-Analysis for Explanation: A Casebook* (eds T. Cook, H. Cooper, D. Cordray, *et al*). New York: Russell Sage Foundation.

MANDELBAUM, A. (1977) A family-centred approach to residential treatment. *Bulletin of the Meninger Clinic*, **41**, 27–39.

MARKS, I. (1986) *Behavioural Psychotherapy: Maudsley Pocket Book of Clinical Management*. London: Wright.

MAY, D. (1975) Truancy, school absenteeism and delinquency. *Scottish Educational Studies*, **7**, 97–107.

MORGAN, R. R. (1975) An exploratory study of three procedures to encourage school attendance. *Psychology in the School*, **12**, 209–215.

OKE, S. & MAYER, R. (1991) Referrals to child psychiatry – a survey of staff attitudes. *Archives of Disease in Childhood*, **66**, 862–865.

PARKER, F. C. & McCOY, J. F. (1977) School based intervention for the modification of excessive absenteeism. *Psychology in the School*, **4**, 84–88.

PARTRIDGE, J. M. (1939) Truancy. *Journal of Mental Science*, **85**, 45–81.

PATTERSON, G. R., DeBARYSH, B. D. & RAMSEY, E. (1989) A developmental perspective on antisocial behaviour. *American Psychologist*, **44**, 329–335.

PRITCHARD, C., DIAMOND, I., FIELDING, M., *et al* (1987) Drug misuse and truancy in normal 4th and 5th year comprehensive children. *Maladjustment and Therapeutic Education*, **5**, 2–16.

REID, J. B. & PATTERSON, G. R. (1989) The development of antisocial behaviour patterns in childhood and adolescence. *European Journal of Personality*, **3**, 107–119.

REYNOLDS, D. & MURGATROYD, S. (1977) The sociology of schooling and the absent pupil: the school as a factor in the generation of truancy. In *Absenteeism in South Wales* (ed. H. Carroll), Swansea: University College of Swansea.

——, JONES, D., ST LEGER, S., *et al* (1980) School factors and truancy. In *Out of School – Modern Perspectives in Truancy and School Refusal* (eds L. Hersov & I. Berg), pp. 85–110. Chichester: John Wiley.

—— & CUTTANCE, P. (1991) *School Effectiveness*. London: Cassell.

RINES, W. B. (1973) Behaviour therapy before institutionalization. *Psychotherapy: Theory, Research and Practice*, **10**, 281–283.

ROBINS, L. (1978) Sturdy childhood predictors of adult antisocial behaviour. Replications from longitudinal studies. *Psychological Medicine*, **8**, 611–622.

—— & PRICE, R. K. (1991) Adult disorders predicted by childhood conduct problems. Results from the NIMH Epidemiologic Catchment Area Project. *Psychiatry*, **54**, 116–132.

ROSENSTIEL, S. K. & SCOTT, D. S. (1977) Four considerations in imagery techniques with children. *Journal of Behavioural Therapy and Experimental Psychiatry*, **2**, 273–279.

ROYAL COLLEGE OF PSYCHIATRISTS (1990) A report of the Child and Adolescent Psychiatry Specialist Section. *Psychiatric Bulletin*, **14**, 119–120.

RUTTER, M., TIZARD, J. & WHITMORE, K. (1970) *Education, Health and Behaviour*. London: Longman.

——, MAUGHAN, B., MORTIMORE, P., *et al* (1979) *Fifteen Thousand Hours: Secondary Schools and their Effects on Children*. London: Open Books.

SCHAFFER, D. (1974) Suicide in children and early adolescence. *Journal of Child Psychology and Psychiatry*, **15**, 275–291.

SCHONFIELD, I. S., SHAFFER, D., O'CONNOR, P., *et al* (1988) Conduct disorder and cognitive functioning: testing three causal hypotheses. *Child Development*, **59**, 993–1007.

SIMEON, J. G., FERGUSON, H. B., KNOTT, V., *et al* (1992) Clinical, cognitive and neurophysiological effects of alprazolam in children and adolescents with overanxious and avoidant disorders. *Journal of the American Academy of Child and Adolescent Psychiatry*, **31**, 29–33.

SKYNNER, R. (1974) School phobia: A reappraisal. *British Journal of Medical Psychology*, **47**, 1–16.

SMITH, S. L. (1970) School refusal with anxiety: a review of 63 cases. *Canadian Psychiatric Association Journal*, **15**, 257–264.

STURGE, C. (1982) Reading retardation and antisocial behaviour. *Journal of Child Psychology and Psychiatry*, **23**, 21–31.

SWADI, H. (1989) Adolescent substance use and truancy: exploring the link. *European Journal of Psychiatry*, **3**, 108–115.

——— (1992) Relative risk factors in detecting adolescent drug abuse. *Drug and Alcohol Dependence*, **29**, 253–254.

TAYLOR, E. (1993) Syndromes of attention deficit and overactivity. In *Child and Adolescent Psychiatry. Modern Approaches* (eds M. Rutter, E. Taylor & L. Hersov), pp. 185–307. London: Blackwell.

———, SCHACHER, R., THORLEY, G., *et al* (1986) Conduct disorder and hyperactivity. I. Separation of hyperactivity and antisocial conduct in British child psychiatric patients. *British Journal of Psychiatry*, **149**, 760–767.

———, ———, ———, *et al* (1987) Which boys respond to methylphenidate? A controlled trial of methylphenidate in boys with disruptive behaviour. *Psychological Medicine*, **17**, 121–143.

TENNENT, T. G. (1971) School non-attendance and delinquency. *Educational Research*, **13**, 185–190.

TIBBENHAM, A. (1977) Housing and truancy. *New Society*, **39**, 501–502.

TYERMAN, M. J. (1968) *Truancy*. London: University of London Press.

WALDRON, S., SHRIER, D., STONE, B. *et al* (1975) School phobia and other childhood neuroses: a systematic study of children and their families. *American Journal of Child Psychiatry*, **132**, 802–808.

WALLER, D. & EISENBERG, L. (1980) School refusal in childhood: a psychiatric paediatric perspective. In *Out of School – Modern Perspectives in Truancy and School Refusal* (eds L. Hersov & I. Berg) pp. 209–230. Chichester: John Wiley.

WALSH, A., PETEE, T. A. & BEYER, J. A. (1987) Intellectual imbalance and delinquency: comparing high verbal and high performance IQ delinquents. *Criminal Justice and Behaviour*, **14**, 370–379.

WARREN, W. (1948) Acute neurotic breakdown in children with refusal to go to school. *Archives of Disease of Childhood*, **23**, 266–272.

WELLS, K. C., FOREHAND, R. & GRIEST, D. L. (1980) Generality of treatment effects from treated to untreated behaviours resulting from a parent training programme. *Journal of Clinical Child Psychology*, **9**, 217–219.

WEST, D. J. & FARRINGTON, D. P. (1973) *Who Becomes Delinquent?* London: Heinemann.

WORLD HEALTH ORGANIZATION (1992) *The ICD–10 Classification of Mental and Behavioural Disorders*. Geneva: WHO.

YULE, W. (1985) Behavioural approaches. In *Child and Adolescent Psychiatry. Modern Approaches* (eds M. Rutter & L. Hersov), pp. 794–808. London: Blackwell.

———, HERSOV, L. & TRESEDER, J. (1980) Behavioural treatments in school refusal. In *Out of School – Modern Perspectives in Truancy and School Refusal* (eds L. Hersov & I. Berg), pp. 267–302. Chichester: John Wiley.

Commentary on the inclusion of material from the third edition with particular reference to Jack Kahn's contribution

In attempting to bring *Unwillingly to School* up to date by incorporating a group of contributors who have taken a particular interest in some aspect of the problem of absence from school, it was felt that something of the original flavour of the book might be lost despite efforts to include writers on many aspects of the problem. This is why some of Jack Kahn's writings have been retained. His awareness of the wide-ranging causes and consequences of school attendance problems, coupled with his ability to convey the complexities of the subject, make the following four chapters from the third edition as relevant today as they ever were. Nor do the case illustrations appear dated in the light of clinical practice in the mid 1990s. Nowadays, the multidisciplinary team in a child and adolescent psychiatry service includes professional workers who did not participate when Jack Kahn was in practice, such as community child psychiatric nurses and occupational therapists. In many instances social workers, psychologists, psychotherapists and teachers still work closely with child psychiatrists although the relationship is often more mutually independent than it once was.

In the light of more recent findings, Jack Kahn was right in questioning too strict an adherence to the categorisation of school attendance problems since mixed pictures are so common. His interest in the developmental aspects of these difficulties is also very much in line with current thinking. The descriptions of treatment in the case history summaries are little different from what happens now. The importance attached to legal, medical, social, family and individual aspects is as relevant now as it ever was. The need for the active participation of many different professional workers in dealing with any particular problem is also very much in line with current thinking in the subject. Although a 'psychodynamic' approach is less fashionable than it once was, the fact remains that many child and adolescent psychiatric services work very much along these lines so that some discussion of it is well worth including.

Finally, the historical and philosophical aspects of Jack Kahn's contribution are important features of the book and justify its inclusion. It is always interesting to take a historical perspective. The philosophical approach, which constantly adjusts the reader's focus to the conceptual basis of what happens in the clinical setting, is so pervasive in Jack Kahn's writings as to be almost unique.

11 An overview

JACK KAHN, JEAN NURSTEN and HOWARD C. M. CARROLL

The term 'playing hookey' came into use after education had been made compulsory towards the end of the nineteenth century. At that time the term probably covered all forms of absence from school without leave, and it is only recently that the different forms that absence may take have begun to be studied. This may be because absence from school is a symptom of disturbance that cannot be kept secret within the family in the way that night fears, bedwetting or food fads may be. Another reason might be that society as a whole has a share in the problem. Not only are parents sensitive to the problem being brought into the open, but a law is seen to be violated and yet initial counter measures may fail. Further, teachers feel that a child's truancy or fear of school is a reflection on them; and social workers may feel failures when they, too, cannot succeed in getting a child to return to school. Everyone is disturbed by the fact that the child seems to be getting away with something. What is going to happen to a child, one is asked, who does not go to school? What about his or her future career? Will he or she be a normal adult? How can the education welfare officer enforce attendance on those who *really* truant, if it is possible to get away with non-attendance by calling it 'school refusal'? The symptom thus becomes a challenge to the teacher, the education authorities, the social service department, parents, the medical profession and to society as a whole.

Individual cases may present a challenge to professional skills; success is demanded where the parent failed, and the processes in which the parents are involved may be repeated. Professional workers may be equally unsuccessful and may find themselves protecting the family from the demands of reality by being too permissive. In these cases the resemblance of the doctor/patient relationship to the parent/child relationship is particularly important; the doctor comes to feel responsible for the child's continuing symptoms in the face of the doctor's efforts. Psychiatrists often feel responsible for a patient's life if they are aware that the patient is suicidal. The child who refuses to go to school is being self-destructive. Contacts outside the family are avoided, the career is jeopardised, and the future is cut off in a way that could be described as social suicide. Sometimes, awareness of these problems cannot be tolerated and the patient has to be moved some distance away – the suicidal patient and the school refusal child to a hospital. The frustration that this topic raises in different groups of professional workers has a social cause in addition to a personal cause, for it is implicit in our society that there shall be equal opportunities for all. We are upset by those who 'contract out' and apparently refuse to take what is being offered them.

As a starting point, the difference between truancy and school refusal needs clarifying. Once the two concepts have been differentiated, it will be possible later to consider common factors. Truants are usually thought of as children who are absent from school without their parents' knowledge or the school's permission. There are other types who are kept at home by their parents because the children can be of some direct help by their presence within the family. Either the child or the parents can initiate absence from school. If it is the child who starts it, unknown to the parent, it can be called truancy; if it is the parent who openly encourages the child to stay away, it can be called school withdrawal.

By contrast, children with school refusal may want to go to school, but they find that they *cannot*. They are suffering from an emotional problem, which is often based on anxiety at the thought of leaving home. It is because they fear leaving home that they cannot go to school. In fact, school refusal is a misleading term as it is usually only the result of another problem, the source of which is the tie between parent and child and its ensuing conflicts.

Those brief definitions show that quite often the social problem of truancy and the emotional and pathological problem of school refusal can be very different. Absence from school is the factor common to both but they are not just different degrees of the same difficulty. They have different causes and are as different as any two other syndromes. Perhaps this may be seen more clearly if the slurred speech of a drunken man and the stammer of a child with a speech defect are compared. Poor muscular co-ordination is the common factor, but the underlying reasons are very different.

Before going on to consider in greater detail truancy and school refusal, it will be helpful to place both forms of absence from school in their proper context. To this end the next section will deal with the incidence of school absenteeism, reasons for absence and the possible problems associated with the use of labels.

School absenteeism

Evidence for the extent of school absenteeism stems from class attendance registers kept by all schools in connection with the legal obligations of local authorities to provide educational facilities for children from the age of 5 to 16 years and those of parents to cause their children to attend school. These registers are taken in the morning and the afternoon and, when completed correctly, provide a valuable source of data, though, like most data, to be interpreted with caution.

The need for such caution has been well explained. Basically the problem stems from the use of averages, which can be misleading simply because the figures cannot reveal the actual pattern of absences. Two individuals (or two groups) could, for example, have the same attendance rates but differ markedly in terms of when they attended. Thus absence for a whole week differs from absence one day a week for 5 weeks.

Having acccepted the need for caution when looking at average figures, it is now appropriate to turn to actual data. At a national level the range of estimates is indeed a wide one. Carroll (1977) examined the relevant literature and found that between 10 and 24% were absent, with 1.2–8% of all pupils absent for 'unjustified' reasons. He concluded that the age of the pupils surveyed, their sex, the time and place for carrying out the surveys and the methods of arriving at the estimates were all factors that contributed to the wide range of findings.

An examination of the likely reasons for absence makes it possible to see how truancy and school refusal stand relative to these other reasons. A particularly valuable study for this purpose is that of the National Association of Chief Education Welfare Officers (1975) who carried out a survey involving some 27 000 pupils in four counties and 12 cities and county boroughs.

With respect to those children absent during a whole week in October 1973, the education welfare officers in the various locations indicated which of eight possible causes were thought to account for the absences. Not surprisingly, the largest proportion of children were considered to be absent because of illness. Truancy, lateness and school refusal, however, accounted for 3.3, 1.6 and 1.3% respectively of the absent children, with the proportion being far greater at the secondary than at the primary level for all three reasons.

Relative to the other seven causes, 'school refusal' accounted, in fact, for the smallest proportion of pupils absent and only about 0.3% of the total population. On the basis of the fact that in 1973 the school population of England and Wales was about 7.5 million (Department of Education and Science, 1978), it may be concluded that in one school week in 1973 there may have been more than 20 000 children who could have been described as 'school refusers' in England and Wales. Should reaction to this figure be one of disbelief that it could be so high, it is perhaps pertinent to add that this may well have been a conservative figure for, in ascribing causes to the absences, the education welfare officers who actually collected the data were provided with the following instructions relating to school refusal: "Only those cases identified by the Officer of the Authority or receiving treatment by a competent agency such as Child Guidance, Psychologists, etc. disregard woolly descriptions by outside agencies."

Furthermore, in commenting on their findings as they related to this group, the National Association of Chief Education Welfare Officers indicated that the figures were probably incomplete as a result of some absent children being categorised in general terms as 'ill' when in actual fact their absence was attributable to school refusal. Although the National Association of Chief Education Welfare Officers divided causes of absence into eight categories, seven clearly defined and the eighth 'other causes' — what they termed a 'rag bag' category — it is possible to deduce from their comments on their findings that it was not always an easy matter to categorise a child's absence. For example, being aware of the fact that more boys than girls are referred to child and adolescent psychiatric clinics and noting that, in their survey, more of the girls than boys were categorised as school refusers while more of the boys than girls as truants, they asked: "Are some of the male truancies really school refusal, or are we again faced with faulty motivation over the education of girls?"

The first part of their question reflects, in fact, a real area of difficulty in the classification of school absentees. Aside from those who are absent because of physical illness or accident, family neglect or being late or on holiday, do the remainder really fall into two exclusive categories of truants and school refusers? The work of Hersov (1960) seems to indicate that there are situations in which the distinction is a meaningful one. In a comparison of the hospital case records of truants and school refusers he was able to demonstrate that the two groups differed in a number of important ways, the overall difference being that the truants' problem took the form of a conduct disorder while that of the school refusers reflected an underlying psychoneurosis. Leaving aside any challenge to the reasoning through which the behaviour of truants comes to be placed in the diagnostic category 'conduct disorder', it is to be noted that the problems of these children must have been quite severe. That being so, it is indeed meaningful to differentiate between extreme cases of truancy and school refusal. On the other hand, for the far larger number of children who miss a significant amount of schooling and whose personal and family characteristics are such that they are not clearly classifiable as either school refusers or truants, is it meaningful to categorise them in these terms? Certainly, in the field of special education, as shown in the Warnock Report (1978), the move is away from the use of categories.

It is not only those working in the field of special education who have become actively concerned about the use of categories and therefore labels. Some social psychologists and sociologists have pointed out that the use of labels, particularly where deviant behaviour is concerned, has a number of consequences that are not always appreciated by those who use them. Fundamentally, what they appear to be saying is that individuals take on certain characteristics, sometimes in addition to those they may have already, when and only when another – usually a professional person – locates and labels them in a particular way. Thus children categorised as truants become truants not because of something inherent in them but because a professional person decides to call them such on the basis of certain observations about them and probably about their family and home. A child of 10 years of age with a reading age of 6 years on a well-standardised, valid and reliable test of reading can, quite correctly and unambiguously within the British school system, be classified as a backward reader in purely operational terms and without inferring a diagnosis and a cause. However, can one classify less severe cases of truancy and school refusal with the same precision and lack of ambiguity?

Labelling has two further dangers: the child categorised, for example, as a school refuser, on whatever basis, is likely to take on, in the eyes of other people concerned, all those characteristics which they have come to associate with school refusal. It could be argued that, for children described as truants, the danger could be even more insidious because of the tendency to link truancy and delinquency. The final danger of terms such as truancy and school refusal is that they can cause the less well informed to conclude that an identifiable cause of the problem lies in the individual when, in actual fact, the problem is far more complex and can involve the individual and the family, neighbourhood *and* school.

Writers on labelling theory such as Szasz (1961) and Hargreaves (1978) certainly raise important issues that workers in child psychiatry would do well to take note of and consider most carefully. If one does not wish to follow them completely, at least one should go part of the way with them and avoid the uncritical use of specific terms, preferring instead to use less loaded (at the moment) names like 'school absentee'. With that important proviso in mind it is now possible to look in detail at truancy and school refusal, keeping in mind one's reservations about the usefulness of a particular term in emphasising the appropriateness of a specific approach to a problem.

Truancy

Beginning with the persistent truant, it can be seen that when the parents are unaware of the child's truancy, it usually follows that the child has been away from home as much as from school. The parents have presumed that the child was attending school by the child's reappearance at home at the appropriate time each afternoon. This type of truancy is often a comparatively normal reaction to surroundings that are unsympathetic or lacking in stimulation. For instance, factors that can lead to truancy based on unfavourable external circumstances can include situations where the educational pressures have been too high for an underachieving child or, more rarely, where they have been too low for a bright child, or where the home circumstances are poor through the parents being unreliable, lacking in perseverance and routine. Truants of this type are rebelling against frustration felt at home or at school. The needs of a child as an individual have been overlooked. Although truants are often underachieving children, they generally seem robust, adventurous and crave constant change. They have few strong ties and have had a lack of warm relationships in early life. The homes are often broken. The parents have usually little energy left over for interest in the child's welfare, and they are able to provide little discipline. The children are often the victims of material and emotional poverty. The dangers implicit in this kind of truancy are the forms of antisocial behaviour that it almost inevitably leads to in the child's everyday life. The mildest form it takes is lying to parents and teacher when the child is beginning to be found out or, should the child decide to return to school, there may be forged notes from home or attempts to impersonate the doctor's voice over the telephone to offer excuses. The more serious dangers arise from the amount of free time that the child has, once away from school organisation.

Some aspects of this type of problem were shown by Royston, who was seen in a child psychiatry clinic. He was a dull boy of 13 years in a school where he found the work too hard. He had lost interest in lessons and had, in fact, given up trying, because not only friends of his own age but even his younger brother had overtaken him. The parents had separated, and the mother had added to the demands already made on Royston when she told him that she expected him to become the man of the house in the father's absence, and that it was his duty to protect her and his younger brother. She was surprised when he did not accept her suggestion as 'a challenge'. His behaviour deteriorated and he began to truant and later to steal. The mother ended a clinic interview by saying that she had been disappointed in Royston for a long time, as she had dreamed of having a son with talent. This boy had too much expected from him at home and at school. More frequently, the type of child that is kept at home by parents is one who comes from a family where education is not valued and where its compulsory nature is resented. Such families often do not conform to society's other demands, or its usual cultural goals. They are sometimes labelled 'problem families'. Boys and girls alike are kept at home to run errands or to supply the mothering needed by the younger members of the family. An example is provided by a 13-year-old daughter, who was at home during each of the mother's many pregnancies. She cared for the toddlers and was often to be seen in the street, pushing a pram with a flock of the youngest children around her, while the mother walked ahead, rather remote and unconcerned, and with the same pony-tail hair style as her more capable daughter.

In truancy and school withdrawal, education welfare officers have an important role, as it is they who visit the home after discussions with the head teacher. As a result of their later interviews with the child and parents, the problem may be resolved and the child return to school, but the family may still need help. Education welfare officers are able to act as a liaison between the family and the social services. Material poverty can be eased to some extent by the provision of clothing and meals by the education department; educational or physical handicaps may come to light and the child be referred to a doctor; problems of overcrowding may be referred to the housing department, and disturbed children to a child and psychiatric service. In a city the size of Birmingham there are some 4000 children away from school each day; some 50 or 60 of these will be truanting. It is only if truanting becomes persistent that the child's case will be brought before the school attendance subcommittee and, in a few instances, the parents subsequently taken to court. Truancy can be persistent, but it may be prevented from becoming chronic by the diligence of the education welfare officer. Some of the most severe cases used to arise in grammar schools and technical schools as, historically, there had been less routine contact between their head teachers and the school welfare section of the education departments.

School refusal

In the first studies school refusal was observed as being very different from truancy. It was given its own pathology, manifestations and needs in treatment. It was accepted that the truant usually comes from a home where there is emotional or material poverty and is likely to be below average intelligence; but the first cases of school refusal to be recognised came from a materially good home, where the emotional climate was more likely to be intense rather than lacking. Such children usually had at least average intelligence. By now it has become possible to recognise that both truancy and school refusal can occur in children at all levels of intelligence, from every social background, and in families of varied aspirations. The main difference now is the action that follows the distinction between the two forms of school absence, and the main task is to find a meaning for the action in terms of the life of the child at home and in the school.

Just as the word 'truancy' covers different forms, so does the term 'school refusal'. It is a comprehensive, umbrella term. The basis of most conditions is the fear of leaving home, and if the child is pressed to do so, anxiety can amount to panic. School represents the outside world and is a different type of reality from the one that the child has experienced at home. Some children find it too much to face and they retreat to something more familiar. School is often the first place where a child has to get along without his mother's support. Most children can make the change without developing neurotic illness and they find the journey to school filled with excitement, but even so, most of us can recall some of the aids that are used to ward off superstitious fears. We might have avoided the cracks in the pavement or the sight of a funeral, or gained irrational pleasure or momentary horror from seeing a black cat, a white horse or a particular number of magpies. If we can remember such incidents in our own life and accept them, we can see that we each have projected our fears, at some time, on to the outside world and found our own methods of dealing with them.

Brenda, a pupil at a grammar school in the A stream, had to be absent from school because of appendicitis. When she recovered she refused to return, as she said that she feared she had fallen behind with her lessons. The family doctor suggested that she should be transferred to a less demanding school, but after this had been arranged she developed a fear of thunderstorms and hated the big picture windows in the new school, as she could see every impending change in the weather. She also dreaded needlework, which was held in silence in the room with the biggest windows. She then completely refused to attend and would scream hysterically if she were pressed to do so. The fears may be irrational but they cannot be discounted. The disturbed child may, too, be showing a concern experienced by many other children to a lesser degree. They may be pointing out, in an unusual way, the things that many find difficult. Some children focus their fears on undressing for physical education (PE), showers or swimming, and many 'normal' children, who have not been brought up to think of nakedness as ordinary, are reluctant about this, especially in senior schools when they are still adjusting to their changing bodies.

However, looking at the focus of the fears and into the precipitating factors must not lead us into thinking that they are causes. The precipitating factor is likely to be just the most recent, disturbing event that has upset an already predisposed child and made his or her fears the easier to focus. John was a 14-year-old only child who was living at home with his mother and father. His refusal to go to school was the crisis that precipitated his referral to a child psychiatric clinic, but both parents recognised that, apart from this, they had a disturbed son. During the previous summer the boy became self-conscious about undressing for PE, being very tall and gangling. His scragginess preyed on his mind and he would often ask his mother if he were getting fatter. At this time John began to get sore throats, or toothache, on Mondays and Wednesdays, the days PE was held; he also complained about travelling on the school bus, as he did not like the horse-play and the smoking that went on. After the 6 weeks' summer holiday, he could not face the return to school and he began to develop headaches and bilious attacks first thing each morning. When a medical examination showed no physical cause, he was referred to a child psychiatric service by the family doctor. The parents were then seen and they described John as a timid, sensitive boy, who would never stand up for himself; he hardly talked at home and, when he did so, it was in a cheeky or bad-tempered manner. The parents were at a loss. Because of his size they felt unable to compel him physically to go to school, and if they tried to persuade him by argument, he became a whining toddler. The mother was shy and timid and still strongly influenced by her own mother. The father was a tall well-built man with a more vigorous personality, though unable to assert himself at home because of the grandmother's influence; in addition he was getting no satisfaction at work, as a minor technical misdemeanour, in an energetic and organising job which he had formerly held, had led to his dismissal. He was currently in a less responsible job that did not work him to capacity; he was distressed that he could influence other peoples' sons, but not his own, as any conversation he tried to hold with John ended in an argument. The school problem, in the boy's case, had revealed a situation of difficult inter-personal relationships with the family. The physical symptoms, the various aches and pains that he developed, are common in children with school refusal. There is no question of malingering, as the symptoms' emotional origin makes them no less distressing to experience.

Many children with school refusal have similar physical symptoms. They may be particularly faddy over food and often refuse breakfast. They lose weight and may, indeed, even lose the use of their legs. If pressure over school attendance is withdrawn, most of these symptoms go into abeyance, although the children remain maladjusted. Others may be at the beginning of a more complete withdrawal from life; school is just one activity of many from which they contract out. They may lock themselves in their bedrooms and refuse to see relatives, friends or officials. An 11-year-old, Pamela, for example, had gained a place in a school with a good academic reputation with ease, and she was the youngest pupil. At the end of the first term she had a bad cold, but although she dreaded her return she somewhat reluctantly did go back. Being the youngest pupil she was asked to present a bouquet on Speech Day, but this was too much for her to face so she refused, and then began to absent from school. The headmistress tried excusing her from assembly, which Pam had said was too stuffy, but the focus for anxiety altered and Pam's fears shifted on to physics, from which she was also excused. She acted normally after 4 p.m. and at weekends, when she felt the onus was removed from her. She later stayed away completely and, in addition, began to restrict her life to such an extent that she stopped going to the choir, to Guides, Sunday school, her music lesson and even the corner shop. She shut herself in her bedroom and, instead of being her bright tomboyish self, she became quiet, unsociable and irritable.

Brenda, John and Pamela have all been chosen to illustrate particular points, but they each have factors in common that are frequently found in cases of school refusal. One striking factor in many cases is the upset that the children experience in relation to a change of school, especially from junior to senior schools. It seems to be a particularly stressful situation for those who have difficulty in settling down when they have first been admitted to school. It does not seem to be the educational pressure that has been too much for them; it is the totally *fresh situation* that is hard to absorb. The children particularly prone to breakdown at this time are those with a parent ill at home. Boys whose mothers are ill seem to be the most vulnerable. They seem to be unusually dependent on them and overconcerned about them. Often these boys have been alone with their mothers due to their fathers' absence in pre-school days, and the mother/son relationship has become particularly close.

Often the symptom of school refusal, although only one of the modes of pathological expression, points to a disorder of the parent/child relationship. Usually adolescents try to free themselves from their dependence on their parents, to emancipate themselves and begin to accept some responsibility for their own actions and ideas. They still need a secure, tolerant background, against which they can try out their different selves. School-refusing children become, at the same time, both more dependent on home and mother, and yet more stubborn in the way in which they take care of their own lives by refusing to go back to school. They want to grow up, but fear their possible failure in the adult role; they fear their increasing size and strength and the awakening of sexual maturity. Regression to behaviour that was appropriate at a younger stage of development is 'preferred' to the risk of growing up.

There is conflict too, within the parents, who may view adolescence as the time when they lose their child. They feel they have little to offer the new individual who is developing, since with the speed of cultural change, their ideas appear outdated to the child, and yet they cannot appreciate the adolescent's strange new loyalties and friends. Even the term 'teenager' can seem dangerous. For treatment, children with school refusal are rightly referred to child and adolescent psychiatry clinics, as help is needed from the whole professional team.

It was not until some children who had, for any reason, repudiated school along with other aspects of an imposed role were referred to child and adolescent services that the term 'school refusal' came into use. The formulation depended upon awareness that help was needed from the whole team of psychiatrist, psychologist and social worker, and on the assumption that the absence from school had an emotional basis. The criteria were: firstly, the parent is trying to get the child to school, but is unsuccessful; secondly, the child has unreasonable anxiety on a number of topics that other children cope with fairly well; and thirdly, the child has recurrent physical symptoms for which no adequate cause can be found.

Treatment of school refusal as a clinical problem

At the time of the first edition of this book, existing literature was confined almost exclusively to psychiatric, psychological and paediatric journals. We were unable to trace references in publications intended for the general medical practitioner or the teacher. Nevertheless, referrals to the then named child guidance clinics were being made by head teachers, general practitioners and parents themselves. In these referrals it seemed to be implied that once the problem had been channelled into a psychiatrically based service, no other profession retained any responsibility. In similar cases, where such referrals were not made, the teacher or the (then) school welfare officer could only feel secure in maintaining existing practice by denying the existence of an emotional problem in the child. There was comfort in the knowledge that one was doing the right thing, even when actions failed to produce the desired result. For a long time any cases not referred to child guidance clinics remained in no man's land, which lies uncomfortably beyond the areas of medical, educational and social services. The family doctor is now being consulted much more frequently.

Levels of study or description

Human activities and problems can be presented in different ways, and descriptions and terms in which they are expressed determine the kind of treatment that they will receive. All such activities can be experienced and studied in the following ways:

(a) In intrapersonal or individual terms, referring in physical aspects to constitutional and organic factors, and in mental aspects to the psychology and psychopathology of the individual.
(b) In interpersonal terms, with particular reference to relationships with significant individuals in the family situation.
(c) In environmental (socio-cultural) terms, i.e. material resources, such as finance and housing; satisfactions from occupational, recreational and cultural activities; of legal requirements referring to community obligations.

These three presentations will be reformulated later as frames of reference for diagnosis and treatment.

The relativity of diagnosis

The choice of the terms of description depends upon a number of factors and is not based on abstract or absolute principles. Sometimes a particular form of behaviour or problem may be appropriately expressed in one of these aspects alone. More often, all three are relevant. Usually one only is selected by either the subject or the professional worker as the dimension in which there is an attempt to understand the situation. The description in any one of these terms serves as a diagnosis, and a diagnosis serves as a decision for intervention. The level of intervention decided upon may depend on several factors: for instance, the kind of service the problem is presented to, the existing state of knowledge, the resources available, and the acceptability of a particular approach to both recipient and to the agency applying the help.

There is then an attempt to convert the problem into the terms understood by the agency that is consulted and is applying the help.

The problem has been made more complicated by the fact that in some cases the symptoms are perceived as being physical ones and then receive treatment at a physical clinical level, although there is a tacit recognition that the symptoms may have no relationship to the underlying cause of the disturbance. In fact, physical symptoms are sometimes more acceptable to parents and are therefore presented by the child. In other cases, even when the problem is recognised as a severe emotional disturbance, there is the attempt to deal with the social symptom by legal or statutory procedures connected with the school welfare service. One might say that, almost everywhere, experts deal with the problem within the discipline in which they are trained and then, in addition, proceed to give amateur advice in other fields. The teacher and education welfare officer become the doctor and hope that their treatment of the behaviour, which is the symptom, will cure the underlying disorder. The doctor becomes aware of the community obligations and says: "The most important thing is to get the child promptly back to school". The doctor is not always able to say how this can be done.

A restatement of the factors noted in school refusal is needed because the condition is now a paradigm of conditions where a large variety of professional workers seem to have equal claim to the treatment and a degree of success. Such topics, being related to the everyday activities of people, are pronounced upon as authoritatively in newspaper articles and by the ordinary lay individual as by the professional worker. All individuals have had conflicts within themselves, within their family and with the community, and know exactly how they should be tackled.

A developmental view

Some insight into the problem can be gained by looking upon it as a failure in one of the developmental stages of the personality of the child at a point where the child passes from life predominantly in the family to life in the outside world. School refusal can be compared with other developmental stages, particularly the transition from feeding at the breast or with bottle to feeding with solids. There is 'food refusal' in some cases, and the battles and issues, moral and medical, that are built up in this situation are strongly reminiscent of those with a child who shows school refusal.

Conflict within the parent

The psychopathology may be viewed as that of conflict. There is the problem of family interaction, with a varying degree of involvement of particular members. First there are those cases where the conflict is mainly within the personality of the parent. There are parents who attempt to keep their children as babies, and the symptoms satisfy something in the mother who wants to see her children independent but can scarcely let them go from her side.

Conflict within the child

The second group are cases where the conflict appears to be mainly within the child. This is the intrapersonal or individual level of diagnosis. There is a variety of clinical categories of psychiatric disturbances where failure of school attendance is an inevitable consequence. These are anxiety and mood disorders. In some cases, the relationship of these with failure to attend school seems to be a direct one. In others the symptom is merely incidental to the underlying disturbance, which has other implications in addition.

Conflict within the family

There are, however, cases where the conflict shows clearly as an equal interaction between child and parent. There are parents who fail to give any direction to their children, yet expect some kind of perfection to emerge spontaneously from them. With a change in the public image of the parental role, parents who do not wish to repeat what they feel to be the rigidity of former generations may still seek the results that authoritarianism was supposed to give. Sometimes a weak tyrant poses as a permissive parent and, when this fails to produce the desired result, complains about the change in the attitude of society. The parent blames the teachers for not enforcing attendance, takes the child to the police or probation officer, and finds neither sympathy nor a cure for the trouble. The helpless parent, who by now is terrified by the power of the child to defy him, has a child who is equally terrified by the impotence of authority.

The normality of stress at points of change

Some cases are transitory disturbances, which occur as part of the instability that accompanies change of circumstances in all people. Some events in life have been called 'crisis points' because individuals at these times run the risk of emotional disturbance. These stages can be at weaning, toilet training, school entry, change of school, school examinations, puberty, school leaving, entry into or change of occupation, change of residence, marriage, childbirth, menopause, retirement, the loss of friends and the death of people closely associated – all these points where people need to accommodate themselves to a change of status or a change of relationships to other people. Some of these events have been imaginatively called not crisis events but 'stepping stones', and to many people each new stage is an opportunity to develop new levels of expression.

Every such stage has the momentary instability that children experience when learning to walk. There is the leaving hold of some person's hand or of an article of furniture, and there is the prospect or reality of falling before reaching another hand or object. Children who fall usually pick themselves up with determination; needless anxiety is conveyed to them by those adults who are equally uncertain of the next step. School entry is such a stage, and so is change of school. When children enter school the mother may feel that they run the risk of injury, or of contamination by infections or parasites, or that they come under the influence of other children and learn from a teacher, in a way over which the mother has no control. Yet in spite of the worries, many mothers confidently look forward, together with the child, to school days. Some, however, fear them more than look forward to them. They may say to the child: "There is nothing to be afraid of", but the tremor of the voice belies their words. Sometimes this fear is transitory in the mother or child and the settling-in period is brief. There is, however, a danger of reactivation of symptoms at each new stage of school life.

Support without intervention

In most cases, the treatment need be no more than the holding of a watching brief, and the kind of reassurance that makes no pretence at face-saving physical explanations. The mother needs support, not criticism; so does the child. More severe cases need psychiatric investigation and treatment, involving both parents and child. There is no short cut. Removal of a child to a residential school sometimes takes him out of a disturbed family arena into a more consistent setting, but does little to solve the basic problems. Punishment is no use if it is *called* punishment. Firmness by the parent in support of the child is different, but in severe cases the parents do not know how to be firm and loving at the same time. They need help in sorting out their own attitudes. The concerted action of the professional persons, if applied with kindness yet with determination, gives parents and the child the feeling of firmness and support which is so fundamentally lacking in their personalities (Senn, 1962).

Treatment as a process directed to the source of the conflict

Psychotherapy aims at dealing with the underlying conflicts or the specific psychopathology, which includes the ambivalence that is a part of ordinary life. It is necessary to help the parents to face the realities of their feelings and the child's. There are parents who are afraid of the realities of death and so their children dare not go to school, not because of what will happen at school in their presence but of what might happen at home in their absence.

Yet to criticise the parents for their failure to give adequate emotional provision to the child is no more helpful than to be punitive to the child.

Institution-determined treatment

Part of the problem of 'treatment' is the rigidity of the concept of therapeutic procedures within each professional setting. There is usually an attempt to confine it within the limits of one of the dimensions referred to above. Failure of the routine measures leads not to critical examination of the institution but to the referral of the child to another agency from whom success is now demanded. Parents, teachers, education welfare officers, probation officers, magistrates, family doctors, paediatricians, psychiatrists, psychologists and social workers may all be involved at some time. It is important for each to have a concept of their role and of the role of other workers. The greatest danger is to offer or to accept a presentation of the problem in a form in which the procedures are inappropriate or inadequate.

Cultural aspects

Pathology is related to the culture and so is treatment. As problems change in their form of presentation, professional workers who are trained, qualified and experienced expect themselves to be able to deal with the new kind of problem for which they have had no preparation. At this stage it is necessary for them to avoid reacting to the problem with the untrained part of their personality. It is also necessary to recognise that when professional workers give a prescription for action to be taken outside their own field they are acting in an unscientific and sometimes irrational manner.

References

CARROLL, H. (1977) *Absenteeism in South Wales: Studies of Pupils, Their Home and Their Secondary Schools.* Swansea: University of Swansea.

DEPARTMENT OF EDUCATION AND SCIENCE (1978) *School Population in the 1980s.* DES Report on Education No. 92. London: HMSO.

HARGREAVES, D. (1978) Deviance: the interactionist approach. In *Reconstructing Educational Psychology* (ed. B. Gillham), pp. 67–81. London: Croom Helm.

HERSOV, L. A. (1960) Refusal to go to school. *Journal of Child Psychology and Psychiatry,* **1,** 137–145.

NATIONAL ASSOCIATION OF CHIEF EDUCATION WELFARE OFFICERS (1975) *These We Serve: A Report of a Working Party Set Up to Enquire into the Causes of Absence from School.* Bedford: NACEWO.

SENN, M. (1962) School phobias: the role of the paediatrician in their prevention and management. *Proceedings of the Royal Society of Medicine,* **55,** 978.

SZASZ, T. (1961) *The Myth of Mental Illness.* New York: Harper and Row.

WARNOCK REPORT (1978) *Committee of Enquiry into the Education of Handicapped Children and Young People.* London: HMSO.

12 Clinical services

JACK KAHN, JEAN NURSTEN and HOWARD M. C. CARROLL

The route to medical intervention often lies through the family doctor's surgery. In many cases this is where successful diagnosis and treatment begins, but for school refusal in particular, complications arise. Often, the sequence of events for school refusal children, on referral to a general practitioner, is roughly as follows:

The parents are able to justify the absence of the child from school by fitting the symptoms into a medical setting. The doctor examines the child, reassures the child and parents and says there is nothing physically wrong, but appears to treat the problem as a physical illness. The doctor gives the child a tonic and suggests a return to school in 2 or 3 days. The child may get there, sometimes accompanied by the parent to the gate or even into the classroom, but may return home in the middle of the morning or at the midday break.

There is a failure to resume attendance the following day. This is sometimes followed by physical investigation, referral to a paediatrician, hospital admission and even a spell in a convalescent home. On the child's return home the difficulty with regard to school attendance still persists, and by this time the child and the family are terrified that something obscure is present. If child and adolescent psychiatry is suggested at this stage, treatment is likely to be refused and a search for possible physical causes is still demanded.

Familiarity with the term 'school refusal' is leading more and more to direct referral from the family doctor to the child and adolescent psychiatry clinic and many clinics have a high proportion of referrals from general practitioners in their total caseload. Community physicians make speedy referrals. The social remedies that may be exerted by the education department, the juvenile court and the social services department are not automatically called upon. Further consideration of the family doctor's role and the paediatrician's is given later.

Failure in treatment

There are cases that fail by falling between different medical services and the reasons for failure can, firstly, arise from the severity of the underlying condition. Severe psychiatric conditions are states where the prognosis is serious, irrespective of the question of school attendance. Secondly, there can be cases where the nature of the problem is denied by the family concerned and where there is a continued attempt to find physical cause. These are the cases where there are repeated requests for a change of school, usually granted but ineffective, or where there is a constant search for physical abnormalities and where sometimes attempts are made to give irrelevant physical explanations in the hope that these will satisfy. Thirdly, there can be failures of professional techniques on the part of the agency consulted, or a failure of co-ordination of a number of agencies acting simultaneously. Occasionally there is a combination of the above three factors. The following is an example.

Case illustration

Richard was a boy aged 10, an only child with fairly elderly parents. He attended a local authority child psychiatric clinic after first being referred to the psychiatric department of a distant general hospital. The transfer was made because of the difficulty in travelling to keep appointments and it was also considered to be advisable because of the need to keep in touch with the education department. The problem was one of refusal to go to school, occurring during the previous few months. The boy had complained of feeling sick and had to run home after having reached the school gates. He was a pale, small boy and had had a number of other symptoms, some of an obsessional nature.

The original report stated:

> "His knowledge of the outside world is completely coloured by anxiety. If he walks down the street he might get run over. If he eats food outside the home he may be poisoned, if he plays with other children they may hit him. He was unusually concerned with hygiene, insisting on washing his hands immediately prior to eating, and refusing to eat if his father smoked at the table. He refused to eat, too, when he was an in-patient at the hospital for a tonsil operation."

At the time of the referral the family were seriously concerned about their residential accommodation. All three were living in one room in the home of some relatives, and were eating, sleeping and watching TV all in the same small area, with joint use of the kitchen and bathroom with other members of the household. They had had a council flat of their own in another area, but had left it voluntarily because the noise in the neighbourhood was upsetting Richard's sleep. They had planned to buy a house of their own, but the purchase fell through and they found themselves outside the rules of eligibility for local authority housing in either their present or previous area. At an early stage of the investigation, the housing need was presented by the parents, with full justification, as part of the problem, and although representations were made to the housing department of the area no help was forthcoming, as their living conditions were by no means exceptional. Moreover, it seemed strange that having made preparations to buy a house 3 years previously, they still found themselves unable to find anything suitable on their own initiative.

Richard was found to be a boy of average intelligence, but was extremely withdrawn. He expressed a wish to attend school, but a different school from the one where the symptoms had arisen. The parents themselves made several suggestions concerning schools that would be better, but at the same time found reasons why these were, in turn, impossible. The family unit had become self-contained and there was little contact with other people in the neighbourhood, or even with their relatives living in the same house. Richard and his parents attended the clinic over a period of 2 months and then an attempt was made by the education welfare department to apply statutory pressure on the boy's return to school.

Immediately, a private consultation was arranged with another psychiatrist, who arrived at a diagnosis similar to that formed in the clinic, namely that the problem went beyond the housing difficulty or even the expression of physical symptoms. The parents could not accept a different interpretation from their own, and decided that psychiatric intervention should cease and that the next development should be a visit to the paediatric department of a hospital, which Richard still attended at the time of writing. Correspondence between the hospital and the local authority has centred on the family's housing needs and on requests that the education welfare officer should not visit the home. The reports say that there is nothing physically wrong and the boy is suffering from an emotional disorder, but the remedy is to be a physical one and Richard is being given 'nerve medicine'. He still does not go to school.

This is a case where the approach was not acceptable to the parents of the child. The parents' environmental needs were real enough and the clinic was powerless to intervene. Acceptance of housing difficulties as the cause of the problem might have permitted the parents and the boy to continue to attend. At the same time, the possibility of supplying the need in the form in which it was expressed would have given all concerned an excuse for the failure of the case to improve. This has in fact been the subsequent position and his continued failure to attend school was attributed to the housing situation.

The boy's obsessional symptoms, his withdrawn personality and his failure to communicate with other children of his own age were part of the family pattern. The parents felt that the boy was justified in not wanting contact with children who were dirty and rough, but they had no alternative plans that would include contact with children of whom they might approve. Their own social difficulties had been solved by withdrawal and their own dissatisfactions were always caused by the actions of other people. For three of them to live in one room in those circumstances, with financial resources that although not ample were by no means of the lowest level, would seem to indicate a positive choice. Was it more than this family were capable of to be asked to examine their own participation in the problem and encouraged to share in finding a solution? Certainly such ideas were unwelcome to them, and they searched around until someone could be found who would share their own view of what was needed. From the point of view of the clinic it is necessary to ask what more could be done to present, in an acceptable form, a therapeutic process that would take a long time and that was not in accordance with the parents' own ideas on the subject. This case is representative of a number where child and psychiatric services fail and where, unfortunately, alternative procedures are equally ineffective. Without treatment, compulsion may also fail.

Clinical intervention

The teamwork of the staff of child and adolescent psychiatric services drawn from three different professions is itself an example of a multidisciplinary approach to problems. Child guidance procedure, as the service was formerly called, is something that has been built up during the past 65 years to deal with a fairly wide group of problems. Many of the early clinics founded in Great Britain were under the aegis of local education authorities. In 1927 the first British clinic was opened by a religious body, the Jewish Board of Guardians, as part of their welfare work among children in the East End of London. At about the same time the London Child Guidance Centre was set up under a voluntary committee and education authorities were, under a Board of Education decision, able to pay for psychiatric treatment of children, carried out at the Tavistock Clinic.

The impetus to the founding of individual clinics, linked with local education authorities, came from the Child Guidance Council, one of the three organisations that later united to form the National Association for Mental Health. With grants from the Commonwealth Fund of America, a group of social workers went for training in child guidance to the USA, where considerable progress had already been made in establishing clinics on the pattern set by William Healy in Chicago in 1909 and who transferred his work to Boston in 1917. At these clinics it had been proposed that problems of disordered behaviour and of the mental life of children needed a threefold approach – medical, educational and social. Specialisation within these functions led to a team consisting of a psychiatrist, a psychologist and a social worker. It became recognised that in whatever aspect of life the symptom might lie, the treatment of a child needed to take into account life in the school and life in the home as well as the individual aspects of mental life.

The psychiatrist represented the doctor concerned with the physical as well as mental aspects. The psychologist had links with the educational world and was able to give information regarding the child's intellectual potential as well as the educational performance of attainment, because the two may or may not be in line. The psychiatric social worker had the duty of obtaining information about the child's family background, using the parents as informants, but was later able to help the child by using casework as a treatment method for the parents on account of their own needs. Teamwork procedures were built up, and it was on this basis that various kinds of child guidance clinics were subsequently instituted in Great Britain and in other countries all over the world. Some clinics employed lay child psychotherapists in the team. Psychotherapists who worked in child guidance clinics had as training a university degree, experience with children, a personal analysis and some four years of theoretical study at one of the two training centres.

By 1939, 46 clinics attached to education authorities had been founded in Great Britain. Other clinics were attached to the psychiatric or paediatric departments of general hospitals or teaching hospitals, and a very small number of clinics organised by voluntary bodies remained.

The 1944 Education Act made provision for special educational treatment of pupils suffering from handicaps of various kinds such as defective sight, defective hearing and intellectual defects. However, the main purpose of the regulations, apart from the ascertainment of the defects, was to see that these children received the most suitable kind of education. Emotional maladjustment was added to the list of handicaps and it was made the duty of each local authority to make provision for special education in such cases also.

There was considerable change in the ideas underlying provision for handicapped children of all kinds. It had seemed to be a basic assumption that most of the handicaps were permanent and not amenable to treatment in themselves. While that may be true in the mechanical sense, it is also true that in almost every handicap there are considerable areas in which development of personality is possible. When education and treatment are combined in a way that allows children to utilise their own levels of ability, while receiving the most suitable stimulus in the form of educational and social experiences, considerable changes may occur. This is particularly true of emotional maladjustment. It was recognised that ascertainment and educational placements were not enough. Psychiatric treatment had also been provided and, although many clinics were originally founded as an educational provision, the links with the school health services allowed them to develop therapeutic facilities for the benefit of the child and the family. (For a full history of the child guidance movement see the *Report of the Committee of Maladjusted Children*, Ministry of Education, Underwood Report, 1955.)

The National Health Service Act was passed in 1946 and came into operation in 1948. It gave the responsibility for treatment of all kinds to the services that were organised locally by the regional hospital boards. It then became possible to separate ascertainment, which remained (along with special education) the responsibility of the education authority, from treatment that became the responsibility of the regional hospital board. In some localities, the school psychological services became separated from the child guidance clinic, and in other areas new clinics were set up by hospital boards. There were some districts where the psychiatric services of the clinic were disbanded before fresh ones could be set up under the new scheme of organisation. It was then that a few regional hospital boards offered to supply local authority child guidance clinics with the services of a psychiatrist. In this way the 'joint' clinic was born, providing the basic pattern of clinic organisation. The local authority provided the building and the services of the psychologist, social worker and sometimes a child psychotherapist and remedial teacher, and the health authority provided the consultant psychiatrist. The nature of the problems referred to these clinics went far beyond those that formerly would have been considered a medical concern. The team approach is justified by the inclusive nature of the treatment offered for a wide range of problems. Treatment of such width and depth would be very onerous for a single professional worker to carry out. The significance of the child guidance clinic team approach lies not only in the range of treatment offered to the patient, but also in the support it gives to the individual worker who is called upon for help in such diverse disease. A team is not formed by merely pulling a number of people together. It needs activity as a team and the sharing of a common language and even philosophy. Its essence can be said to be the study and the professionalisation of the use of relationships. A danger that must be guarded against lies in allowing this co-ordination to reach such a point of specialisation that communication with outside workers becomes difficult.

The value of a team is due in no small measure to the fact that each member has some share in shaping the final diagnosis, which is the decision for action. Nor can the child's treatment be something separate from the remainder of his life, which is spent at home and in the school. Decisions that involve alteration in school and home circumstances therefore necessitate participation of the teacher and parents too. It is unsatisfactory to make decisions where the responsibility for carrying them out is to be handed to someone who has not shared in the discussion of the problem.

The essence of the team approach is that its appropriate member takes the most prominent part in each particular treatment planned. Thus it is not the head of the clinic who automatically takes on the main burden of the treatment, but rather it is the different level of diagnosis, be it individual, interpersonal or environmental, which determines this. Treatment may be limited to one factor, but there are also many cases when all three aspects of disturbance can receive simultaneous treatment.

The making of a diagnosis can be part of a therapeutic process, i.e. investigations can be carried out in a way that may clarify the problem for the parent as well as for the professional observer. Moreover, the way in which investigations are carried out involves the use of interpersonal relationships, and these may be the very areas in which the child and parents feel disturbed. They may have been accustomed to provoking and receiving hostile reactions from professional people and it is necessary to avoid allowing the investigation in the clinic to become a repetition of previous damaging experiences.

Five examples are described below in some detail, but the general principles guiding treatment at different levels and with different participants are discussed in later chapters. In each of the cases described, there was close contact with the family practitioner. There was an attempt to diagnose the underlying pathology, which led to a variety of treatment plans. The examples are based on real situations, but some details have been changed.

Illustrative cases

Case 1

Sandra, aged 9 years: a case suitable for short-term treatment with mother and child by a social worker and a psychiatrist. The family doctor stated:

> "Sandra was happy at school until her move from the Infants' School to the Junior School. Since then she has made many scenes about going to school – screaming and throwing herself on the floor. Questioning her gives no clear indication of her dislike of it; she does not want to go, she does not like being shouted at, and it makes her feel 'funny' – this is as near the truth as I have been able to get. She is not apparently upset by the other children. She is distressed by Assembly when there is rather a crush, and we were able to have her excused from this some time ago."

The mother, seen by the social worker, cried and twisted her handkerchief throughout the interview. It seemed that life was just too much for her. The father has an ulcer and has to have a special diet. The mother felt that it was all she could do just to keep going if she had no problems. Sandra was spoken of as a nice-looking girl who "answered well when spoken to, but she has become temperamental" and often "upsets me, after which she sulks, but then apologises. She takes things too much to heart." There is another child, Diane, who is 6 years of age.

When seen by the psychiatrist, Sandra reluctantly agreed to draw, saying her sister Diane was able to draw very well. On a second interview both children were brought and both occupied themselves drawing while in the waiting room. Sandra drew a snowman while Diane drew a snowman plus a house and a girl, and one wondered if Diane always overtook Sandra in performance. Although Sandra was self-depreciating, she showed a wish to be in the limelight, and her favourite drawing was of a single dancer framed by a proscenium arch. Sandra's picture of herself and her wish to excel were discussed with her on a superficial level. With her mother, some benefit was obtained by ventilation of her anxieties about some of the very real troubles through which her family was passing. In four visits Sandra and her mother had achieved sufficient relaxation to justify cessation of regular appointments, with the proviso that they could approach the clinic if they felt it necessary. No further approach has been made, and enquiries at the school through the educational psychologist indicated that the position is satisfactory.

Case 2

Derek, aged 12 years: a case suitable for long-term treatment of the child and parents by a psychiatrist and a social worker. The family doctor considered Derek sufficiently disturbed to justify a domiciliary visit. The doctor presented the following notes:

> "First seen by me for this illness one month ago. Complaining of feeling dizzy, tingling all over, cannot breathe, throat feels blocked (for all the world like an adult hysteric). I have not seen a picture like this at this age in my experience of fifteen years. On examination, nothing abnormal detected. Diagnosis – hysteria. I had a long discussion with him and the parents and his very sensible school master, and much reassurance was given to the boy that there was nothing to fear; everyone was on his side. There would be no punishment and he could safely confide in his master or parents. He improved temporarily. Last Monday the whole condition flared up acutely; he retired to bed, could not breathe, had night terrors and was quite unable to go to school. We can hardly leave him like this much longer, hence my plea of urgency. The father is a very pleasant man, trying with partial success to understand his son, whom I think he frightens. The mother, herself recently depressed and neurotic, is also a very nice person."

More of the history is contained in the following report to the doctor, just after the psychiatrist's visit to the home:

> "I saw Derek and his parents at their home and the home visit was justified both by the intensity of the symptoms and the fact that the symptoms in their acute form are more likely to respond to treatment . . . The immediate symptoms were that Derek had been complaining – as mentioned in your letter – of dizziness, tingling sensation, inability to breathe, and feeling of constriction of the throat. He had improved a little, but after the half-term holiday he felt unable to return to school. He had been lying in bed in a state of panic. The parents told me about the boy's fear of choking and stated that he swallowed some chewing gum recently, and felt that it was still in his throat. On one occasion he drank out of a chipped glass and was convinced that he had swallowed the missing piece. His father wondered whether these anxieties had begun at the age of 18 months, at the time when the younger child was born. The father took Derek to stay with the maternal grandmother 200 miles away, during the time of the other child's birth. At the grandmother's suggestion the father left the house by the front door,

while she distracted the boys attention at the back of the house. During his stay at the grandmother's the boy became seriously ill and delirious, and at one point was not expected to recover. After his return home, he did not wish to let either parent out of his sight. Derek had always been a bad sleeper and even now will not fall asleep until he has seen both parents go to bed. He will come downstairs several times to make sure they are still in the house. Once they are upstairs he falls asleep without trouble. School entry was difficult. He had to be dragged to school, by his mother and this continued for a whole year. He subsequently settled down at school until the change to Secondary School. This involves a long journey by bicycle, and the mother claimed that she is not unduly nervous about this. The mother, nevertheless, strikes me as being a very anxious individual, who is made more anxious by the boy's symptoms and who, therefore, reinforces the boy's fears. She appears to be able to make an easier contact with the younger child, Elizabeth, who, incidentally, is a couple of inches taller than Derek. The father has been at a loss to deal with the problem and has carried a load of guilt since the incident at 18 months. The result of this has been that, although blustering at times, he has been inconsistent in giving the boy the normal authoritative framework. This case is one of a large group of problems of school attendance. The clinical diagnosis is hysteria and the underlying process is a failure of organisation of the personality. Parental anxiety and inconsistency interacts with the new pressures of secondary education, and we have had to recognise that the problem goes beyond the additional complication of adjustment to adolescence. Derek will be accepted for treatment along with his parents."

Case 3

Mark, aged 9 years: a case suitable for the main treatment to be by the social worker with the parents. The parents themselves referred Mark on the suggestion of the head teacher, but the family doctor was brought into the picture immediately and he was well aware of the problem. When Mark started school at 5 years, he had cried bitterly at first, but after a few weeks settled down. On a move to another area he settled well at his new infant school, but was reported by the head teacher to be very quiet and withdrawn. At the junior school, difficulties began after an attack by a gang of boys who damaged his bicycle. He refused to go to school for a while, but later resumed attendance when accompanied by his mother. He would cry on the way to school and also during the day while actually in school. The doctor wrote:

"This child apparently makes persistent scenes when he is going to school. He cries a lot but will not say why. Some time back, he was the victim of a certain amount of bullying. While he used to cry at school as well as on the way, he now confines his woe to the journey there. He seems a nice child to me, though I gather from letters from a former school mistress, that he was never particularly intelligent. I think some of his trouble may stem from the fact that his father, who has had some medical training, tries to analyse all their minds too closely and is rather a domineering character. Mark's older sister has also been to me at one time on her father's suggestion, because of her anxiety state.

Since I have known her, the mother has always been very highly strung and rather afraid of her husband."

The following are extracts from the initial psychiatric report.

"The parents stated that difficulties began in June this year at the end of a week's holiday. Mark refused to go to school the following week and wept when pressed to go. On arrival at school he complained of 'tummy ache' and was sent home and when taken to you, nothing physically abnormal was found. After a few attempts to maintain attendance the teacher felt that they could do nothing for him, as he wept all day and upset other pupils. A fortnight before the end of the summer term, he stopped attending school. The class teacher and the head teacher were sympathetic but found the problem to be without explanation. At home, immediately the boy was told he need no longer go to school that term, the symptoms stopped. At the end of the summer holdiay, the boy again became anxious. In the meantime he had been transferred to a nearer school but there was still difficulty. He manages to attend school as long as his mother accompanies him all the way. Mark is the younger of two children. His sister attended a grammar school, and is now working as a secretary. The father works in a highly specialised technical post. He has gained promotion in his work. He had been brought up in a religious and strict household. The mother is two years older than the father and had a deprived childhood, having been orphaned during infancy. She was in domestic service after leaving school and she feels inadequate in comparison with her husband. The family situation is that the father and daughter can feel identified with one another, and the mother feels to have no place and no purpose in the home, except in relation to Mark. If Mark became independent of her, she would feel to have no justification within the family. The problem is one of 'school refusal' in which the underlying process is in the relationship between the child and his parents. Mark is a small child having a bright appearance but with some degree of timidity. Mark tries to fulfil his parent's separate needs. He attempts to make models and drawings which he offers to his father for criticism, and his father then seeks to help him achieve a perfection which is beyond the boy's capacity. The models are never satisfactory until the father takes over the making of them. I discussed with the father the need to find something within the boy's capacity that he can find approval for, rather than to seek to make the boy conform with his picture of what he himself might have been like. With regard to the mother, the boy's symptoms have been of value in keeping the boy dependent upon her."

In this case it was considered that most of the work necessary was with the parents. The father for a time continued to justify his attitude of helping Mark to achieve more perfect standards of school work, whereas Mark, when he attended school, was more likely to attempt to gain attention by clowning. He frequently approaches father and mother for affection, and they give it. It became evident that what he was seeking was the approval rather than affection, and approval seemed to elude him. During the course of interviews, the marital problems of the parents became the dominant theme, and whereas both parents had been ready to discuss what they could do to help

Mark, their real need for each of them was to achieve some satisfaction in their own lives. While trying to help Mark, each parent had been attempting to fit him into a mould that was shaped by their separate moods. Mark was trying to do the impossible thing of satisfying demands that were incompatible. The boy and the parents were seen at regular intervals over a period of 13 months, when the family situation improved sufficiently for the case to be closed.

Case 4

Alistair, aged 9 years: a case where environmental change was appropriate, along with treatment of the mother by the psychiatrist. Alistair was the fourth of a family of four boys, there being a 5-year age gap before he was born. The parents were a little older than the average parent of a boy of Alistair's age. When first referred to the clinic at the age of 8 the parents were interviewed by the psychiatric social worker to whom they stated that the problem occurred following a rebuke during class by a new teacher. On the following day, Alistair went to school but returned home at 9.30 a.m. not having got as far as the classroom. He was immediately taken back to school by the mother, who took him to see the headmaster. After this he showed some reluctance to go to school, wanting the mother to take him each morning; and since then either she or the father had done so. Alistair seemed happy each day on his return from school. He expressed great dislike of assembly, held every 2 days and on these occasions had run off from school several times without being noticed. Although previously a healthy child he had begun to complain of headaches or migraine, and on several occasions these ailments had kept him at home. He was said to complain of the noise in the school yard before school begins, and disliked making his way into the building. In consequence, his mother often took him right into the school building, handing him over to a teacher. Reflecting on Alistair's minor ailments, the parents stated that they thought he had had a tendency to migraine since he was 5 years old, i.e. when he had started school. The parents said that Alistair had a number of nervous habits — nose picking, nail biting, and when upset in any way he became very quiet. Alistair was born at home after a fairly difficult and prolonged labour and was a large baby. Both parents had hoped that he would be a girl. The parents were worried about him and determined he should attend school. They were somewhat critical of any action of the teachers, to whom Alistair attributed the reason for his wish not to attend. Shortly after the interview with the social worker, an appointment was made for Alistair and the parents to see the psychiatrist, but the parents wrote saying that he was much better and they thought that seeing a psychiatrist might cause a setback. A further referral was made 1 year later, when the boy had run out of school where he had been left by the mother in the care of the head teacher. He dashed out of the head teacher's arms so quickly that he ran across the road in the path of a motor-car and narrowly escaped being run over. On this visit to the clinic the mother gave account of many of the details of the school arrangements, which had been altered several times on her suggestion in order to accommodate the school life to Alistair's needs. Somehow or other the changes never made the position better, but it appeared that the changes had never been made *exactly* in the way that the mother hoped. There was an expectation that the psychiatrist should at this stage begin treatment with the boy "to find out what had been causing it", so that the parents could be informed how to deal with the problem. In this case, it was felt important that the boy should *not* be seen subsequently by the psychiatrist. Arrangements were made for the boy to attend a remedial teacher, dealing with a small group of four or five boys in a free atmosphere, with various practical activities as well as lessons. He attended this class without trouble three half-days a week, and continued with his attendance with varying degrees of difficulty at his ordinary school. The parents were seen by the psychiatrist, and although considerable pressure was applied by them in order to change this routine, the arrangement was accepted and maintained by the parents, who in the end benefited by the psychiatrist's ability not to be manipulated. Although both parents were unusually competent socially, each had deep anxieties about illness and death. It could be safely stated that Alistair was afraid to go to school not because of what was happening at school when he was there, but because of his fear of what might happen to one of the parents at home in his absence. This fear was not one that was confined to Alistair alone – the parents' anxieties were being actively and continually conveyed to the boy. The mother's forceful personality was a façade covering a good deal of tenderness, which she had felt unable to express in a masculine household. To have given way in the clinic to her domination would have been damaging to the feminine side of her, yet a brusque brushing aside of her fears or a criticism of her failure would have been equally injurious. She needed the knowledge that her vigour might be resisted and, at the same time, that she herself could be accepted. This was a case where time was on the side of therapy, and the boy's natural process of growth and development gave her a better reward than his previous closeness to her. His compliance with her unspoken demands to remain near her, which was in conflict with her verbal instructions to get off to school, was succeeded by a degree of independence that did not completely separate him from her.

Case 5

Michael, aged 11 years: a case suitable for intensive treatment for the child by a psychiatrist with supportive interviews for the parents by a social worker. The family doctor stated:

> "I gather that on going to each new school he has had some trouble in adjusting himself to the change. Now that he has gone to the comprehensive school, where the machinery seems fairly large to him, he is at his lowest ebb. He is unsure of the boys and his own ability, and any harsh word from a teacher leaves him

completely unable to cope. He seems intelligent, but unable to make friends and not worried by this. I would be grateful if you could help him to adjust himself, and I have prescribed a small dose of minor tranquillizer in the meanwhile."

The following are extracts from the psychiatric report sent in reply:

"Michael and both parents were seen by me. They gave an account of difficulties regarding school attendance from the age of 5 onwards. The first occasion was associated with the fact that he had been locked in a w.c., and that the teacher in charge of the playground had had a loud voice. After six months this teacher left the school, and Michael had no trouble for a short while. The family moved to their present address when Michael was 6 years old; then he had measles, which kept him away from school for nearly one term. When he began school in the new term he was afraid of other boys, and used to sob each night and again each morning before going to school. Again the trouble settled down, but a year later, when moved to the annexe, he again complained that the teacher had a loud voice. He cried at night, had diarrhoea, headaches and picked up other complaints, such as colds and tonsilitis, which provided justification for his being kept at home. The present trouble is associated with his transfer to the large comprehensive school. It is said that on the first day, the form master spent the morning telling the boys of the Do's and Don'ts – the discipline of the school – and Michael came home terrified. He returned to school in the afternoon, but sobbed all night and refused to go the following morning. The mother visited the headmaster and was asked to bring the boy that afternoon, but the mother had difficulty in getting him across the entrance to the school. That night he seemed happier, but two days later began to have diarrhoea. He was away for a few days and then went to school the following week, still having diarrhoea each morning. He was less worried about the form master but had anxiety about each master in turn as fresh subjects were introduced. His fears finally remained fixed on one master only. Michael is the elder of two children, having a sister aged $5\frac{1}{2}$. His developmental stages were said to be normal and the mother described the pregnancy as being normal until the father revealed that she had been sick all day and every day, and had vomited until she had brought up blood. Michael teethed early and began to suffer from dental decay, having to have extractions at the age of 3. Four teeth were extracted on each of two occasions, and on the second occasion he screamed and subsequently refused to see any dentist. He was thought to have tonsilitis after the younger sister was born, but the doctor considered it due to what he called nerve trouble and it cleared up. After the move to their new address, he had a swelling in the neck due to a blocked salivary duct. He was admitted to hospital, but as the swelling had gone down no operation was performed.

The father is an individual of unusual personality, who probably finds difficulties in his relationships with many people. Many of the details of the medical history were given in a way which implied blame on different people. He had a religious conversion at the age of 18 and had done Church work and Youth work. Michael sometimes rebels against the father's religious doctrines, and is inclined not to participate in the family prayers which his father holds. He is able to ask his father questions on religion that the father is unable to answer. The mother is an anxious individual, who speaks intensively with a deep voice. In his interview with me, Michael kept his face averted from me at the beginning. He talked readily, but evaded the topic of his anxiety. He is in the third stream at school which is the lowest of the streams and he is finding difficulty in mathematics and science. He does not like playing rough games with other boys. His main leisure interest is his train set. Michael is suffering from a personality difficulty, which finds expression in the symptoms of school refusal. The physical symptoms are due to a conversion reaction and are triggered off by incidents or by difficulties at school. The underlying problem, however, is that of abnormal relationships between the family as a whole and anxiety in the enclosed family circle. Michael is somewhat rebellious, and this gives us hope that he may be able eventually to achieve a better adaptation to the outside world. At the moment the responsibility for all difficulties has been successfully attributed either to faults of other people or to physical illness. Cure can only come when the child is able to accept some responsibility for his part in the problems. Treatment is likely to be resisted at first, and at this stage we may have to be content with the usual sequence of improvement as he settles down, with perhaps another recurrence at a new stage."

Michael continued to attend the clinic in spite of the doubt as to the acceptability of treatment and was seen each week by the psychotherapist. The parents were seen less frequently. Unusual views were expressed without self-questioning, and the father described visions, which the boy also saw, in a matter-of-fact way. Michael continued to attend school, but one would be cautious about predictions of his ultimate level of adjustment.

13   The need for a multidisciplinary approach

JACK KAHN, JEAN NURSTEN and HOWARD C. M. CARROLL

School refusal is a disturbance that illustrates the problem of the boundaries of medical concern. Physical illness poses no such problems. Its recognition follows a well-defined practice. The patient complains of a symptom, and the doctor looks for and finds a sign that confirms some altered body activity. The doctor prescribes a treatment that, if successful, restores the patient to the original state of good health. For each symptom there is only a limited range of signs to look for, and it is part of the background of examination and treatment that no more of the patient's life is examined than is necessary for this purpose. The doctor's professional relationship is limited to the area of the patients life that is concerned in the illness, and no unnecessary questions are asked. It is assumed that, even if patients have some dissatisfaction in some other aspects of their lives, they do not wish to be asked questions about it unless they are seeking to have something done about it. Although it could be part of medical skill to be sensitive to areas of disturbance other than those that are first presented, a doctor does not intrude *personal* opinions about the patient's marital, occupational or social shortcomings. This is the essence of the professional relationship within the field of medicine. Professional persons in other fields, too, have a role in a limited area. They enter into a close relationship with the patient (or client), use their skill for the benefit of the patient and receive payment for this either directly from the patient or from some community organisation on the patient's behalf. They do not go beyond this relationship.

There is no problem as long as illness is thought of in terms of physical disturbance alone. However, when the disturbance is in the behaviour, the thoughts or the feelings of an individual, boundaries of relevant questions and examinations are harder to draw. If the symptoms of the disorder include disturbances of relationships with other people, then the relationships that will be established between the patient and the therapist are inevitably affected by the disturbance. Thus professional helpers or therapists are unable to stand the disturbance and be objective in the way that they can be in the diagnosis and treatment of physical illness.

Patients themselves distinguish between what seems to be a limited disturbance and those that are disturbances in their essential personality. A patient may say "My kidneys are troubling me", and there is no doubt that the implication is that the "me" which is being troubled is something separate from the physical self. Another patient may recount a whole list of physical complaints and then add "and I do not feel well in myself".

Although doctors are liable to be consulted about disturbance of feeling and of behaviour, they are less certain of their professional role. A further difficulty in such complaints is that the help may be sought not by the individuals concerned but by others on their behalf. A patient suffering from a phobia may prefer to deal with the problem by avoiding a situation in which the symptoms appear. A child with school refusal might prefer to avoid school rather than seek treatment. Parents, education welfare departments and other representatives of the organised community have a duty to enforce obligations such as school attendance, and this concern may take the form of seeking treatment for the child. It is, in any case, a part of normal community organisation to arrange for the enforcement of laws and to provide penalties for non-observance of the law.

Whenever a treatment is suggested for a condition called to attention because of non-observance of the law, it has to be decided whether the disorder can be recognised as a clinical condition irrespective of behaviour or whether the non-observance of the law is in itself considered to be a disease. In the latter case therapists are expected to accept the community standards of normality as their own. They must not give preference to the declared aim of the individual whom they are called upon to treat if that aim is at variance with community obligations. Nevertheless, as clinicians they have no power to enforce or impose any predetermined type of behaviour or attitude to society. All they can do as clinicians is to help patients to see the motives and consequences of their behaviour in a new light.

When disturbed behaviour is accepted as a medical concern, doctors have to go beyond the ordinary bounds of medical enquiry. Their questions go beyond the physical processes and functions of the body. They enter into the same field as the parent, the teacher, the parson, the policeman and the magistrate, but doctors' means are different. Wootton (1963) has stated that

"Today moral problems, marital problems, and problems of deviant behaviour [are] constantly brought into the doctor's consulting room. In every broadcast discussion on moral issues, be it teenage sex, illegitimacy, adoption, or anything else, the presence of a psychiatrist now tends to be thought indispensable."

It is sometimes implied that psychiatrists have no limits to their enquiries, but some limitations there must be. Perhaps the limitations should be that no enquiries should be made, and no information should be permitted to be divulged, unless it is going to be useful in the treatment that the therapist has to offer. The limitations thus become the *relevance* of the information that is given, or sought, *to the treatment* which the therapist can carry out. There are communications that may be offered and accepted in a psychoanalytical framework, where they become the basis of interpretation, but these same communications would be inappropriate in a therapy that is based on adjustment of the environment.

In a general way the aim is to understand the whole human but, to do that, observers would have to stand outside themselves. The 'whole' human would include relationships with other people, not excepting the observer. We sometimes believe that we are examining the whole human simply because we are beginning to extend the accustomed areas of investigation. The process of diagnosis is thus seen to be the result of investigations within an acknowledged framework. Diagnosis, moreover, needs to be related to some subsequent decision of procedure that can be called treatment, otherwise it could become a private system of thought which cannot be communicated to others outside the system. Formulations are therefore the process of learning about that section of the patient's life which is unsatisfactory and for which some alteration is being sought. Are we entitled to call any disturbance an illness if the individual does not present it to some medical agency for help? Ryle (1963), in a survey of his own general practice, found that he referred 8% of the children in his care to child guidance clinics. This, although in accordance with estimates of the need for referral made in the Underwood Report (1955), is ten times the national percentage of referrals to child guidance clinics. He asks the question whether the effect of arrival at a clinic through a referral (and the acceptance of the referral), as against the non-arrival of presumably similar cases, should be the criterion for the kind of treatment offered in child guidance clinics?

Here we must state clearly that there are not, and there are not likely to be, sufficient child psychiatric clinics, or staff to serve them, for the number of patients that would be referred if every doctor was presented with, or dealt with, a similar proportion of cases. We must state frankly that we do not know the fate of the presumed other nine-tenths. It may be that no one complained or that no one notices that complaints are made, or it may be that some alternative procedure is adopted. There is no reason to assume that those about whom there is no complaint fare well. Such knowledge as we have is confined to the cases that are presented for diagnosis and treatment, and even those may meet with different kinds of therapeutic procedure in different types of clinic or therapeutic agency to which they may be referred.

All workers, however, are in agreement in the belief that they deal with only a fraction of the total incidence of the type of problem brought to them. It is felt there is inadequate provision for existing demands, and therefore thought is given to ways of adapting the services to meet the present and potential load. Suggestions are made that it would be more efficient for psychiatrists, child psychotherapists, psychologists and social workers to come out of the clinics and work with general maternal and child welfare clinics, school clinics, teachers and others whose work takes them into the daily lives of large numbers of children at the point where special problems are liable to arise. This may well be the point at which progress can be made and many experiments are being carried out in this direction. There is the hope that problems which can be recognised at an early stage would be easier to treat and also the possibility that contact of psychiatric personnel with other professional workers would be a kind of in-service training.

One needs the warning that such experiments need to be conducted from the base of a strong clinical service, because wherever psychiatric personnel venture out into other professional fields their colleagues seem to gain the courage to make more clinical referrals to be dealt with at a purely psychiatric level. Prevention with regard to psychiatric problems is an elusive process as compared with physical illness, where there often appears to be a relatively simple cause impinging upon the life of a hitherto normal person. Emotional disorders, however, do not seem to have a beginning because individuals are born into families where conflict already exists and where the disorder bridges the generations. The value of taking psychiatric personnel into various allied fields might be that of providing the background knowledge from which concepts can be built up jointly with other workers, and the result would be that preventive mental health work would become a function that lies outside the profession of psychiatry. Ideas of mental hygiene similar to those of physical hygiene could evolve and this would be the professional area of those such as health visitors, school doctors and teachers who ordinarily work with the healthy population, as well as those in whom some disorder is suspected.

The extension of preventive services (which would include sensitisation to the presence of established disorders at early stages) needs a framework of diagnosis that must be related to a theory of the development of personality. It is necessary to have knowledge of the importance of emotional factors during development, and disorders then can be linked with the personal and family history. In some cases disorders will be thought of as a result of prolonged damaging experience, and in some cases it will be considered to be due to the absence of provisions that are necessary for normal development. In this latter sense emotional disorders must be considered as deficiencies, and one has to ask not "What was it that went wrong?" but "What was it that did not go right?"

Child and adolescent psychiatry services

The authors' view is that progress will come from a recognition that satisfactory therapy is not a single process. The disorder should not be treated as a single symptom that can be cured by removing the form of expression. The disorder is one which is related to the personal, family and environmental life of individuals, and the general scheme of the treatment must cover all the areas. The final aim must be a shared therapeutic process. Where the disorder can be considered the result of deficiencies in satisfactory relationships at critical stages of development, treatment must be the provision of experiences that have been missed. This becomes a kind of maturation process. It is therefore like growing up, and consequently it takes time.

Such a therapeutic process may be undertaken at a psychiatric level in which the individual learns to make an adaptation to family and society as well as to personal needs, but it would seem feasible to bring the environmental services into the treatment instead of regarding them as fixed points to which the individual must adapt. If the family and educational background are to be made therapeutic, these also must be capable of adaptation and the parents and teacher should be able to examine their separate participation. They should be able to examine their attitudes to themselves and to examine the concept of their own role rather than saying: "This *child* must be made to attend school, obey, become independent, concentrate."

Only too often the parent, the teacher, the education welfare officer and the magistrates arrive at decisions that seem right, but which are unsuccessful in their aim; and, being right, they go on feeling that they have no option but to give the mixture as before in stronger doses.

With the teacher, for example, it might be helpful to recognise that this is a problem that necessarily reflects the child's total attitude to the school. The roots of the problem may be elsewhere and alterations in the educational process are unlikely to have a positive effect. In fact alterations that are made for the purpose of curing the symptom are more likely to do harm because of the implied acceptance of an incomplete presentation of the problem. The question can then be asked: "What is the range of the emotional disturbance that can be *resolved* in the school, and what are the problems that can *be prevented* in the school?" These are questions that are now being considered in the training of teachers. The building up of a philosophy of education which includes the study of a wider range of aspects of personality development is occurring as in other professions.

Failure of school attendance is a problem that has compelled families, schools and representatives of the organised community to examine the basis of their attitudes. It is no longer acceptable to say that because the system works well enough for the overwhelming majority of children, there is no need to question it for the sake of a small proportion who, for some reason, do not fit in. As a community we have become concerned with the small minorities who fall outside the normal range either in their interest, equipment, in their experience, or even in their response to normal obligations.

We are concerned because we no longer think of the small minority as showing a process that is separate and distinct from the remainder. We acknowledge that disturbance is not an all-or-none process but proportionate, and that the same processes which occur in those who are apparently distinctive (because the symptoms show) also occur in some degree in those who are symptom free. It may even be fortuitous as to which particular individuals suffer a symptom. We are more than ever one community that includes the strong and weak, rich and poor, healthy and sick: we accept the responsibility for those who begin life with handicaps or who become inadequate temporarily or permanently at some point of their development: we are more ready to accept emotional and social disturbances as requiring help. We are beginning to recognise that sometimes the disorder seems to lie mainly in the individual, sometimes in the family relationships and sometimes in the interaction between the family and society. There are times also when it is the environmental process (in this case the educational process) that seems to be the area which requires adjustment.

It has already been suggested that the nature of treatment varies with the way that a problem is envisaged and formulated. The place of the child and adolescent psychiatry clinic has been emphasised and yet it must be recognised at the same time that there are many areas of this country where child and adolescent psychiatry provision is insufficient. The Court Report (1978) placed new emphasis on the child guidance team and on co-operation between the various services concerned with child health. The following substantial extract is therefore given from the DHSS Health Services Development, Court Report on Child Health Services:

"Further progress needs to be made in the integration of child guidance and hospital psychiatric services for children and adolescents. This does not mean fusion of all existing services into a new one, but rather that there should be co-ordinated planning and working. The psychological, psychiatric and social services for children, adolescents and their families need to be brought together so that in-patient, day-patient and hospital out-patient care, services in centres outside hospitals, and consultative services to schools, to social services provision, and to other services form a comprehensive whole. Staff from the National Health Service, the Local Education Authorities (primarily their School Psychology Service) and Departments of Social Services should continue to work together as multidisciplinary teams working at an agreed local base. Where the base is in the community the team may be identified collectively as the child guidance team: this phrase should be understood as having a functional rather than an institutional meaning. Members of the team from all disciplines should spend a substantial proportion of time working with schools and other community agencies as part of a comprehensive service. They should also maintain close links with their 'parent' services. Child psychiatrists need to have links with other medical services especially general psychiatry and paediatrics. It would facilitate this if they all had a hospital appointment (either a linked or honorary appointment in an appropriate grade) at least for a small proportion of their time. It is not however acceptable for social workers to be employed on an occasional basis: a full-time commitment to the team should be the usual arrangement.

In Ministers' view there should be both formal arrangements at an administrative level to ensure joint planning and organisation of services — the planning exercise that has been carried on locally as a result of the 1974 circular can perhaps be regarded as a pilot for this — and also collaboration between all the services involved on a personal level, for example through joint or linked appointments or informal contact on a day to day basis."

A problem nevertheless remains. There are times when there is demand for a distinction between a clinical disorder and disturbed behaviour. When the appearance of a form of behaviour is held to be a symptom of a clinical disorder, there are requests for criteria with which to discriminate those incidents that call for treatment by legal machinery by the personal social services from those that will be referred for psychologically based treatment. The distinction cannot be made on the success of one or other procedure because failures occur with all. People recognise the appropriateness of surgical and medical treatment of physical conditions even when the conditions are thought in advance to be incurable. The prediction of incurability does not absolve medical or social services from the responsibility for the care of people who suffer.

Similarly there are many people who behave in an antisocial way who are subjected to various judicial processes, being fined or imprisoned without any alteration in their social conduct, and in practice there may be no constructive alternative to those procedures. The decision for the application of the different procedures should come from the meaning that can be given to the behaviour in terms of the individual's inborn qualities, developmental history, experiences and relationships with other individuals in the community, and in terms of the resources available for the primary processes of provision.

Human problems may be described simultaneously in more than one set of terms and it may be possible or necessary to carry out treatment on more than one level. The development of individual capacity on a personal level, within a community, presents individuals with complex problems and conflicting demands. There is a need to develop the capacity for individual expression and satisfaction and, at the same time, the need to restrict activities to a form that is acceptable to the community. When there is a disturbance of adaptation to community living, consideration may be necessary for both the individual and social component of the problem.

There are limitations to the effectiveness of any single approach whether it be educational, social, legal or clinical. The value of the child and adolescent psychiatry contribution is that it is the agency which goes furthest towards a comprehensive approach. It is manifestly wrong to accept environmental or physical explanations for a disorder in which there is a continuing emotional disturbance. Yet this frequently happens.

Where a single approach is applied and maintained in the absence of improvement, the choice of that approach is often affected by the social class of the person concerned. School refusal was recognised first in children of middle-class families where individual consideration was more likely to occur than remote administrative decisions. The distinction between truancy and school refusal is still less likely to be recognised in lower social classes and so-called problem families, and the term 'school refusal' is still more likely to be used for children in families with whom it is possible to enter into a co-operative exploration of the various factors involved. Since the problem demands the team approach, both in the clinic and between agencies, it is necessary for all the professional workers involved to ask how far the present practice meets the needs. Advance is likely to follow from consideration of the following.

(a) The training provided for the different professional workers should be relevant to the therapeutic procedures undertaken. In many professions individuals trained and qualified for their job are unjustifiably expected to undertake procedures that are unrelated to their training.

(b) Problems dealing with the emotional aspects of personality drain the emotional resources of the professional person concerned. This impact on the professional worker gives rise to the need for support. This support or renewal can come from extensions of the training or from co-operation with colleagues in other professions of a level of equality. Without the support of training, or of a team, the defences are likely to be a denial or evasion of the true nature of the problem.

(c) The child and adolescent psychiatry clinic offers:

   (i) A clinical service. This is the main function.

  (ii) A consultative and advisory service acting in co-operation with other agencies. This is not a substitute for clinical service but should be a means of extending the range of problems that can be dealt with within the boundaries of professional work of other departments.

 (iii) Theoretical concepts regarding the development of personality and the meaning of disorders which penetrate into the general culture as part of the interchange of knowledge between different professions.

 (iv) The philosophy of the shared approach. The framework of the clinic carries the medical tradition of making an examination of a presenting disorder that leads to a rational diagnosis and to treatment procedures based on the diagnosis. Medical or clinical authority, however, should never be used with regard to levels of examination in which members of the clinical team have had no training. It is as wrong for the medical person to make an authoritative decision on a social problem as for members of social agencies to come to decisions on clinical disorders. When a diagnosis includes clinical, social and educational factors it should be a shared diagnosis.

(d) Liaison with other agencies means that each will need to examine the procedures it uses and the way in which co-operation will affect them. When the prescription for treatment is likely to be carried out by another agency or person, that agency or person should have as great a share in the diagnostic process as possible. Those who are satisfied with the methods that they already use are unlikely to be prepared to change them. A professional worker may wish to deal with a problem by excluding those who do not fit in with a particular setting, or by requesting treatment that would alter a child in a way that would make him or her acceptable in the framework. The alternative is a process of consultation in which the setting as well as the disturbance in the child can be examined concurrently. In the words of Lord Adrian (1963), which hold good today:

> "Training the mind to stand up to all the hostile experiences of childhood and adult life involves problems outside the sphere of organic or of psychological medicine, problems for parents and teachers, and for the society which has set the standards of behaviour. *Ensuring mental health and a useful life for each individual is in fact a priority for the whole community* ... In time it may become one of the highest priorities in clinical medicine, but we must wait for further developments before this can happen." (our italics)

There is, nevertheless, a considerable amount of knowledge that we already have and there is no justification for withholding the professional practice which is based on that knowledge. The most valuable tool which exists at present is the joint participation by workers of different disciplines who have built themselves into a professional team. The next step is to reformulate the theoretical ideas that the members of the team took with them into child and adolescent clinics and to translate them into a form that is utilisable by other professions who are called upon to deal with similar problems in other professional settings. Every action is affected by the nature of the situation in which it takes place. Theory has to be selected and applied within a frame of reference that is applicable to the situation.

Professions have boundaries in which they have authority to act. The authority may come from a long tradition that is accepted both by the professional worker and by those who are the subjects of the worker (server and served). The authority may be newly granted on a statutory basis by changes in the law which may be designed to extend or improve the social services. There are also the boundaries and limitations of financial provision, whether this be direct payment on a private basis or the indirect payments made through local or general taxation to salaried professional workers. Beyond all this, the workers need to have a competence that is based on some theoretical formulations which can be conveyed through training.

It is the formal expression of ideas that allows professions to become distinguished from the general unorganised friendly support within and between families which was the precursor of social services. Professions thus must develop their own specialist knowledge and techniques and, at the same time, develop the ability to communicate with other professions about problems in which they share responsibility.

In the topic of school refusal there is always something new because the study of social problems utilises the current themes that occupy every profession at the point where it is growing. *Unwillingly to School* was originally written by a psychiatrist and a psychiatric social worker. It was not to be expected that any members of any other professions that were referred to in the preceding pages would be able to accept the account given as representing their own image and, in any case, the account must be incomplete. It is hoped that what has been written may provide a stimulus for different viewpoints to be expressed by others, while at the same time giving support to the idea that they will become integrated into a comprehensive view of multidisciplinary work with the problem of school refusal.

References

ADRIAN, LORD (1963) Comments. *Proceedings of the Royal Society of Medicine*, **56**, 825.
COMMITTEE ON CHILD HEALTH SERVICES (1978) Fit for the future (Court Report). London: HMSO.
RYLE, A. (1963) Lecture to the Association of Child Psychology and Psychiatry. London.
UNDERWOOD REPORT (1955) Report of the Committee on Maladjusted Children. London: HMSO.
WOOTTON, B. (1963) *The Law, the Doctor and the Deviant.* London: Allen and Unwin.

14 The psychodynamic approach and frames of reference

JACK KAHN, JEAN NURSTEN and HOWARD M. C. CARROLL

Within multidisciplinary work one of the most important contributions of child guidance clinics in their early days was the introduction of what became called the psychodynamic approach. The word psychodynamic referred to forces in the mind, and it was assumed that the disturbances of thought, feeling and behaviour, which were dealt with, could be understood as an altered balance of mental processes.

Some clinics operated on psychoanalytical lines, emphasising the dynamic conceptual model but not excluding others: structural, economic, historical and object relations. Some were based on other schools of psychodynamic psychology (Jungian and Adlerian being the main alternatives). Some were eclectic and were subject to the criticism that its members placed themselves above all the separate schools, presuming to select the ideas or phraseology on personal good judgement or whim. Others, still under the eclectic label, acknowledged the discipline of studying and experiencing a particular school and, using that experience as a base, extended their practice by absorbing into themselves the concepts of a variety of schools.

Members of the three professions in the staff of early child guidance clinics (psychiatrists, psychologists and psychiatric social workers) had an original profession (medicine, teaching and social work), and it was the shared interest in the psychodynamic approach that turned them into a multidisciplinary team. All could (and many did) practice psychotherapy as a result of further training and experience. Some came straight into child guidance following a training within their field.

A fourth profession gradually grew up with a specific training in child psychotherapy, for specialist work with children, and with a commitment to the treatment facilities of the clinic. Child psychotherapists now have their own professional organisation in the UK (Association of Child Psychotherapists), which includes members of different training schools. Child psychotherapists distinguish themselves by their concern with the patient's 'inner world'. They are concerned primarily with the treatment of emotional disturbance in children and young people, but they also work in a consultative capacity in a variety of settings that touch the growing individual. In *The Child Psychotherapist* (Boston & Daws, 1977) Dora Lush explains how this member of the team helps the child to recall early emotional experiences that seem to have shaped the child's present difficulties and disturbances. Using case material, including a case of 'school refusal', she demonstrates the work that takes place directly with the child and the close collaboration with colleagues in the team. She concludes:

> "Psychotherapists do differ amongst themselves, but all have a great deal in common, namely their orientation towards the unconscious meaning of behaviour, thoughts and feelings as the crux of any solution. Apart from his child psychotherapist's knowledge of child development and unconscious processes it enables him to make a valuable advisor contribution to the work of a clinic generally, and to many other institutions and settings concerned with the education and welfare of young people."

The psychotherapeutic process

Each school of psychodynamic psychology has its own corpus of recorded utterances and theoretical structures. There are, however, some common principles of psychotherapy that can be discussed under the headings of transference, communication, interpretation, insight and utilisation.

Transference

Psychotherapy is a difficult process for individuals who cannot confess their need for relationships with other individuals. It might be a relationship with another individual that is felt to be the abnormality, or it might be some inner feelings of distress or anxiety in those cases where the ordinary defences are ineffective. The seeking of relief from anxiety can become the motivation for psychotherapy.

Psychotherapy begins when individuals feel the need for help and find that they may obtain it only by selecting a particular therapist. Thereby, the beginnings of some kind of relationship with the therapist is necessarily formed. Within this relationship there develops a repetition of previous behaviour and experiences, which had occurred in relation to other individuals in the patient's life. The relationship with the therapist begins even before the patient and therapist meet, because all individuals have some image of the person they expect to encounter, or of the person they think would supply their needs. The therapist is expected to fill this image, but the image itself may contain contradictory factors. The therapist is expected to be able to understand all the patient's thoughts and to be powerful enough to impose his or her ideal pattern of normality on to the patient. Patients want this, yet at the same time would challenge any idea that this could in fact be possible. They resent the idea of having their thoughts pried upon and their life manipulated.

All individuals have had some similar ideas during infancy in relation to their parents. They had endowed their parents with the power to read their thoughts, in both benevolent and hostile roles. They begin to repeat their infantile fantasies at this later stage of their life when they enter into the relationship with the therapist. They may feel warm to the therapist in the belief that they are going to receive benefits, and in the recognition of the therapist's wish to help. They may feel hostile to the therapist in the disappointment with the therapist's failure to live up to this image or, contrariwise, in the face of the therapist's attempts to do so! These feelings are called transference relationships because they are, at least in part, transferred by the patient to the therapeutic situation from previous relationships. There are positive and negative transference feelings. These are not separate stages, but they are experienced simultaneously, although one or the other may predominate at different times.

Transference feelings are not exclusively a feature of therapeutic situations. Every relationship in an individual's life is affected in some way by expectations derived from previous experiences. The special feature of the psychotherapeutic situation is that these things are discussed openly. Thus, during the course of treatment, links can be shown to exist between the feelings and behaviour that are being expressed in the present and previous feelings and behaviour that are recalled from the past. Patients become able to identify and isolate some of the irrational parts of their day-to-day behaviour. They then eventually become able to take responsibility for the consequences of their own acts, instead of blaming the effects on something in their past or on the actions of other individuals in the present.

The process of psychotherapy includes a number of other features, which all occur against the background of relationship referred to above. For instance, counter-transference enters into the relationship. Psychotherapists are not passive observers. They have their involvement, which derives from their own past experience, and there must be some irrational component in this. The therapist should continually seek to be aware of this component and be prepared to discuss it with the patient along with the material provided by the patient.

The relationship between patient and therapist has, in addition to the transference features, some qualities in its own right. All individuals grow in their personalities through the taking in of qualities belonging to the individuals with whom they are in close relationship. Children take into themselves the qualities of their parents. This applies also to patient and therapist, and some of the relationship involves the taking in of qualities from the therapist as an individual acting in his or her own right, and not merely as an object to whom feelings are being transferred. Sometimes, when patients are deficient in satisfactory parental figures on whom to model their life, they take in something from the personality of the therapist as a first time experience.

Communication

The above are non-verbal communications and interactions, but some of the communications are in words – patients make their presentation of their complaint, or their denial that there is anything wrong with them. They may ask questions of the therapist, or they may reply to questions that come from the therapist. They give an account of the background of their lives and they describe their present situation and their problems as they see them. Within limits, all this is possible for adults; but communication is an emotional process and children may find it difficult to speak freely on what it is that disturbs them. Children have become accustomed to presenting problems in the way that they believe adults expect them to do. They may be unfamiliar with the right to express their own feelings. When children are taken to a doctor because of some physical ailment, they may expect their mother to tell the doctor where they feel the pain. When the doctor asks the child some questions, the child looks at mother before replying.

Symptoms, even when reported accurately, are reported within a framework that is provided for the child by the adult world. Symptoms become a means of communication of feelings of distress, to someone who is trained to understand them. If there is an attempt to convert symptoms that are presented to us in one form into another kind of expression, it cannot be expected that the translation will be accepted easily. When an individual is complaining of a pain or sickness, and the therapist believes that this presents anxiety about an intolerable situation, this may not be so readily believed by the patient. There are, however, many ways of communication. Physical symptoms may be symbolic representation of an emotional state. There are colloquialisms in everyday speech that recognise this; everyone knows what is meant when someone says, "Charlie makes me sick!" There are, in fact, people whom, and situations which, do make one vomit. A person may be a "pain in the neck" or a problem may be a "real headache".

Other kinds of symbolisation depend upon the use of art forms. Music can express and communicate emotion, while drawings and paintings can convey feelings as well as meanings. Children are accustomed to drawing and to playing, and these activities have a number of functions. They can be enjoyable in their own right or they can carry children's recollection of previous situations. They can be used to portray or to play out the plans for future activities, or they may be a means of communication with another individual who is expected to participate. The psychotherapeutic process with a child includes the use of painting, drawing and playing of various kinds. The art product and the play are not therapeutic in themselves; they can be part of the process of communication within the framework of the therapy.

Interpretation

The material communicated becomes available as part of the treatment if its meaning can be interpreted by the therapist to the patient. Interpretation can be used by the therapist for communication, too, and communication is therefore a two-way process. Interpretation can be verbal or non-verbal. There may be a direct recounting to the patient of the apparent meanings of the communications from the patient, but the behaviour of the therapist in acceptance of the communications may also have an interpretation value to the patient.

Insight

Insight is not an intellectual process in which the patient learns the equivalent meanings of a set of symbols. It is an understanding, reached from the first time, of the range and depth of alternative meanings that our thoughts, feelings and behaviour can express. It involves a reconciling of opposite, and a toleration of ambiguity and of double meanings that our actions can involve. Such understanding can only be achieved with the relief of some emotion that had previously closed up within the defensive system. When the achievement of insight is accompanied by obvious expression of emotion, it is called 'abreaction'. Sometimes this 'abreaction' is looked for as the main vehicle of therapeutic progress. It should not, however, be the end of treatment. The cure takes place not in the therapist's room but in the ordinary life of the individual. It is here that individuals must be able to release and utilise the emotions that were locked up in the disturbed pattern of mental life which their symptoms represented.

Utilisation

Making use of insight is the test of cure, which can be said to exist when patients are able to take responsibility for their feelings, their thoughts and their behaviour, and when they do not need the shelter of evasions, denials or symptoms. Thus psychotherapy becomes a way of taking more responsibility and should not be lightly undertaken. Psychotherapy may be carried out by a psychiatrist. Some of the casework of social workers, quoted elsewhere, has much in common with psychotherapy, utilising a psychodynamic approach, although many present-day social workers seek their professional inspiration in other forms of psychological and sociological theory. Psychologists, likewise, may derive their professional image from their choice of the psychodynamic schools or from alternative theories in academic psychology. Thus for the psychiatrist, the social worker and the psychologist, psychotherapy offers a treatment method for which an additional training of varying degree of completeness may be taken, but it is a deplorable fact that many professional workers undertake a practice that they call psychotherapy but for which they have not sought any preparation. This is a problem of which Freud became aware at the early stages of his work. He makes mention of a time in 1904 of physicians in hospitals who gave an order to a young assistant to undertake a 'psychoanalysis' without troubling to enquire about the actual procedures that Freud used. He compared it with a passage in *Hamlet* (Act 3, Scene 2), where Hamlet suspects that Rosencrantz and Guildenstern have been sent to discover his secret thoughts. Taking a recorder from one of the players, he passes it to Guildenstern and asks, "Will you not play upon this pipe?" Guildenstern protests that he has not the knowledge. Hamlet replies:

> "Why, look you now, how unworthy a thing you make of me! You would play upon me; you would seem to know my stops; you would pluck out the heart of my mystery; you would sound me from my lowest note to the top of my compass; and there is much music, excellent voice, in this little organ; yet cannot you make it speak.'Sblood, do you think I am easier to be played on than a pipe? Call me what instrument you will, though you can fret me, yet you cannot play upon me."

At a later stage we shall attempt to demonstrate that some principles of psychotherapy have passed into the possession of a variety of professions, and that through psychotherapy there is a greater public awareness of the nature of emotional problems. The formal practice of psychotherapy, however, requires respect for the intricacies of the human personality and, consequently, requires a disciplined training.

Theoretical framework

Two points have become abundantly clear. The first is that, notwithstanding the pioneer role of child guidance clinics in the identification, understanding and treatment of school refusal, there is no prospect that child guidance clinics will ever have sufficient staff to deal with all the cases that could possibly be referred to them. The second is that a number of other professional services have an involvement in, and responsibility for, some aspects of the problems of the child and family in cases of failure of school attendance. The school psychological service may have been the first point of contact for the school, and the educational psychologist may then have taken on the task of dealing with the problem. The family doctor may be consulted by the parents as mentioned previously, a specialist paediatrician may be brought in or the social service department may have an original involvement with the family or be brought in later to carry out statutory duties following court proceedings. The education department (administration, teaching staff, counselling service and education welfare department) has a continuing responsibility. There is a need for a theoretical framework in which to enclose the activities of all these different professional workers – not borrowed from psychiatry with its utilisation of a medical model and not merely dependent upon views of child upbringing and family relationships. Each activity should have its justification and authorisation within the professional practice of the worker concerned. Therefore, it is necessary to offer a chart of different frames of reference within which it is possible to make observations, draw conclusions and act, in a coherent sequence.

The first frame of reference is based upon the medical model in which there is a complaint (the *symptom*); an examination (distinguishing characteristics or *signs*); a pathology (altered structure or functioning, i.e. *anatomical* or *physiological* changes); and a cause (the *aetiology*). The pathology gives a basis for treatment; the aetiology for prevention. This medical diagnostic model has been transferred to mental illness and fits some regular syndromes except that, in the absence of a physical pathology, a *psychopathology* is described. The psychopathology is distinguished from the normal psychological processes in a way that follows the relationship of pathology to the normal anatomy and physiology. The medical model thus is used in the figurative sense when applied to mental disorder. It is sometimes used even more remotely from physical medicine when we speak of social pathology, and when we ask how to recognise, treat or prevent some undesirable behaviour. It is, however, possible to preserve some rationality in the use of the diagnostic medical model if we recognise that there are different dimensions of diagnosis: diseases, dysfunctions, deviations and descriptions.

Diseases are specific entities, each of which are separable from the normality of the individual and separable from other diseases. This is best exemplified in the acute illness, which is an episode in the life of an otherwise normal individual. The patient was well, is now ill, will receive treatment and, one hopes, will be well again. Some mental disorders can fit fairly comfortably into this dimension, but for most disordered mental states there is not sufficient separation of symptom from the features of a normal personality. Moreover, even for some physical disorders this dimension is inadequate for the disabilities of a chronic illness that resist treatment, and which persist into the family and working life of the adult or the school life of the child.

It is necessary to come to terms with the fact that mental illness requires a different conceptualisation from that of somatic medicine. The rational principles of diagnosis need modification when applied to disturbances of thoughts, feelings, behaviour and relationships. Aetiology is never a single cause; there are a number of components that operate within a matrix of the constitutional factors which we call the temperament. The present state must be related to past experiences in terms of beneficial and harmful events; deprivation must be related to provision, and it may also be necessary to speculate on the way in which crises at various developmental stages can make an individual more vulnerable or more resistant to present stress. In order to consider all these factors, a new dimension of diagnosis (Kahn, 1969, 1971), different from that of specific diseases, needs to be invented.

This dimension is that of *disorder of function.* The question here is not whether a person has or has not got an illness. Rather is it the question of which activities or performances are adversely affected. Most chronic diseases, whether of soma or psyche, fit into this second dimension.

There is yet a third dimension, that of *deviation from a statistical normality.* This applies particularly to behaviour that is considered to be abnormal and also to some clinical syndromes which are merely an intense form of an experience common to all humanity. In this third dimension the complaints are relative to the culture, to race, religion, colour, social class, geographical area and the epoch in time in which one lives. What is normal or abnormal varies from district to district, from generation to generation. Descriptions form the fourth dimension, in which the words as presented by or on behalf of the patient, are translated into Latin or Greek, and a new word becomes the diagnosis. The value of using a descriptive word, which adds no new information, comes from the belief that what is named is understood. Thus, *difficulty with words* becomes *dyslexia*; and *overactivity* becomes *hyperkinesis* or, more simply, *hyperactivity.* The danger of using this dimension comes from the belief that all cases of dyslexia (or hyperkinesis) have the same pathology and the same aetiology. It becomes a barrier against exploring the non-medical (social or education) aspects in the child and the interaction in the family. The consideration of these dimensions has implications for treatment. For *specific diseases* we think in terms of cure, and the responsibility is purely medical.

Disorders of functions enter into various living activities and the treatment is shared by those who have skills in particular areas. Children live and grow in the family, in the school, in the neighbourhood. Other professional services are involved with their individual, family and educational life. *Expression of the disorder is multidimensional, the causation multifactorial and the treatment multidisciplinary.* It is proper to speak of intervention in any single area as 'treatment', and thus we have remedial education, speech therapy, physiotherapy as well as psychotherapy. At the same time, the child and the family might be involved in receiving the benefit (or otherwise) of administrative, legal, religious and environmental services.

In *deviation from the normal*, particularly where behaviour is concerned, there may not necessarily be a medical contribution at all. The treatment may be purely legal or social action. The aim is to bring the behaviour into conformity. An alternative aim might be to enlarge the public tolerance of the behaviour that is described as abnormal. In such instances, professional workers may have an educative function as when reporting on a single case or, in their public role, when they take a share in the shaping of popular opinion. The deviations are not the exclusive domain of the child psychiatry clinic or hospital unit and many problems of thoughts, feelings and behaviour are neither medical nor psychiatric until someone makes them so. The psychiatrist comes into the study of some human problem only by invitation and this invitation may not be wholehearted. It is as if the psychiatrist is expected to claim authority in every problem of living, only to have that claim challenged even while his or her help is being sought.

With regard to *descriptions*, the main task is to accept the professional responsibility for redefining a complaint in more appropriate terms, which can be related to treatment. Thus, in some cases, where there is a recognisable pathology, the notion can be transferred to the dimension of a specific disease. In others, the dimensions of dysfunction or deviation may be more appropriate and the professional responsibility may lie with different services concurrently or consecutively, according to the way that the disturbance is perceived. Gradually, however, in passing from diseases to deviations, we have been emerging from the diagnostic frame of reference, and other frames of reference become applicable. In these alternative frames of reference, we no longer seek the polarities of normality and abnormality.

In the diagnostic frame of reference it was assumed that abnormality can be distinguished from normality and that there are separate varieties of abnormality. The diagnostic labelling is a step towards finding an appropriate treatment.

New theoretical frameworks

Other frames of reference are appropriate in cases where distress is connected with:

(a) Interaction with others who are participants – *relationships*.
(b) Stages of individual development – *maturation*.
(c) The absence of necessary supplies required to maintain life at the different stages of development – *provision*.

These three frames of reference will be elaborated, but there remain social, political and economic frames within which it is possible to study the background in which distress is experienced and where help may be provided. There is also the religious frame of reference, in which human beings seek meanings of existence and ideas of purpose.

The choice of frame of reference may become a choice of what action, if any, is to be taken when complaints are made. It may happen that a framework is chosen in which the scale is so large that any possible action can only have a minimal effect on a particular case. Such a choice is made to justify action on that larger scale, or even to justify inaction on the grounds that only a change in the structure of society could be effective. For our own professional work we concentrate on adding the frames of relationship, maturation and provision to the diagnostic framework. This does not exclude us from involvement with activities in other frames of reference in our personal and public lives.

Relationships

It is possible to enter into the framework of relationships in order to benefit an individual suffering from a disorder. The target of treatment is not the disorder itself, but the relationships of an individual with a family or some other grouping. Relationships have their polarities: isolation is opposed to interaction. The word 'interaction' can be changed slightly to alter a degree of approval or disapproval: for example co-operation, interdependence, dependency, inadequacy, in descending order on the scale of approval. So too with isolation: withdrawal, solitude, individuality, independence, in ascending order. Thus one should leave behind ideas of normality and abnormality (in the sense of disease entities) for the specific purpose of group therapy or family therapy. The group process has been utilised in treatment, in counselling and in an educational setting (Thompson & Kahn, 1970) and in residential settings (Ward, 1993).

Group therapists have drawn on a variety of theories for their practice: individual psychotherapy; sociometric techniques; learning theory; and existential philosophy. In practical methods there are variations ranging from spontaneity in word and deed to carefully controlled measures directed towards a predetermined aim. Family therapy is a rapidly developing practice that now has a profuse literature. It would seem that many family therapists have little in common with one another other than the label under which they operate. Theory and practice varies, some looking upon the family as pathogenic and seeking to rescue the identified patient from its painful influences, others looking for the hidden strengths of a divided family in a manner comparable with those psychotherapists of the individual who direct their efforts to the positive features of the patient's personality. Just as individual psychotherapy recognises ambivalence (the simultaneous love and hate within the individual), some family therapists recognise the family as a unit that has simultaneous integrating and disruptive forces. The therapy is directed to the family process; it is not the simultaneous treatment in one another's presence of the individual pathology of the separate members of the family.

Maturation

This framework is utilised whenever the question of landmarks of development is raised: "Should he be walking? . . . talking. . . able to read?" The expectation is that certain stages of physical maturation, and certain capacities, should be present at specified ages. There is also the idea that certain stages of development are in themselves a vulnerable phase where instability is to be expected. The stages are cultural and biological, and include school entry, a change of school, puberty. It is thus necessary to be familiar with stages of development from a number of viewpoints.

(a) Norms of development derived from measurements of stages of growth and attainments of special skills in a child population. The child is compared with a broad range of children of the same age.

(b) The different factors of personality (physical, intellectual, emotional) grow at different rates. Even within physical structure alone, different tissues reach final maturity at different ages in the same individual. For example, Tanner (1962) gives charts of rates and growth of skeletal, central nervous system and reproductive systems, showing that, in early adolescence, the growth of these tissues is out of phase in that different proportions of the final adult composition have been reached in the separate tissues.

(c) The rate of growth in girls differs from that in boys.

(d) There is a widely held impression that growth ceases at the end of adolescence when adult life is set to begin. This applies only to physical growth, which is limited by the completion of skeletal development (earlier in girls than in boys). However, intellectual and emotional development may continue in various ways throughout life.

(e) Piaget & Inhelder (1969) have given stages of cognitive growth where, instead of comparing one child with a population, it is possible, and profitable, to ascertain the point at which a young person has arrived in a sequential scale of development.

(f) Emotional growth is referred to in the historical model of psychoanalytical theory. Erikson (1950) has added a cultural dimension in his eight stages, each of which encloses a task to be performed in adaptation to external demands.

The maturational framework includes the polarities of immaturity and maturity, each term, when slightly altered, being able to convey either approval or disapproval, according to context. This development frame of reference has been enthusiastically taken up as the basis of a method of treatment in crisis theory.

Provision

Surprisingly, the polarities of provision and deprivation, also, are not the equivalent of normality and abnormality. The word deprivation, which is sometimes used as a description masquerading as a diagnosis, should refer to the absence of some specific provision that is considered to be necessary for normal development. Necessary provisions, however, are envisaged in relationship to what is available in any particular culture, and therefore provision is a relative term. Deprivation, too, has values attached to it, even to the extent of the adding of a moral component, with the implication that deprivation helps to build character. We shall, therefore, avoid the use of the word deprivation and, instead, attempt to describe the primary processes of provision which we consider to be essential. We shall give three and then add one more.

(a) *Nurturing.* This means food, clothing, shelter, protection from injury and disease, and providing treatment if these should occur. Nurturing also includes the non-material provision of love. But love is none the less physical because, in order to be conveyed, it involves touching and being touched. Nurturing is given first because, without it, the infant cannot survive.

(b) *Teaching.* This means the bringing of the perceptions of the external world of people and objects to the infant, and then giving the words, which are the names of the people and objects. Just as the child's physical growth depends upon food, intellectual growth depends upon people, objects and words – the words standing for the people and objects in their absence and forming the material of subsequent complex thought.

(c) *Training.* This involves the do's and don'ts that are brought to the infant in the prohibitions and obligations in behaviour. These three primary processes are provided, in the first place, in the home, continued in the school and, later, in various ways, in adult life. At school there is nurturing and discipline as well as teaching. Nurturing continues in adult sexual relationships and in family life, and there is an extra entitlement to it when a person is physically ill. Teaching and training continue each time people enter into a new social or occupational situation. There are also implications of these three processes in most forms of therapy that do not aim specifically at some identified pathology. This is expressed in confidently made statements, such as:

> "I know what that child needs, he needs love."
> "I know what that child needs, he needs a different school."
> "I know what that child needs, he needs discipline."

Any one of these statements may have good justification. Any one of them may be used in the case of failure of a school attendance. What is often lacking, however, is the perception of the value of each component in the balance of all three. At this stage we wish to add a further primary process of provision: experimenting.

(d) *Experimenting.* Nurturing, teaching and training give to each infant the possessions of the previous generation. Nurturing gives the material possession; teaching, the knowledge that is available; and training, the standards. But change occurs, and each new entrant to a family (each new entrant to a school or a profession) is part of the process of change. Change occurs through experimentation, which reveals a choice. The infant experiments with food and learns to spit out instead of swallowing: with materials, when using a toy not envisaged by an adult: with words, when making a mistake which is funny, finding that it can be done deliberately, and has learned how to make a joke. The capacity to experiment grows when the parent, the teacher, and later the therapist, learn how to accept an ambiguous communication and an unanticipated response.

Specific types of therapy can be related to these four primary processes.

Caring (an aspect of nurturing) is an accompaniment of most methods of treatment. In some systems of therapy, the main communication is the experience (perhaps for the first time) of being demonstrably cared for.

Teaching is the process utilised in some forms of didactic therapy and some types of casework at ego level, when the therapist provides an opportunity to explore alternative ways of dealing with a hitherto impossible situation.

Training is implied in forms of behaviour therapy, in which desirable responses are encouraged and undesirable ones inhibited. It is understood that aims and objectives can be agreed and the therapy is directed towards achieving those objectives.

Experimenting is an idea underlying those forms of psychotherapy in which interpretation is not seen as a direct equivalent or translation of an original communication or of a symptom. Rather it is an addition to the number of models that are possible. Here the final aim cannot be declared in advance and there is recognition of the complexity of unconscious mental processes. Although a patient may seek help because of distress (or may be brought to treatment because his behaviour is unsatisfactory to someone else), the treatment is directed to the exploration of ideas and potentialities that are as yet unknown.

Detailed treatment approaches follow in subsequent chapters.

References

BOSTON, N. & DAWS, D. (1977) *The Child Psychotherapist and Problems With Young People.* London: Wildwood House.

ERIKSON, E. (1950) *Childhood and Society.* New York: W. W. Norton.

KAHN, J. (1969) Dimensions of diagnosis and treatment. *Mental Hygiene,* **53**.

—— (1971) Uses and abuses of child psychiatry. *British Journal of Medical Psychology,* **44**.

PIAGET, J. & INHELDER, B. (1969) *The Psychology of the Child.* London: Routledge and Kegan Paul.

TANNER, J. (1962) *Growth At Adolescence.* Oxford: Blackwell.

THOMPSON, S. & KAHN, J. (1970) *The Group Process As A Helping Technique.* Oxford: Pergamon Press.

WARD, A. (1993) *Group Processes.* Birmingham: Ventura Press.

15 Psychiatric diagnosis

JOHN SCOTT WERRY

In this chapter the role of psychiatric classifications in the study and management of severe school attendance problems is discussed. For completeness, other psychopathological classifications are mentioned but only briefly since they lie outside the main scope of this discussion, although this is not to devalue or diminish them.

There has been a long-standing interest in psychiatric disorders and symptoms associated with school attendance problems (see Atkinson *et al*, 1985; Hersov, 1985; Berg, 1991, 1992), dating at least from 1932 when what came to be called school phobia was first described (Hersov, 1985); though Carl Jung is said to have noted the role of emotional factors as early as 1911 (Berg, 1991). However, as Berg (1992) notes, modern psychiatric classifications like the third edition of the *Diagnostic and Statistical Manual of Mental Disorders* (DSM–III; American Psychiatric Association, 1980) and the *International Classification of Diseases* now in its tenth revision (ICD–10; World Health Organization, 1992) have shifted attention away from the earlier symptom- or problem-based-type classifications to psychiatric disorders. Thus, interest in school attendance problems as an entity in themselves has declined markedly in the last decade or so. While there can be little doubt that this new focus on diagnostic categories has brought great clinical and heuristic benefits (Werry, 1992), there have been some losses as well, in that the power of psychiatric classifications to explain all severe school attendance problems and point a path to management is limited (Berg, 1992; Berg *et al*, 1993). This may leave clinicians in a quandary when confronted with a severe school attendance problem that does not fit any particular psychiatric label or where a diagnosis offers little guidance to specific management. There is also a danger of neglecting a valuable collection of previous clinical knowledge (Ollendick & King, 1990).

Nevertheless, a substantial psychiatric literature (see Atkinson *et al*, 1985; Hersov, 1985; Berg, 1991; 1992; Berg *et al*, 1993) shows that associated psychiatric disorder appears common enough in children with severe school attendance problems, especially in certain subgroups such as those referred to clinics, to be worth considering in the initial assessment of most children with such problems.

Classifications of child psychiatric problems

Medical

These are characterised by the disease model: diagnoses are categorical (i.e. yes/no), qualitative (i.e. portraying abnormality or disorder) and describing a set of characteristic attributes such as defining symptoms, aetiology, specific treatment, outcome, differential diagnosis and associated features (such as epidemiological, family and social factors). Medical classifications have strengths and weaknesses (see Werry, 1992). Strengths include their power to convey understanding to parents, and to address symptomatology, correlates, outcome and specific treatment. Weaknesses lie in the unreliability and unknown validity of some categories, their inability sometimes to prescribe a sufficiently comprehensive course of management to be clinically useful and the high degree of co-association (comorbidity) of some disorders leading to multiple diagnoses. There is, however, no necessary connection between this type of classification and a medical treatment for the disorder, though one may not always get this impression from recent research.

Two medical-type systems now dominate, each of which has evolved through a number of revisions: DSM–IV (American Psychiatric Association, 1994) and ICD–10. DSM–IV is characterised by more disorders, especially subcategories, by explicit, but not always objective, 'operational' diagnostic criteria, by greater rigidity and, increasingly, by a larger volume of high-quality research and greater use of structured methods of data capture. The current version is so new that most of the data relevant to severe school attendance problems relates to earlier revisions, most notably DSM–III, DSM–III–R (American Psychiatric Association, 1980, 1987) and ICD–9 (World Health Organization, 1979).

In an attempt to expand the scope of medical systems to take account of criticisms from clinicians of the failure to address important aspects of patients beyond their 'disorder', both classifications added extra axes to take care of medical disorders, stress, holistic and intellectual function, but none of these seems to have attracted much real interest clinically or in research in children (see Werry, 1985, 1992).

Personality/dimensional

In contrast, this classificatory model views symptomatology as a quantitative departure from characteristics found in all children or, put another way, as exaggerated normal personality traits. Definitions of abnormality are usually normative/statistical (e.g. more than two standard deviations), derived from whole populations and have no relationship to any 'disease' process (which is most unlikely to fit neatly to any normal distribution curve). The dimensional approach, which has been studied as extensively as medical classifications in child psychopathology (see Quay, 1986), has advantages of lack of stigma, a sounder psychometric base (since it grew out of empirical statistical methods) and greater power of prediction in research (see Werry, in press). It is also much better able to explain comorbidity or cases of mixed disorders as expected, coincidental concurrence of high scores on more than one dimension in a minority of the population. This is well illustrated in the study of school attendance problems by Bools *et al* (1990), which found two main dimensions associated (emotional/neurotic and conduct) but also that a small number of children scored high on both. The greatest value of the dimensional model may be in terms of mass detection, in description, in research and as a dependent variable measure of outcome; but it is probably, as yet, less useful in management than the medical or functional models.

Functional

This model is concerned with the functional relationship between types of problem behaviour or symptoms and environmental factors or stimuli causing and perpetuating them and is shared by psychodynamic, family and behavioural approaches. It is doubtful that most of these are yet so well internally organised that they could be considered as true classifications and are best regarded primarily as treatment techniques, though there are a few examples of attempts to develop a true classification system of school attendance problems (see Ollendick & King, 1990). Indubitably, this is the way that clinicians finally approach much of the management of most children including those with severe school attendance problems; but this is largely a default position because, as in the rest of medicine, psychiatric classifications should lead logically to a powerful, specific treatment but regrettably this is still less frequent than desirable in the clinical situation.

Frequency of psychiatric disorders in school attendance problems

Before discussing individual disorders, the question of the frequency of psychiatric disturbance of any type in severe school attendance problems is addressed. Though severe school attendance problems occur in under 10% of clinic referrals (Berg, 1991, 1992), older studies gave the impression not only that psychiatric disorders were commonly associated, but that one type, 'school phobia', predominated. However, community-based studies, which have been done only recently (Bools *et al*, 1990; Berg, 1992, Berg *et al*, 1993), have shown that the vast majority of children with school attendance problems are never referred to psychiatric facilities. Correlates of school attendance problems, such as socio-economic status, gender and parental psychiatric disorder, in community samples differ substantially from those from psychiatric clinics. Further, these studies have shown that a substantial proportion, even a majority, of children with attendance problems have no psychiatric disorder and in those that do, school 'phobia' was less common than other disorders (Bools *et al*, 1990; Berg, 1992; Berg *et al*, 1993).

However, the community samples have had rather high refusal and presumptively incomplete detection rates and/or in themselves are biased in that they are not random samples but children referred to statutory agencies. This suggests that the frequency of psychiatric disorders and other epidemiological features of chronic severe school attendance problems remain to be established. Nevertheless, community studies do confirm that psychiatric disorder is reasonably commonly associated with severe school attendance problems, so that discussion of the particular psychiatric diagnoses concerned should be valuable.

Psychiatric disorders and school attendance problems

While in this section the various diagnostic conditions that may cause or be associated with school attendance problems are discussed, it is beyond the scope of this chapter to indicate what are the implications of each diagnosis, for example for management. These should be sought in other parts of this book and/or standard modern texts of child and adolescent psychiatry.

A problem with studies in this area is that until the mid 1980s few applied systematic measures of diagnosis or symptoms (including school attendance) or employed proper controls for error (Atkinson *et al*, 1985). Also, older studies did not use current classifications though some diagnostic categories have persisted from previous versions with only minor changes. Nevertheless, the older literature has clearly pointed which of the modern categories might be important and drawn attention to the value in diagnosis of such factors as acuteness of onset, age and duration (Atkinson *et al*, 1985; Hersov, 1985; Berg, 1991, 1992). In general, these have indicated that there are two broad diagnostic groupings. In the first, known as *school refusers*, who are more likely to be female, white and from higher socio-economic groups (Last & Perrin, 1993), absence from school is generally known to carers and children resist going to school with displays of anxiety, anger or misery in the home. In the second, *truants*, where boys and disadvantaged groups predominate, the child pretends to go to school, conceals the absence and avoids school, not out of fear but, like Huckleberry Finn, to do other more interesting things notably delinquent acts especially in urban areas. School refusers usually have some kind of anxiety/dysphoric disorder (neurotic disorders) while truants may have disruptive (conduct) disorders. However, while confirming these two broad groups, recent studies (Bools *et al* 1990; Berg *et al*, 1993) have shown that they are not absolute, that mixed cases occur and quite a proportion of children with school attendance problems have no apparent psychiatric disorder at all.

Studies of the recent classifications of psychiatric diagnosis in children and adolescents, while generally an improvement, have revealed some difficulties. Interdiagnoser reliability varies with category and subcategory and in some cases is quite unsatisfactory (see Werry, 1992). Resort to structured methods of interviewing results in great improvements but does not obviate problems entirely (e.g. Silverman, 1991; Silverman & Eisen, 1992). There are varying disagreements between parental and child reports, complex interactions between age and type of symptoms (externalising or internalising) and such methods are often too cumbersome for clinical use.

Perhaps the biggest problem in DSM—III, which now hardly a study does not illustrate, is that of comorbidity or concurrence of more than one disorder (Anderson *et al*, 1987; Bernstein & Borchardt, 1986; Biederman *et al*, 1991; Last *et al*, 1987*a*; Last & Francis, 1988; Werry *et al*, 1987*a,b*). This problem of mixed cases has been known for a long time as current and previous versions of ICD and DSM before the third revision illustrate. The causes of this are complex but underline the need for great care in diagnosis, not just blinkered focusing on one set of symptoms or one diagnosis. The study of attention deficit disorder graphically illustrates this problem, where from 1966 to the mid 1980s the often-associated conduct disorder (Werry *et al*, 1987*a,b*; Biederman *et al*, 1991) was ignored so that it is difficult to know how much of the vast literature on attention deficit disorder is true of that disorder, or really reflects conduct disorder or the admixture of the two disorders (Werry *et al*, 1987*b*; Werry, 1992).

Another problem for any reviewer is that while ICD—10 and DSM—IV now resemble each other more closely, there are still significant differences in terminology, criteria and placement of individual disorders within the overall system. In children, ICD—10 deals with some comorbidity by 'mixed' disorders (of conduct and emotions) while DSM—IV insists on dual or multiple diagnoses (comorbidity). An effort will be made to present material in ways reflecting both nosologies but this will not always be possible. In general, there is more research on DSM than ICD, which necessarily gives the former apparent predominance. There is also reason to believe that though ICD is the official classification in all countries, DSM is actually the one in most general use, despite its often-alleged problems of medicalisation, overinclusiveness, rigidity and pseudoprecision (see Werry, 1985, 1992; Wilson, 1993).

Anxiety disorders

In ICD—10 this group of disorders is found within the neurotic, stress-related and somatoform disorders whereas in DSM—IV they are a self-standing group. However, both have anxiety disorders important in school attendance problems found in the section on child and adolescent onset disorders. Paradoxically, ICD—10 now has more of these than DSM—IV. There are also important differences in DSM—IV from DSM—III (elimination of overanxious and avoidant disorder, both now integrated into adult disorder of generalised anxiety disorder and avoidant personality disorder respectively) and in ICD–9 from ICD–10 (greater specificity and subcategorisation of the emotional disorders) that makes for some difficulties in interpreting research within the new systems.

The symptomatology relevant to school attendance problems in this group of children has been well described (see Atkinson *et al*, 1985; Hersov, 1985; Ollendick & King, 1990; Berg, 1991). As noted, school absence is termed school refusal and is known to parents right from the beginning in that the children try to remain at home to avoid school and usually publicly refuse to go to school when asked or urged; but this distinction is not absolute, especially in adolescents who may go to friends' houses or hide until parents have gone to work. As a result, in these days of working mothers, the child's absence may take more time to be detected. The frequency of school refusal in the total school population has not been well researched though it is felt to be rare before adolescence, when it increases substantially (Berg, 1992). One Venezuelan study found a prevalence of 0.4% in 3–13 year olds (de Aldaz *et al*, 1987). However, the frequency in clinic samples is much higher at 5–7% (Berg, 1992) and it is from this group that most of the research emanates. This is likely to bias the results towards severity of the disorder, comorbidity and dysfunctional families.

The key to diagnosis lies in obtaining a history of classical symptoms of anxiety around going to school though these may be obscured by *secondary escape–avoidance types of behaviour* such as complaints of physical illness, semi-plausible reasons for not going to school and tantrums/disruptive behaviour when attempts are made to urge or force the child to school. Anticipatory anxiety (e.g. towards the end of weekends or vacation) is highly characteristic. However, objective signs of anxiety may not be present except when the child is being urged or forced to school. The onset may be sudden or it may gradually increase from one or two days every so often to every day and continuing for weeks or months.

In one of the few studies of school attendance problems using ICD–9, Bools *et al* (1990) showed that in a sample referred to the statutory authority for school attendance problems, the general category of emotional disorder of childhood with anxiety and fearfulness accounted for about one-quarter of cases and nearly all were girls. However, in ICD–10 and DSM–III/IV terms, these children would be now further subclassified as follows.

Separation anxiety disorder

This DSM–III/IV category did not occur in ICD–9 but does in ICD–10. The essential feature is an abnormally intense and developmentally inappropriate fear of separation from the primary attachment figure (usually the mother or other parent). This feature, however, may not be readily apparent if the child has resorted to illness as a strategy for school avoidance but will be discernible with proper history taking. According to Last & Francis (1988) the key diagnostic feature not found in other disorders is that *separation anxious children always remain at home and/or in the presence of the primary attachment figure when avoiding school.* They also have separation anxiety behaviour evoked in other situations besides school (e.g. at night when parents wish to go out). The fear of separation may take the form of fear that something may happen to the parent and this may be exaggerated if the parent has health problems, died or departed (Hersov, 1985; Ollendick & King, 1990; Berg, 1991). School is conspicuously absent as an explanation for their anxiety. In one study of children from an anxiety disorders clinic (Last *et al*, 1987*b*) separation anxious children were reported more often to be female, prepubertal, likely to have associated externalising behaviour problems (Last *et al*, 1987*c*), from lower socio-economic groups and their mothers more (and very) likely to have both anxiety and mood disorders compared with children with true school phobia (see below). Unfortunately for diagnostic parsimony, separation anxiety disorder was also found to have a 92% comorbidity with other disorders, mostly anxiety disorders, so that school refusal due to a pure separation-type school refusal uncomplicated by other disorders seems unlikely. Further, de Aldaz *et al* (1987) found that in the group which was most attached to and dependent on their parents (presumptively those with separation anxiety disorder) that it required some prominent stress, most notably change of school, to precipitate anxiety. McFarlane (1987) found that children exposed to a disastrous bush fire developed marked increases in anxiety when away from their parents at school. This suggests that separation anxiety disorder may sometimes act more as a risk factor for school refusal than as the immediate precipitant.

The exact frequency of separation anxiety disorder as a cause of school refusal is contentious (Berg, 1992) with some asserting it is almost always present (Tonge, 1988; Gittleman-Klein & Burrows, 1990) while others stress that many cases are due to other types of disorders (de Aldaz *et al*, 1987; Last & Francis, 1988; Berg, 1992). Unfortunately, there are very few studies that have attempted to examine this issue critically using current classifications rather than simply assuming that school refusal was a homogeneous entity (usually due to separation anxiety). In an adolescent community sample, Berg *et al* (1993) found separation anxiety disorder was the commonest cause of school refusal and more frequent in females, but occurred only six times in 80 cases suggesting that it is an infrequent cause of school attendance problem in adolescents not referred to clinics. In one of the few community surveys using random sampling of a total school population, de Aldaz *et al* (1987) found that children with separation anxiety and dependency were only slightly more common than other causes of school refusal. However, the frequency of school refusal as a cause of school attendance problems is much higher in clinic cases (Last & Francis, 1988) and, as noted above, children seen there are likely to be more severely disturbed. While there is agreement that it is the commonest cause of children seen clinically with school refusal, the diagnostically best study suggests that there is a substantial minority, perhaps one-third, with other diagnoses (Last *et al*, 1987 *b*).

In summary, though separation anxiety came to be regarded as diagnosable simply by school refusal, it is now clear that though separation anxiety disorder is important, school refusal may result from a number of other diagnoses (Atkinson *et al*, 1985; Last & Francis, 1988; Berg, 1992; Berg *et al*, 1993). It is therefore necessary to ascertain that the criteria for separation anxiety disorder are present, and not to assume that they must be just because there is school refusal.

Phobic disorders

These disorders are characterised by morbid (that is exaggerated or unnecessary) fear of some specific, circumscribed stimulus that is is seen only in direct association with this stimulus, in this case some aspect of school (in contrast to separation anxiety disorder where the fear relates to all situations where the child is to be separated from the primary carer(s) or attachment figure(s) of which school may be the only one of many). If the fear is of some simple quasi-life-threatening event (e.g. being bullied) it is called a *specific or isolated phobia*; if the fear is social (e.g. failure, criticism by a teacher, ostracism by a group of peers) a *social phobia*; if of going outside or of being in crowds or places where escape might not be possible, *agoraphobia*. Since the latter is not centred on school and thus not a true school phobia, and presents other complications because of its relationship to panic disorder, it will be discussed separately below.

There is a significant difference in the way that these disorders are organised in ICD–10 and DSM–IV in that there is a separate ICD–10 classification for these disorders within the child disorders group (phobic anxiety and social anxiety disorders of childhood) in addition to those in the general neurotic/phobic anxiety group (ICD–10) or anxiety disorders (DSM–IV) group as outlined above. The criterion for using a childhood rather than the adult diagnosis is that the fear should be developmentally appropriate (age-related), such as fear of animals. This seems likely to me only to cause confusion but final judgement must await formal research data.

The idea that some children might refuse to go to school solely because of phobias restricted to the school situation is not new (e.g. Berg *et al*, 1969), but seems to have become submerged by uncritical enthusiasm for the separation anxiety hypothesis. Because of the latter, there is very little good research on true school phobias. What there is has been reviewed by Last & Francis (1988) and much of the good data stem only from one set of studies in a specialised anxiety disorders clinic by Last and colleagues. These showed that school phobias (social or specific) were valid diagnoses distinctive from separation anxiety and other anxiety disorders in that children with isolated school phobias differed from those with separation anxiety disorder and other anxiety disorders in number of fears, in gender ratios (more males), in socio-economic status (higher), age (adolescent), in comorbidity (lower), in associated externalising behaviour problems (lower) and in rates (lower) and type of maternal disorder. However, between a half and two-thirds of the children with school phobias had another comorbid anxiety disorder – overanxious disorder (in DSM–IV this is now melded into generalised anxiety disorder), other phobic or panic disorder (Last *et al*, 1987*b,c*). Thus the diagnosis in practice may be more difficult to separate out from other anxiety disorders.

How frequent true phobias are as a cause of school attendance problems is difficult to determine. In the only other study using current classifications, in a sample of 80 children selected from schools on the basis of an absence rate of at least 40% absence during the term (trimester), Berg *et al* (1993) found one case of specific phobia and two of possible social phobia though all anxiety disorders were infrequent. However, among cases of *school refusal* phobic disorders seem prominent. Among children seen in the special anxiety disorders clinic, Last *et al* (1987*b*) found 19 cases as compared with 35 of school refusal resulting from separation anxiety disorder. In a survey of a total school population aged 3–13 (de Aldaz *et al*, 1987), phobic-type disorders (*n*=24) accounted for almost as much school refusal as separation anxiety/ dependence (*n*=28), though this study did not use modern diagnostic categories and some of the phobic group may have been adjustment disorders (see below).

School phobic disorders are therefore clearly important as a cause of school refusal but require much more study. Attempting to make the distinction from other anxiety disorders such as separation anxiety disorder is not an idle pursuit since there is a well-established literature on phobic disorders and their management (Marks, 1987; Ollendick & King, 1990).

Other anxiety disorders

It is possible that other kinds of anxiety disorder might result in school refusal.

Agoraphobia (fear of being in situations where escape might not be possible usually because of social embarrassment) and its often associated disorder, *panic disorder*, in which the person is struck by a sudden discrete period of intense fear for no apparent reason, should theoretically occur in an occasional case of school refusal but so far have not been reported. This may be because these disorders have been reported only rarely before age 15 (Klein *et al*, 1992). However, Abelson & Alessi (1992) point out that the category of separation anxiety disorder and other forms of school 'phobias' may in fact be obscuring detection, or alternatively may be but developmental variants, of panic disorder (which nearly always leads to agoraphobic disorders). There seems little to dispute their suggestion and that of others (e.g. Berg, 1992) that panic and agoraphobic disorders and their link to school refusal merit closer examination.

Overanxious disorder, which is characterised by general worrying about everything but especially social performance in general, has been reported in association with school refusal, particularly where it is of the true phobic type (Last *et al*, 1987*a*; Last & Francis, 1988). However, this has been less as a direct cause than a predisposing or vulnerability factor, rather like a personality dimension, upon which a specific school phobia could develop. There have been doubts about the reliability and validity of this diagnostic category especially its real distinctiveness from other anxiety disorders (Werry, 1991) and it has now been relegated to emotional disorder 'other' in the child section of ICD–10 and amalgamated with the adult generalised anxiety disorder in DSM–IV, so the role of this type of disorder in school refusal will have to be looked at anew.

Obsessive–compulsive disorder may theoretically occasionally present as school refusal, for example where the child is too preoccupied with rituals to be able to leave the house or where there are particular fears of contamination at school. The pervasiveness of the disorder, especially at home, and the correct diagnosis should soon become apparent.

Reaction to severe stress and adjustment disorders

It is clear from the literature on school refusal that many children may suffer a transient reluctance to go to school consequent on some clear and obvious stress (such as going to a new school, bullying, or an accident on the way) and that most of these are dealt with quickly and efficiently by parents. Unlike ICD–10, DSM–IV usefully allows these minor problems, if brought to the attention of professionals, to be classified as non-disease *'V'codes (problems that are the focus of attention)*. However, in some cases the response may be more severe and/or more obdurate and a psychiatric condition, therefore, a possibility.

Where the event is real enough and the response is understandable empathically (this differentiates it from a phobia), characterised by any kind of disabling distress, and occurs within 1 (ICD–10) to 3 (DSM–IV) months of the event, an *adjustment disorder* should be tentatively diagnosed. It is likely that adjustment disorders are a common cause of more short-lived school refusal, though most of these are unlikely to be seen clinically. If it persists more than 6 months the diagnosis should be reviewed. Adjustment disorders in children are poorly studied in general and difficult to diagnose reliably, though there is no doubt about their occurrence and importance, in particular their presaging of the development of more serious disorders (Newcorn & Strain, 1992). De Aldaz *et al* (1987) classified 49% of their 57 refusers as having "problems in adaptation to changes in the school environment", but from the description many of their children probably had separation anxiety disorder instead (or possibly some as well).

Where the event is catastrophic (e.g. a serious accident, a near-miss, sexual assault or being held hostage) and there is an immediate disabling reaction that subsides within a short time, *an acute stress reaction* may be diagnosed. Where the condition arises within 6 months of such an event and where it is accompanied by intrusiveness of thoughts about the event, avoidance of situations associated with the event, impairment of concentration and in younger children behavioural regression, then *post-traumatic stress disorder* should be considered, consulting diagnostic manuals for exact criteria required. There is some controversy about the number and type of diagnostic criteria in children (Green *et al*, 1991), for example visual flashbacks are said not to occur in children (Bernstein & Borchardt, 1991), but adolescents have more typically adult-type symptoms. Few of the studies of disaster, even those that occurred in or close to school, seem to have reported school refusal though one study found it in only one of 25 children involved in the hijacking of a school bus (Terr, 1983). This suggests it is a rather infrequent occurrence. An Australian study of serious bush fire (McFarlane, 1987) showed that children became more anxious about being separated from parents so that the impact of a catastrophe may appear in other ways than post-traumatic stress disorder.

Depression

Depression in children is somewhat contentious and depressive symptoms may occur in most other disorders. However, true depression certainly occurs in children, though more commonly in adolescence (see Harrington, 1992). It is characterised by a marked change in behaviour and function due to a pervasive mood of sadness, nihilism or pessimism and loss of interest in formerly pleasurable activities. It may be mild or severe, brief or durable and with or without psychotic and melancholic features (like weight changes, sleep disturbances, diurnal fluctuation in mood) and with or without agitation or anxiety. It may occur once or be recurrent, and may be associated with manic episodes (bipolar type). It has a strong tendency to be familial, so that in children a history of parental depression is commonly reported.

Depression has been noted in association with school attendance problems for some time (Hersov, 1985). Using empirical multivariate statistical methods, Kolvin *et al* (1984) found that school refusers aged 9–14 fell into two groups, one where anxiety and one where depression dominated (45%). The depressed group had a higher association of parental depressive disorders, recent life events and a history of organic factors in early life. Among community samples with school attendance problems, what would now be classed as depression has been found, but only infrequently (de Aldaz *et al*, 1987; Bools *et al*, 1990; Berg *et al*, 1993). However, in clinic referrals the situation is quite different and depression may figure more prominently (Kolvin *et al*, 1984; Bernstein & Borchardt, 1992). However, most recent studies, except that of Kolvin *et al* (1984), have shown a very high comorbidity of mood with anxiety disorders in children and adolescents and also in their parents (Last *et al*, 1987*a*; Bernstein & Borchardt, 1991), raising questions about some aetiological interdependence of these two disorders. Since recognition of the possibility of comorbidity is only recent, these findings on the possible frequency of primacy mood disorders in school refusal do not diminish the well-established primacy of anxiety disorders but merely indicates the need for a broader brush when making diagnoses.

Somatoform disorders and psychological factors in physical illness

This is a group (in ICD–10 two groups) of disorders characterised by physical symptoms that seem to have no basis in disease or psychological factors/ symptoms which cause, or are prominently associated with, physical diseases. There are several subcategories depending on the type of physical symptoms (e.g. conversion or quasi-neurological, pain, hypochondriasis), whether or not they are multiple (somatisation disorder) and whether or not true physical disease is present.

Physical symptoms such as stomach aches, general malaise and headaches are common in school refusal (Atkinson *et al*, 1985; Hersov, 1985; Berg, 1992) and there seems good reason to think that school refusal may be often misdiagnosed as physical illness, at least initially. When signs of illness such as fever, cough or vomiting symptoms are absent or symptoms rapidly evaporate after the decision is made that the child can stay at home only to reappear next morning or Monday mornings, discerning parents or doctors have little trouble making the correct diagnosis. When the symptoms are more persistent or generalised (e.g. chronic fatigue syndrome) or where the parent has some conscious or unconscious reason for wanting the child at home, feels that the child is really ill or is generally overprotective, or the doctor is resistant to the recognition of psychological factors, then illness may become reinforced until a somatoform disorder becomes established. In these situations, school refusal is unlikely to be the only problem and evidence of more general psychopathology in child and/or parent should be apparent. These cases can be difficult to diagnose and to manage since parents can nearly always find a doctor who will confirm suspicion of illness and commence a series of protracted investigations or specialist referrals, all of which prolong absence from school and the prospect of chronicity. The size of this problem is unknown since it will not be easily detectable as a form contributing to school refusal so firmly are child, parent and/or doctor convinced that illness is present.

A rather different problem is presented when the child has a definite physical illness especially a chronic or disabling one and has a school attendance problem. Studies (see Berg, 1992) have shown that children with physical illnesses, including quite disabling ones, lose very little time from school. Thus, a high index of suspicion is required when a child with a physical illness seems to be spending an excessive time off school. An opinion from a specialist who knows how other children with similar levels of disability cope should be sought.

Conduct and oppositional defiant disorders

Conduct disorder is characterised in both ICD–10 and DSM–IV by a repetitive pattern of antisocial behaviour (defiance, lying, fighting, running away, cruelty and substantial crimes) extending well beyond the norm for that child's peer group. A salient feature is an exploitative selfish core to interpersonal relationships in which the child/adolescent does or takes what he (males predominate) wants, when he wants it and without regard to the rights or feelings of others. The pattern of antisocial behaviour varies but tends to be more shocking and felonious in males, in large urban areas and in violent societies like the USA. It is one of the oldest, more robust and better researched categories of psychiatric diagnosis in children (Quay, 1986) though attempts at subcategorisation have generally shown poor reliability. It is associated with male sex, attentional and reading problems, poor school achievement, parental adversity and disorder notably alcohol and drug abuse and criminality. The role of adverse sociological factors is well established but that of genetic and neurological factors in aetiology is attracting more interest and some kind of interaction in many cases seems possible (Lewis, 1990). School attendance problems are common and take the form of truancy rather than school refusal, that is absence from school without due cause and with attempted concealment from parents or guardians (Berg, 1991). Community studies (Bools *et al*, 1990; Berg *et al*, 1993) have generally shown that among those children with school attendance problems who have associated psychiatric disorders (a minority), *conduct disorder is the most common diagnosis*. This differs sharply from clinic referrals where school refusal and emotional disorders predominate. However, as with conduct disorder in general (Anderson *et al*, 1987), comorbidity occurs in a significant minority, especially with emotional disorders (Bools *et al*, 1990), although in studies not centred on school problems the highest comorbidity is with attention deficit hyperactivity (hyperkinetic) disorder (Werry *et al*, 1987*a,b*; Biederman *et al*,

1991). Conduct disorder is chronic, often carries a poor outcome and is highly resistant to any treatment (Quay, 1986; Lewis, 1990). School attendance problems are usually only a part of a very serious picture.

Oppositional defiant behaviour was created in 1980 in DSM–III but has been incorporated into ICD–10. There is considerable controversy about its reliability and distinctiveness from conduct disorder (Anderson *et al*, 1987; Werry, 1992) and indeed it looks very like a middle-class version of conduct disorder in which the children are rather better socialised and in which defiance and generally oppositional behaviour predominate rather than frank antisocial behaviour. Berg *et al* (1993) did find one case in their sample of 80 adolescents with school attendance problems, so it may be the cause in an occasional case.

Attention deficit hyperactivity (hyperkinetic) disorder (ADHD)

This well-researched disorder is characterised by inattention–distractibility, impulsivity and hyperactivity. Learning, school adjustment and peer relationship problems are frequently associated. This would be predicted to set the scene for school attendance problems which, because of the commonly comorbid conduct or oppositional defiant disorder, could take either truancy or refusal forms. Yet this seems seldom reported in treatises on ADHD. Again, Berg *et al* (1993) found only one case among a total of 80 with psychiatric diagnoses in their community sample. Thus it seems that ADHD is only an infrequent cause of school attendance problems though this may well be an artefact of underreporting.

Other disorders

Any severe psychiatric disorder, notably schizophrenia, schizotypal, bipolar manic depressive disorder, avoidant (personality) disorder (extreme shyness), anorexia nervosa and so on where anxiety in or about social situations is a feature could result in school attendance problems. However, these should be readily apparent (unless prodromal) and merely illustrate the need for an open mind and a comprehensive diagnostic approach in all cases of school attendance problems.

Conclusions

School attendance problems are probably associated with psychiatric disorders in about half of cases, though definitive epidemiological rates remain to be established and are likely in any case to vary with the socio-cultural nature of the locality and what premium is placed on education. The majority of those who do have a psychiatric disorder are truants with conduct disorders from deprived backgrounds who are rarely seen in clinics. Mental health professionals tend to see those with school refusal who usually have some kind of emotional disorder but, occasionally, may have practically any psychiatric disorder. Among the emotional disorders, separation anxiety disorder is probably the most common, but true phobic disorders are also quite frequent. As with anxiety disorders in general, such children are likely to have other comorbid disorders most notably other anxiety and/or mood disorders.

It is also likely that there is a substantial group of children misdiagnosed as having physical illnesses when what they really have are somatoform psychiatric disorders or psychological complications of physical illness. Despite the recent upsurge in psychiatric epidemiological studies, the size of this group remains uncertain.

The value of making a psychiatric diagnosis will depend on the technical knowledge associated with that disorder but, as in most of psychiatry and indeed in much of medicine as well, diagnosis will give but a variable portion of the clinical picture and management plan. Nevertheless, it is most unlikely that making a psychiatric diagnosis will contribute absolutely nothing; so it is a procedure that is to be encouraged in all cases of severe school attendance problems.

Because of the wide variety of disorders that may be associated with school attendance problems, each case must be approached with an open mind, first as to whether or not any disorder exists and, if so, as to which of the many possible disorders may be present. As such, it is dependent on comprehensive history-taking from a variety of informants and on competent examination of the child, including physical examination where that is indicated.

References

ABELSON, J. L. & ALESSI, N. E. (1992) Discussion of 'child panic revisited'. *Journal of the American Academy of Child and Adolescent Psychiatry*, **31**, 114–116.

AMERICAN PSYCHIATRIC ASSOCIATION (1980) *Diagnostic and Statistical Manual of Mental Disorders* (3rd edn) DSM–III). Washington, DC: APA.

—— (1987) *Diagnostic and Statistical Manual of Mental Disorders* (3rd edn, revised) DSM–III–R). Washington, DC: APA.

—— (1994) *Diagnostic and Statistical Manual of Mental Disorders* (4th edn) (DSM–IV). Washington, DC: APA.

ANDERSON, J., WILLIAMS, S. M., MCGEE, R. O., *et al* (1987) DSM–III disorders in pre-adolescent children. *Archives of General Psychiatry*, **44**, 69–76.

ATKINSON, L., QUARRINGTON, B. & CYR, J. J. (1985) School refusal: the heterogeneity of the concept. *American Journal of Orthopsychiatry*, **55**, 83–101.

BERG, I. (1991) School avoidance, school phobia, and truancy. In *Child and Adolescent Psychiatry: A Comprehensive Textbook* (ed. M. Lewis), pp. 1092–1098. Baltimore: Williams & Wilkins.

—— (1992) Absence from school and mental health. *British Journal of Psychiatry*, **161**, 154–166.

——, NICOLS, K. & PRITCHARD, C. (1969) School phobia – its classification and relationship to dependency. *Journal of Child Psychology and Psychiatry*, **10**, 235–241.

——, BUTLER, A., FRANKLIN, J., *et al* (1993) DSM–III–R disorders, social factors and management of school attendance problems in the normal population. *Journal of Child Psychology and Psychiatry*, **47**, 1187–1203.

BERNSTEIN, G. A. & BORCHARDT, C. M. (1991) Anxiety disorders of childhood and adolescence: a critical review. *Journal of the American Academy of Child and Adolescent Psychiatry*, **30**, 519–532.

BIEDERMAN, J., NEWCORN, J. & SPRICH, S. (1991) Comorbidity of attention deficit hyperactivity disorder with conduct, depressive and other disorders. *American Journal of Psychiatry*, **148**, 564–577.

BOOLS, C., FOSTER, J., BROWN, I., *et al* (1990) The identification of psychiatric disorders in children who fail to attend school: a cluster analysis of a non-clinical population. *Psychological Medicine*, **20**, 171–181.

DE ALDAZ, E., FELDMAN, L., VIVAS, E, E., *et al* (1987) Characteristics of Venezuelan school refusers. Toward the development of a high-risk profile. *Journal of Nervous and Mental Disease*, **175**, 402–407.

GITTELMAN-KLEIN, R. & BURROWS, G. D. (1990) Anxiety disorders. In *Handbook of Studies on Child Psychiatry* (eds B. J. Tonge, G. D. Burrows & J. S. Werry), pp. 173–192. Amsterdam: Elsevier.

GREEN, B. L., KOROL, M., GRACE, M. C., *et al* (1991) Children and disaster: age, gender and parental effects on PTSD symptoms. *Journal of the American Academy of Child and Adolescent Psychiatry*, **30**, 945–951.

HARRINGTON, R. (1992) The natural history and treatment of child and adolescent affective disorders. *Journal of Child Psychology and Psychiatry*, **33**, 1287–1302.

HERSOV, L. (1985) School refusal. In *Child and Adolescent Psychiatry: Modern Approaches* (2nd edn) (eds M. Rutter & L. Hersov), pp. 382–399. Oxford: Blackwell Scientific Publications.

KLEIN, D. F., MANNUZZA, S., CHAPMAN, T., *et al* (1992) Child panic revisited. *Journal of the American Academy of Child and Adolescent Psychiatry*, **31**, 112–114.

KOLVIN, I., BERNEY, T. P. & BHATE, S. R. (1984) Classification and diagnosis of depression in school phobia. *British Journal of Psychiatry*, **145**, 347–357.

LAST, C. G., STRAUSS, C. C. & FRANCIS, G. (1987*a*) Comorbidity among childhood anxiety disorders. *Journal of Nervous and Mental Disease*, **175**, 726–730.

——, FRANCIS, G., HERSEN, M., *et al* (1987*b*) Separation and school phobia: a comparison using DSM–III criteria. *American Journal of Psychiatry*, **144**, 653–657.

——, HERSEN, M., KAZDIN, A. E., *et al* (1987*c*) Comparison of DSM–III separation anxiety disorder and overanxious disorders: demographic characteristics and patterns of comorbidity. *Journal of American Academy of Child and Adolescent Psychiatry*, **26**, 527–531.

——, & FRANCIS, G. (1988) School phobia. In *Advances in Clinical Child Psychology, Vol. II* (eds B. Lahey & A. Kazdin), pp. 193–222. New York: Plenum Press.

——, & PERRIN, S. (1993) Anxiety disorders in African-American and white children. *Journal of Abnormal Child Psychology*, **21**, 153–164.

LEWIS, D. O. (1990) Conduct disorder. In *Child and Adolescent Psychiatry: A Comprehensive Textbook* (ed. M. Lewis), pp. 561–573. Baltimore: Williams & Wilkins.

MARKS, I. M. (1987) *Fears, Phobias and Rituals*. New York: Oxford University Press.

MCFARLANE, A. C. (1987) Post-traumatic phenomena in a longitudinal study of children following a natural disaster. *Journal of the American Academy of Child and Adolescent Psychiatry*, **26**, 764–769.

NEWCORN, J. & STRAIN, J. (1992) Adjustment disorder in children and adolescents. *Journal of the American Academy of Child and Adolescent Psychiatry*, **31**, 318–327.

OLLENDICK, T. H. & KING, N. J. (1990) School phobia and separation anxiety. In *Handbook of Social Anxiety* (ed. H. Leitenberg), pp. 179–214. New York: Plenum Press.

QUAY, H. C. (1986) Classification. In *Psychopathological Disorders of Childhood* (3rd edn) (eds H. C. Quay & J. S. Werry), pp. 1–42. New York: John Wiley.

SILVERMAN, W. K. (1991) Diagnostic reliability of anxiety disorders in children using structured interviews. *Journal of Anxiety Disorders*, **5**, 105–124.

—— & EISEN, A. R. (1992) Age differences in the reliability of parent and child reports of child anxious symptomatology using a structured interview. *Journal of the American Academy of Child and Adolescent Psychiatry*, **31**, 117–124.

TERR, L. C. (1983) Chowchilla revisited: the effect of psychic trauma four years after a school-bus kidnapping. *American Journal of Psychiatry*, **140**, 1543–1550.

TONGE, B. J. (1988) Anxiety in adolescence. In *Handbook of Anxiety (Vol. 2)* (eds R. Noyes, M. Roth & G. D. Burrows), pp. 269–287. Amsterdam: Elsevier.

WERRY, J. S. (1985) ICD–9 and DSM–III: classification for the clinician. *Journal of Child Psychology and Psychiatry*, **26**, 1–9.

—— (1991) Overanxious disorder: a review of its taxonomic properties. *Journal of the American Academy of Child and Adolescent Psychiatry*, **30**, 533–544.

—— (1992) Child psychiatric disorders: are they classifiable? *British Journal of Psychiatry*, **161**, 472–480.

—— (in press) Classification. In *Handbook of Anxiety Disorders in Children and Adolescents* (eds T. H. Ollendick, W. Yule and N. J. King). New York: Plenum Press.

——ELKIND, G. S. & REEVES, J. C. (1987a) Attention deficit, conduct, oppositional and anxiety disorders in children: III. Laboratory differences. *Journal of Abnormal Child Psychology*, **15**, 409–428.

——, REEVES, J. C. & ELKIND, G. S. (1987b) Attention deficit, conduct, oppositional and anxiety disorders in children: I. A review of research on differentiating characteristics. *Journal of the American Academy of Child and Adolescent Psychiatry*, **26**, 133–143.

WILSON, M. (1993) DSM–III and the transformation of American psychiatry. *American Journal of Psychiatry*, **150**, 399–410.

WORLD HEALTH ORGANIZATION (1979) *The International Classification of Diseases* (9th revision). Geneva: WHO.

—— (1992) *The ICD–10 Classification of Mental and Behavioural Disorders: Clinical Descriptions and Diagnostic Guidelines.* Geneva: WHO.

16 The role of the educational psychologist in dealing with pupil absenteeism

HOWARD C. M. CARROLL

Introduction

I feel that the best way that I can pay my tribute to Jack Kahn is to offer a perspective on the role of the educational psychologist which is, as far as I can judge, congruent with the current views and practices of educational psychologists in Britain, even though it may not be entirely consistent with ideas put forward in previous editions. If there is inconsistency, it is partly because the profession of educational psychology has grown and in many ways has come of age. No longer are educational psychologists part of the traditional child guidance clinic team. Instead, they function within local education authority educational psychology services, which are run and predominantly staffed by educational psychologists, many of whom will have chartered status within the British Psychological Society.

Certainly, educational psychologists have acquired their own specialist knowledge, something that is recognised by Her Majesty's Inspectorate (HMI) (Department of Education and Science, 1990). Furthermore, collaboration and communication with other professionals continue to be essential components of their daily work (Russell, 1992), some of which has to do with children with school attendance problems. For example, of the various categories of problem dealt with by educational psychologists in the mid 1970s, those to do with pupil absenteeism were the fourth most frequently occurring type of problem (Division of Educational and Child Psychology, 1978). Necessarily, dealing with pupil absenteeism involves educational psychologists communicating with other professionals, though the extent to which responsibility is shared is likely to be variable.

Before considering further the role of the educational psychologist in relation to pupil absenteeism, it will be helpful to say what is meant by the term 'pupil absenteeism', to justify its use rather than the diagnostic labels 'school phobia' or 'school refusal', and to describe the contemporary educational psychologist in a little more detail.

Pupil absenteeism

This is an umbrella term and is used to cover truancy (including post-registration truancy), school phobia/refusal, parental condoned absence and any other form of absence for which labels have yet to be found. The term has merit in that:

(a) unlike the term truancy (absence from school without parental consent or knowledge), it does not necessarily imply that the problem lies within the child; and

(b) unlike the terms school phobia/refusal (the principal manifestation of a neurotic disorder, characterised by severe reluctance to attend school (Galloway, 1983), or a symptom of the family's 'neurosis' (Malmquist, 1965)), it does not necessarily imply that the problem lies within the child and/or his/her family.

For educational psychologists, particularly those who heed the warning of Hargreaves (1978) that there is a danger in using labels which imply a problem within the child, the term is a useful one whether it is used in connection with casework, when the initial focus is the absenting pupil, or in systems work where the problem is seen to be occurrng at a school level.

Preference for the term is not meant to imply a devaluing of alternative terms which certainly have their place, particularly when they are properly applied by specialists who have much experience of working with certain kinds of cases, e.g. school phobics/refusers and their families who are treated by child psychiatrists, social workers and some clinical and educational psychologists.

The contemporary educational psychologist

Since the pioneering days of Sir Cyril Burt, the first educational psychologist (Department of Education and Science, 1968) there has been a gradual increase in the number of educational psychologists employed by local education authorities in Britain, with occasional spurts resulting, for example, from the Summerfield Report (Department of Education and Science, 1968) which led to a doubling of the number of training courses for educational psychologists in the 1970s, and the Warnock Report (Department of Education and Science, 1978), which led to the 1981 Education Act. This had the effect of causing local education authorities in England and Wales to increase significantly the number of educational psychologists they employed, in order to meet the statutory requirements of the Act in connection with the mandatory involvement of educational psychologists in the statementing process. For example, during 1987–89 the number of formal assessments carried out by educational psychologists in Sheffield increased by 56% (Lindsay *et al*, 1990).

As revealed by a recent HMI survey of one-third of educational psychology services in England, the majority had an educational psychologist: statutory aged pupil ratio of between 1:4000 and 1:6000, though none had achieved the educational psychologist: children/young people in the age range 0–19 years ratio of 1:5000 as recommended by the Warnock Report in 1978 (Department of Education and Science, 1990). From these figures it may be deduced that the typical educational psychologist provides a service to two comprehensive schools, about 11 feeder primary schools and probably one special school. If one accepts the Audit Commission/Her Majesty's Inspectorate (1992) estimate that about 16% of pupils could have special educational needs during their school life, it may be appreciated that the potential if not the actual demand for the services of the educational psychologist at an individual case level are considerable.

With respect to the training of the typical educational psychologist, (s)he has an honours degree in psychology or its equivalent, a teaching qualification, has taught for a minimum of two full years, has a postgraduate qualification (usually a Master's degree or Diploma) in educational psychology and, after working full-time for a year as an educational psychologist, preferably under the supervision of a chartered educational psychologist, is eligible to be registered by the British Psychological Society as a chartered educational psychologist. After completing their training some educational psychologists pursue various short courses in order to update their professional knowledge and/or acquire further skills, though there is no professional requirement for them to do so and few, if any, of the courses lead to formal qualifications.

As for what educational psychologists actually do, this has been the subject of at least three major studies (Department of Education and Science, 1968, 1990; Wedell & Lambourne, 1980) and six books (Chazan *et al*, 1974; Gillham, 1978; McPherson & Sutton, 1981; Quicke, 1982; Jones & Frederickson, 1990; Wolfendale *et al*, 1991). From Gillham onwards the impression one gains from these books is of a profession that is critically questioning what it does and how it does it, a state of affairs which makes it difficult to describe with any real sense of confidence what most educational psychologists do. The problem has been exacerbated by recent Government legislation, in particular the 1981 and 1993 Education Acts, the 1988 Education Reform Act and the 1989 Children Act, and the challenges they pose for the profession. For example, should educational psychologists allow themselves to be reduced to mere contributors to the statementing process; should they follow the recommendation of HMI (Department of Education and Science, 1990) and make better and more frequent use of their knowledge in the fields of learning processes and child development; and/or should they concentrate on offering to schools consultation services, in-service training for teachers (INSET) and/ or systems-based project work? Of course, these are not mutually exclusive alternatives, nor do they cover all the possible roles that could be taken on by educational psychologists. Unfortunately, there are no easy answers to the questions posed. Certainly, as reflected in the following list of titles of publications produced by the British Psychological Society's Division of Educational and Child Psychology, educational psychologists are indeed trying to come to terms with current challenges.

(a) Effective Applications of Psychology in Education: Annual Course Proceedings 1990 (Gledhill & Reason, 1990).
(b) A Psychology for the Community: Proceedings of the 1991 DECP Annual Course (Lunt & Sheppard, 1991).
(c) New Concepts, New Solutions? Proceedings of the 1992 DECP Annual Course (Gray, 1992).
(d) Psychologists and Social Services (Peake, 1992).

Given the problems inherent in attempting to describe the changing role of the educational psychologist on the basis of what members of the profession have written about their roles, an alternative approach will be adopted, namely that of describing the core curriculum of the final year of an educational psychologist's training, something which has been developed by the British Psychological Society's Division of Educational and Child Psychology Training Committee (1990) and which covers the following areas:

(a) personal skills and communication
(b) collecting information and assessment
(c) intervention approaches
(d) disabling conditions and special educational needs
(e) professional practice
(f) research and evaluation
(g) issues in child development.

At a process level trainees are expected to develop a problem-solving approach to their work. One of the clearest short accounts of this is provided by Cameron & Stratford (1987) in an article entitled, "Educational psychology: a problem centred approach to service delivery". The approach is located within the wider framework of applied psychology, in particular behavioural psychology, and can be used at different levels, namely:

(a) with individual clients
(b) with direct-contact people
(c) with organisations
(d) at a policy level.

The first level corresponds to casework in which the educational psychologist is directly involved in intervention; the second, to indirect intervention ranging from working with the child's parents/teacher(s) to providing training courses for groups of parents or INSET; the third, to working at a systems level, e.g. with the school as an institution; and the fourth, to being involved in committee work at the highest possible level within a local education authority. It is the first three levels that have the greatest implications for the role of the educational psychologist in connection with dealing with pupil absenteeism, though as will be seen from the following section, the levels, particularly the first two, overlap.

The role of the educational psychologist in dealing with pupil absenteeism

When a school refers a child to the school psychological service because of a concern resulting from poor school attendance, it is likely that the school makes the referral because it is also worried about other aspects of the child's behaviour. When the school suspects, often on the basis of previous experience of the family and perhaps wrongly (Brown, 1983), that the cause of the absence probably lies within the family, e.g. parental condoned absence, it is more likely that the school would refer the problem to the Education Welfare Service rather than to the Educational Psychology Service.

Faced with such a referral, the educational psychologist is likely to follow the kind of sequential strategy outlined by Wedell (1970) in which the educational psychologist gathers further information about the problem, e.g. from the key teacher(s), the parents and the child; formulates and tests out what Wedell referred to as a diagnostic hypothesis, e.g. that the child's absence is due to a combination of school and home-based factors and was precipitated by a particular event; and sets in motion an intervention plan aimed to get the child to attend school on a regular basis and which might, for example, take the following form:

(a) arranges for the child to be given additional support at school because of attainment problems
(b) sets up a social skills training programme because the child has difficulty making friends
(c) discusses with the parents strategies for helping their child to attend school on a regular basis
(d) plans with the teacher(s) ways of smoothing the child's path back to school
(e) evaluates the outcome of the intervention.

Descriptions of such multi-pronged intervention approaches are to be found in the literature, e.g. Blagg (1987) in connection with school phobia and May (1989) with respect to poor attenders in a primary school. However, in the case of the approach outlined here it is worth adding that:

(a) the sequential strategy presented constitutes an oversimplification of Wedell's

(b) Wedell presented his strategy as an approach to dealing with learning problems, e.g. reading, and as such its focus is the child rather than the interaction of the child with his/her environment

(c) educational psychologists vary in terms of the proportion of time they spend interviewing those who know most about the referred child and the time they spend interviewing/assessing the child. Some would argue that most is to be gained by working primarily with the key adults, for example with parents as equal partners (Wolfendale, 1989), whereas others, for example Gersch (1990), would stress the importance of obtaining the child's/young person's perspective on the problem

(d) many educational psychologists would probably argue that today they do not have as much time as they used to for engaging in intervention, whether indirect – their preferred approach in the mid 1970s (Wedell & Lambourne, 1980) – or direct.

There is a surprising paucity of articles containing accounts of the way in which educational psychologists in Britain deal with pupil absenteeism at an individual case level. What literature there is relates to school phobia/refusal, e.g. Chazan (1962), Lowenstein (1973), Bowdler & Johns (1982) and Blagg (1987), though Galloway (1980, 1985) provides valuable insights into dealing with persistent absentees. Thus, in his case study of Albert (Galloway, 1980), a picture is painted of a truant with difficulties at home and problems at school, only some of which could be tackled by the school following the presumed involvement of the educational psychologist.

Chazan's account was based on 33 school phobics who had attended a child guidance clinic between 1949 and 1959. Part of the recommended treatment for 19 of them was a change in school and, as the educational psychologist member of the team, it is probable that Chazan and his predecessor(s) played an important part in arranging the placements. The treatment appears to have had the desired effect since 29 were back in school in less than half a year of referral.

Educational psychologists can also be involved in easing the return to school of pupil absentees by arranging for them to be placed in the sort of unit described by Church & Edwards (1984), a teacher and educational psychologist respectively. However, another educational psychologist (Topping, 1983) has provided evidence that demonstrates the relative ineffectiveness of such units which, furthermore, were not a form of provision favoured by the Elton Committee, which was set up to enquire into discipline in schools (Department of Education and Science, 1989). Instead, the Committee preferred the establishment of teams of professionals, some of whom would/should be educational psychologists who would have as their role that of providing schools with support for dealing with their problem pupils, among whom would be those with attendance problems.

With respect to children who cannot be made to go to school, either by their parents or by professional workers, it is possible to provide home tuition. In the case of the now defunct Inner London Education Authority, for example, it was chronic school phobics/refusers who were educated thus (Smith, 1983) and, in Smith's study of the Southwark Home Tuition Centre, they constituted nearly one-third of all those in receipt of home tuition, a proportion twice that noted by Seaton (1983) in his survey of three Welsh and four English local education authorities, and nearly three times that for the north-west of England (Petrie & Taylor, 1980). According to Smith, the main aim of the Southwark home tuition programme was to prepare the pupils for return to school. However, from Smith's article it would appear that children of primary school age received only about 6 hours tuition per week, a figure that is comparable to the 5 hours per week in four of the authorities and 5–10 hours in three of the authorities surveyed by Seaton. Compared to the 25 hours per week that primary school pupils normally spend in class, the amount of home tuition would seem to have been far from adequate. It is hardly surprising, therefore, that of three methods of treating school refusal investigated by Blagg & Yule (1984), namely behaviour therapy, hospitalisation and a combination of psychotherapy and home tuition, the combination proved least effective in that 10% of the 20 so treated returned to school successfully, compared to 38% of the 16 hospitalised school refusers and 93% of the 30 dealt with by means of behaviour therapy. However, five of the latter group, one of the hospitalised and none of the home-tuition group were less than 11 years of age. Given that both behaviour therapy and psychotherapy are more successful with pre-adolescent than with adolescent phobic children (Miller *et al*, 1972), it is possible that, had fewer of the school refusers in Blagg & Yule's study been of primary school age, the difference in the success rates of the three forms of treatment might not have been quite so great.

Whereas Chazan's presumed contribution to the treatment of school phobics reflected the traditional role of the educational psychologist in a child guidance clinic, the approaches of Lowenstein (1973), Bowdler & Johns (1982) and Blagg (1987) are in keeping with a trend for educational psychologists to take direct responsibility for the treatment of school phobics by means of behaviour therapy. The reasons for this were presented by Kahn *et al* (1981), namely that:

(a) in British universities undergraduate students of psychology receive a good grounding in learning theory and sometimes its application to specific areas such as behaviour therapy

(b) training in intervention techniques now plays an important part in the final year of an educational psychologist's training

(c) as a consequence of (a) and (b), together with what they might learn on short courses taken after completing training, qualified educational psychologists have the knowledge and confidence to use certain forms of behaviour therapy in their intervention work with school refusers.

Lowenstein (1973), for example, applied negative practice and desensitisation procedures, whereas Blagg (1987) made use of the far more dramatic and even traumatic method of *in vivo* flooding, although the technique is not used in isolation. Much work has to be carried out with the family and the school in order that the intervention can succeed.

Bowdler & Johns (1982) describe three approaches that had been used by educational psychologists to deal with pupil absenteeism. The first was the traditional child guidance clinic approach; the second has much in common with the detailed procedures described by Blagg, except that operant conditioning and systematic desensitisation rather than *in vivo* flooding were the forms of behaviour therapy employed; and the third approach took the form of a preventative action research project aimed at the whole school

The need for this third kind of project in connection with school refusal is implied by Pilkington & Piersel (1991) from the University of Nebraska-Lincoln. They challenge the normally held views about school phobia and argue that school refusal should be seen not as a form of neurotic behaviour but "as a normal avoidance reaction to an unpleasant, unsatisfying, or even hostile environment" (p. 290) and that, as such, more attention should be given to the environmental factors, particularly those within the school. They go on to suggest that by bringing about school changes in response to the needs of school refusers all students would benefit. Unfortunately, they weaken their case by employing the terms 'school refusal' (used by them to cover all forms of school avoidance, including truancy) and 'school phobia' interchangeably, and fail to show that their criticisms of the separation anxiety theory, which they consider underpins explanations of school phobia, apply to the views held about school refusal as defined by them. However, their wish to emphasise the importance of school factors and the need to do something about them in order to reduce 'school refusal' reflects developments in Britain where several educational psychologists have written about adopting a whole-school approach to dealing with pupil absenteeism, e.g. Gregory (1980), Bowdler & Johns (1982), O'Hara & Jewell (1982), Gupta (1990) and Moore *et al* (1993).

The impetus for educational psychologists developing a whole-school approach to pupil absenteeism can be traced back to chapters by Reynolds &

Murgatroyd (1977) and by Carroll (1977*a*) in *Absenteeism in South Wales: Studies of Pupils, their Homes and their Secondary Schools* (Carroll, 1977*b*) and chapters by Gillham and by Burden (1978) in the challenging book *Reconstructing Educational Psychology* (Gillham, 1978). Carroll argued that greater account should be taken of school factors when dealing with pupil absenteeism; Reynolds & Murgatroyd demonstrated that factors within the school could in part account for poor school attendance; Gillham questioned the value of psychometrics, reflected the growing dissatisfaction of many education psychologists with their image as 'testers', and pointed the way toward alternative methods of working by educational psychologists; and Burden, in his seminal chapter, "Schools' systems analysis: a project-centred approach", showed other educational psychologists how they might adopt a systems-based approach to working with schools to deal with school identified problems. Since then:

(a) Rutter *et al* (1979) and Mortimore *et al* (1988) have published the results of major research studies at the secondary and primary level respectively that have demonstrated a probable causal relationship between school factors and pupil outcome measures which, in the case of Rutter *et al*'s study, included attendance.

(b) Bos *et al* (1990), in a study of truancy, drop-out and class repeating in 36 secondary schools in Holland, failed to identify school organisational variables that had a significant effect on truancy rates.

(c) Carroll (1992), unlike Mortimore *et al* (1988), has been able to demonstrate that, with respect to primary school attendance, it is possible to identify 'effective' and 'problem' schools.

(d) Reynolds, whose contribution to this book develops these points more fully, has written/edited two books on school effectiveness (Reynolds, 1985; Reynolds & Cuttance, 1992) and is currently co-editor of *School Effectiveness and School Improvement: an International Journal of Research, Policy and Practice*, and through these publications has provided much evidence to show that school process variables do have an effect on school outcome measures.

(e) Frederickson (1990), in the book by Jones & Frederickson (1990), *Refocusing Educational Psychology*, has provided a re-evaluation of the systems approaches used in their practice by educational psychologists and has advocated that educational psychologists make use of Checkland's soft systems methodology (Checkland, 1981; Checkland & Scholes, 1990), which Frederickson argues has advantages over other systems approaches for the kind of work in which educational psychologists engage.

Gregory (1980) was the first educational psychologist to present a model for planning and evaluating action research concerned with the problem of pupil absenteeism at a school level. The model, developed originally by Ainscow *et al* (1978), is based on the systems approach and takes the form of identifying the needs of the school, e.g. improving overall pupil attendance; specifying the objectives to be achieved, e.g. improving the attendance of some pupils; negotiating ways of attaining the objectives and planning how to achieve them; and evaluating the process of attaining the objectives and the actual outcomes.

Bowdler & Johns (1982) adapted Gregory's model for their work in an inner-city comprehensive school. In their paper they indicate what might have been done to improve the school's attendance record, describe what was actually done and report that, during the project year, the attendance rate was 86% compared to 80% for the previous 2 years. However, without an adequate control group (could one ever have one?!) it is not possible to know whether attainment of some/all of the objectives caused the improvement in attendance. Proponents of action research would argue that in research of this kind it is impossible to provide adequate controls and that it is far more important for those involved in the research to examine process issues in order to improve their approach 'the next time round'.

O'Hara & Jewell (1982), in keeping with the behavioural approach put forward by Cameron & Stratford (1987), describe a method for dealing with school non-attendance that has much in common with Gregory's model, though unlike Bowdler & Johns they did not try out their model. Basically their article contains a number of useful ideas for obtaining information from the school and home about possible causes of pupil absenteeism, and for improving the attendance of both individuals and groups by implementing various strategies for working with pupils, parents and teachers.

Surprisingly, Gupta (1990), a senior educational psychologist in Essex who describes how he worked with a comprehensive school to improve its attendance, makes no reference to the articles of fellow educational psychologists cited here. However, in keeping with Gregory's suggestion that an action research project could be based on improving the attendance of some pupils, Gupta, the school's educational welfare officer and the staff of the school concentrated their attention on Year 8 poor attenders rather than the whole school. Gupta describes how they identified the poor attenders, lists the strategies that were developed for improving their attendance and demonstrates the possible effects of the intervention on subsequent attendance. He also provides a useful evaluation of the possible child, family and school factors that might have caused the attendance problems of his poor attenders. Perhaps his most important finding was that proper monitoring of each pupil's attendance and the provision of support for form tutors and persistent non-attenders and their families had a significant effect on attendance.

The most recently reported research project on truancy was carried out by a team of ten educational psychologists from Leicester in a community college that had asked for the help of the educational psychologists in dealing with the college's truancy problem (Moore *et al*, 1993). The approach to the project that was adopted by the team was based on the soft systems methodology previously referred to. In order to test out hypotheses about the possible causes of truancy (including post-registration truancy) from/in the college the team spent a whole week interviewing selected staff and Year 10 students, tracking certain students in and out of class, and meeting together to share their findings. At the end of the project they wrote reports for the college, discussed their findings with the college executive and, 4 months later, the project leader received feedback from the vice-principal about changes that had been made as a consequence of the project and which it was hoped would lead to reduced truancy. However, although the senior educational psychologist was able to report that the beneficial effects of the project on her/his team were still in evidence nearly 2 years after the project he did not present attendance data to show whether the project might have had an effect. Given the cost of the project in terms of time, effort and the salaries of the ten team members, it is surprising indeed that changes in attendance were not monitored!

Conclusions

The chapter in Kahn *et al* (1981) on the role of the educational psychologist ended with a section entitled, "Extended boundaries". This refers to the boundaries of awareness of the child psychiatrist, the social worker and the educational psychologist in the traditional child guidance clinic team and is about the benefits to team members, as well as to patients, of team members working together. If this chapter was to end in the same way, today's educational psychologist would find it difficult to recognise herself, would feel uncomfortable with a term like 'patient' and would question whether she spends much time working in a clinic context. In 1977, for example, it was found that, with respect to the total time educational psychologists spent working in different settings, 67% was spent in schools and units and 13% in child guidance centres and clinics (Wedell & Lambourne, 1980). With the phasing out of child guidance clinics in many areas and their replacement by hospital out-patient clinics in child psychiatry departments, it seems likely that educational psychologists in the 1990s probably spend even less time working in child guidance clinic contexts than they did in the 1970s.

Given that, in the project reported on by Moore *et al* (1993), the whole team was made up only of educational psychologists and that the function of the team was not to work directly with the college staff in order to reduce the truancy problem, but to provide them with possible reasons for the problem so that they could decide for themselves what to do about it on the basis of the eport provided, the question has to be asked: have educational psychologists moved too far away from working with other professionals? Furthermore, in their desire to avoid the mantle of the hero innovator, have they opted out of the task of working with other professionals in order to deal with a problem, in this instance, one of truancy?

The thrust of Kahn *et al*'s section on extended boundaries is that the contributions of a single professional group in dealing with a problem are limited and that the coming together of different professionals produces a better solution and, in doing so, has the potential for broadening the horizons of all involved. If this is true for other kinds of school phobia/refusal, it is even more true for pupil absenteeism. That being so, educational psychologists should beware of becoming too independent and should look for ways of engaging in teamwork that involves other professionals. It is perhaps salutary to recall that the development of systems work by educational psychologists can be traced back to Burden attending on a chance basis a Royal Society, not a British Psychological Society, conference on systems theory (Burden, 1978). Since the profession of educational psychology has come of age, its members no longer need to prove to themselves that they alone have all the answers. In the case of pupil absenteeism, one is faced with a multi-faceted problem. As such, it demands to be dealt with by a multi-professional team.

References

AINSCOW, M., BOND, J., GARDINER, J., *et al* (1978) The development of a three part evaluation procedure for inset courses. *British Journal of In-Service Education*, **4**, 184–190.

AUDIT COMMISSION/HER MAJESTY'S INSPECTORATE (1992) *Getting in on the Act: Provision for Pupils with Special Educational Needs: the National Picture*. London: HMSO.

BLAGG, N. (1987) *School Phobia and its Treatment*. London: Croom Helm.

—— & YULE, W. (1984) The behavioural treatment of school refusal – a comparative study. *Behaviour Research and Therapy*, **22**, 119–127.

BOS, K. T., RUIJTERS, A. M. & VISSCHER, A. J. (1990) Truancy, drop-out, class repeating and their relation with school characteristics. *Educational Research*, **32**, 175–185.

BOWDLER, D. J. & JOHNS, P. (1982) Non-attendance at school: three approaches. *Association of Educational Psychologists Journal*, **5**, 32–37.

BRITISH PSYCHOLOGICAL SOCIETY (1990) Core Curriculum for Educational Psychology Training Courses. Leicester: BPS.

BROWN, D. (1983) Truants, families and schools: a critique of the literature on truancy. *Educational Review*, **35**, 225–235.

BURDEN, R. (1978) Schools' systems analysis: a project centred approach. In *Reconstructing Educational Psychology* (ed. B. Gillham), pp. 113–131. London: Croom Helm.

CAMERON, R. & STRATFORD, R. (1987) Educational psychology: a problem-centred approach. *Educational Psychology in Practice*, **2**, 10–20.

CARROLL, H. C. M. (1977a) The problem of absenteeism: research studies, past and present. In *Absenteeism in South Wales* (ed. H. C. M. Carroll), pp. 4–29. Swansea: Faculty of Education, University College, Swansea.

—— (1977*b*) *Absenteeism in South Wales.* Swansea: Faculty of Education, University College Swansea.

—— (1992) School effectiveness and school attendance. *School Effectiveness and School Improvement*, **3**, 258–271.

CHAZAN, M. (1962) School phobia. *British Journal of Educational Psychology*, **32**, 209–217.

——, MOORE, T., WILLIAMS, P., *et al* (1974) *The Practice of Educational Psychology.* London: Longman.

CHECKLAND, P. B. (1981) *Systems Thinking, Systems Practice.* Chichester: John Wiley.

—— & SCHOLES, J. (1990) *Soft Systems Methodology in Action.* Chichester: John Wiley.

CHURCH, J. & EDWARDS, B. (1984) Helping pupils who refuse school. *Special Education: Forward Trends*, **11**, 28–32.

DEPARTMENT OF EDUCATION AND SCIENCE (1968) *Psychologists in Education (The Summerfield Report)*, London: HMSO.

—— (1978) *Special Educational Needs (The Warnock Report).* London: HMSO.

—— (1989) *Discipline in Schools (The Elton Report).* London: HMSO.

—— (1990) *Psychological Services in England: Report by Her Majesty's Inspectors.* London: Department of Education and Science.

DIVISON OF EDUCATIONAL AND CHILD PSYCHOLOGY (1978) Psychological services for children. *Bulletin of the British Psychological Society*, **31**, 11–15.

FREDERICKSON, N. (1990) Systems approaches in EP practice: a re-evaluation. In *Refocusing Educational Psychology* (eds N. Jones & N. Frederickson), pp. 130–164. London: Falmer Press.

GALLOWAY, D. (1980) Problems in the assessment and management of persistent absenteeism from school In *Out of School* (eds L. Hersov & I. Berg), pp. 149–170. Chichester: John Wiley.

—— (1983) Truancy. *The Encyclopedic Dictionary of Psychology* (eds R. Harre & R. Lamb). London: Blackwell.

—— (1985) *Schools and Persistent Absentees.* Oxford: Pergamon Press.

GERSCH, I. (1990) The pupil's view. In *Meeting Disruptive Behaviour* (eds M. Scherer, I. Gersch & L. Fry), pp. 117–140. London: Macmillan Education.

GILLHAM, B. (1978) (ed.) *Reconstructing Educational Psychology.* London: Croom Helm.

GLEDHILL, M. & REASON, R. (1990) Effective Applications of Psychology in Education: Annual Course Proceedings 1990. *Educational and Child Psychology*, **7**, 3–96.

GRAY, P. (1992) New Concepts, New Solutions? Proceedings of the 1992 DECP Annual Course. *Educational and Child Psychology*, **9**, 3–66.

GREGORY, P. (1980) Truancy: a plan for school-based action-research. *Association of Educational Psychologists Journal*, **5**, 30–34.

GUPTA, Y. (1990) A study in the improvement of school attendance in a comprehensive school. *Links*, **16**, 11–16.

HARGREAVES, D. (1978) Deviance: the interactionist approach. In *Reconstructing Educational Psychology* (ed. B. Gillham), pp. 67–81. London: Croom Helm.

JONES, N. & FREDERICKSON, N. (1990) *Refocusing Educational Psychology.* London: Falmer Press.

KAHN, J. H., NURSTEN, J. P. & CARROLL, H. C. M. (1981) *Unwillingly to School.* Oxford: Pergamon Press.

LINDSAY, G., QUAYLE, R., LEWIS, G., *et al* (1990) *Special Educational Needs Review 1990.* City of Sheffield Education Service.

LOWENSTEIN, L. F. (1973) The treatment of moderate school phobia by negative practice and desensitization procedures. *Association of Educational Psychologists Journal*, **3**, 46–50.

LUNT, I. & SHEPPARD, J. (1991) A Psychology for the Community: Proceedings of the 1991 DECP Annual Course. *Educational and Child Psychology*, **8**, 3–84.

MALMQUIST, C. P. (1965) School phobia. A problem in family neurosis. *Journal of Child Psychiatry*, **4** 293–319.

MAY, S. (1989) *An Investigation into the Effects of Social Skills Training on the School Attendance of a Group of to 9 Year Old Children.* Unpublished MEd dissertation, University College of Swansea.

MCPHERSON, F. & SUTTON, A. (1981) *Reconstructing Psychological Practice.* London: Croom Helm.

MILLER, L., BARRETT, C., HAMPE, E., *et al* (1972) Comparison of reciprocal inhibition psychotherapy and waiting list control for phobic children. *Journal of Abnormal Psychology*, **79** 269–279.

MOORE, L., CLARE, H., CORFIELD, S., *et al* (1993) A school-based action research project on truancy. *Educational Psychology in Practice*, **8**, 208–214.

MORTIMORE, P., SAMMONS, P., STOLL, L., *et al* (1988) *School Matters: The Junior Years*. Wells: Open Books.

O'HARA, M. & JEWELL, T. (1982) Non-attendance at school: a behavioural approach. *Association of Educational Psychologists Journal*, **5**, 28–32.

PEAKE, A. (1992) Psychologists and Social Services. *Educational and Child Psychology*, **9**, 3–89.

PETRIE, I. & TAYLOR, D. (1980) Home teaching in the North West: a pilot survey. *Child Care, Health and Development*, **6**, 65–71.

PILKINGTON, C. L. & PIERSEL, W. C. (1991) School phobia: a critical analysis of the separation anxiety theory and an alternative conceptualization. *Psychology in the Schools*, **28**, 290–303.

QUICKE, J. (1982) *The Cautious Expert*. Milton Keynes: Open University Press.

REYNOLDS, D. (1985) *Studying School Effectiveness*. London: Falmer Press.

—— & MURGATROYD, S. (1977) The sociology of schooling and the absent pupil: the school as a factor in the generation of truancy. In *Absenteeism in South Wales* (ed. H. C. M. Carroll), pp. 51–67. Swansea: Faculty of Education, University College, Swansea.

—— & CUTTANCE, P. (1982) *School Effectiveness: Research, Policy and Practice*. London: Cassell.

RUSSELL, P. (1992) Boundary issues in new contexts – implications for educational psychology practice. In *The Profession and Practice of Educational Psychology* (eds S. Wolfendale *et al*), pp. 170–184. London: Cassell.

RUTTER, M., MAUGHAN, B., MORTIMORE, P., *et al* (1979) *Fifteen Thousand Hours: Secondary Schools and their Effects on Pupils*. London: Open Books.

SEATON, N. D. R. (1983) *Home Tuition Services for Children: A Survey of LEA Provision*. Unpublished MEd dissertation, University College of Swansea.

SMITH, S. (1983) School refusal – a practical approach. *Association of Child Psychology and Psychiatry News*, **15**, 3–8.

TOPPING, K. (1983) *Educational Systems for Disruptive Adolescents*. London: Croom Helm.

WEDELL, K. (1970) Diagnosing learning difficulties. *Association of Educational Psychologists Journal*, **2**, 23–29.

—— & LAMBOURNE, R. (1980) Psychological services for children in England and Wales. *Occasional Papers of the Division of Educational and Child Psychology*, **4** (1 & 2).

WOLFENDALE, S. (1989) *Parental Involvement: Developing Networks Between School, Home and Community*. London: Cassell Educational.

——, BRYANS, T., FOX, M., *et al* (1991) *The Profession and Practice of Educational Psychology: Future Directions*. London: Cassell.

17 Family therapy

JUDITH LASK

For many years both researchers and clinicians have been interested in the families of children and adolescents who do not attend school and when a referral is made to a child psychiatry setting, work with parents, carers or family is usually part of the package of help provided (e.g. Leventhal *et al*, 1967; Hersov, 1985). This chapter highlights some of the main findings relating to the family context of children who are unwilling to go to school and briefly outlines some of the basic principles of systems theory and their application to these kinds of difficulties. Although there is a dearth of research evidence relating to the application of family therapy approaches to school attendance problems (Huffington & Sevitt, 1989), systems theory provides a useful framework for thinking about the relationships between child, family, the school and other wider systems (Imber Black, 1988) and the different models of family therapy suggest a range of interventions many of which are commonly part of service provision.

The family therapy literature has generally not made the usual distinction between the families of children who are phobic of school, those who truant and those who show difficulties in adjusting to the school environment. Each of these problems, all of which can have serious implications for the future, tends to be viewed as the result of a unique interaction between family relationships, individual characteristics and wider systems (Dowling *et al*, 1985). Similar therapeutic approaches may be used across a range of problems but these will be tailored to suit individual families rather than categories of problem. However, as family therapy techniques become more developed, and demands to justify the economics of service provision become greater, there is an increased interest in identifying which kinds of interventions are most successful in which circumstances. Part of this process must be to identify more clearly the family and wider system patterns that may be associated with particular presenting problems and to build on the information already provided by research.

The families of those unwilling to go to school

Studies have tended to look at particular characteristics or relationships within families rather than overall patterns of interaction and have been particularly interested in exploring the similarities and differences between school phobics and truants, the two broad subgroups of non-attenders. Among the demographic differences described is the tendency for phobic children to come later in the birth order and to have older mothers than children who truant (Berg *et al*, 1972). The families of truants also tend to come from larger families (Hersov, 1960), lower socio-economic groups and to have experienced a range of adversity including paternal unemployment (Farrington, 1980). Much of the evidence relates to clinic populations and we know much less about those children who regularly truant but do not come to the notice of the helping professions.

Although this kind of information is interesting and points to the importance of family and wider systems in the development of particular problems, it is information about family relationships that is of particular value to the family therapist who will be trying to identify helpful ways of intervening. This information has tended to be limited to particular dyadic relationships partly because of the theoretical orientation of researchers but also because of the real difficulties in studying patterns of family interaction (Hetherington & Martin, 1972; Loader *et al*, 1981; Huffington & Sevitt, 1989). There has been a strong tendency to concentrate on the mother–child relationship, which in part reflects the traditional mother-centred approach to child psychiatry (Skynner, 1974). The tendency for school-phobic children to be dependent on and overprotected by their mother has been widely noted (Johnson *et al*, 1941; Kahn & Nursten, 1962; Berg, 1980). Less attention has been given to relationships with fathers or the role that they play in mediating the relationship between mother and child (Skynner, 1974). In their study of adolescents presenting with school phobia Huffington & Sevitt (1989) noted a tendency towards an oppositional relationship between father and index child. Even less attention has been given to the role of siblings, although they will often provide a bridge from home to school and an important base for the development of supportive peer relationships.

Bowlby (1973) suggested four main patterns of interaction in school refusal. These all involve shared anxieties about the safety of a parent or child. Other authors have also given clinical accounts of family patterns and interactions over generations (Malmquist, 1965; Crumley, 1974).

In a study of the self-perceptions of the families of victims and bullies in schools Bowers *et al* (1992) found that the families of children who are victimised tend to be very cohesive while those of bullies have low cohesion. This study was based on the Circumplex model of family functioning (Olsen,

1986) in which moderate cohesiveness and flexibility are associated with optimum family functioning. This mirrors findings relating to the families of school phobics and truants. Currently there is renewed interest in the role of bullying and non-school attendance and Reid (1983) suggests that being bullied leads to loss of confidence and self-esteem in social relationships and may lead to absenteeism to escape the torment. It would be helpful to know more about the types of family relationships that protect children or increase vulnerability, both in relation to bullying and school refusal.

Huffington & Sevitt (1989) noted the tendency of school-phobic adolescents to be sad, lacking in initiative and separate within their family. As children they were likely to have had a mutually dependent relationship with their mothers together with chronic separation difficulties. However over time this developed, resulting in an apparent lack of closeness with mother and hostility towards father.

Truancy has been related consistently to marital disharmony (Farrington, 1980), inconsistent discipline (Hersov, 1960), physical punishment by parents and a lack of interest in the value of education (Fogelman & Richardson, 1974; Olwens, 1980). Clinical experience and various case studies in the literature suggest that marital disharmony is also often a feature of the families of school phobics but that this is likely to be less overt, often with a strong family tendency to avoid conflict.

Non-clinic populations

Family therapists, like other clinicians, have the task of helping children and families overcome difficulties. It is important to ask questions not only about families who involve outside agencies but also about those families who experience difficulties but overcome them effectively without recourse to professional help. Many children stay away from school from time to time without developing some of the emotional problems associated with school phobia or the delinquent behaviour associated with truanting (Fogelman *et al*, 1980) and studies indicate that many children show a reluctance to go to school (Moore, 1966; Newson & Newson, 1977). It would be helpful to know what factors prevent the development of more serious difficulties.

Research issues for family therapists

The problems associated with assessing complex family interaction have already been mentioned and have been fully discussed elsewhere (Frude, 1980; Kinston & Loader, 1984; Huffington & Sevitt, 1989). Available research helps the therapist to focus on certain issues or formulate hypotheses about a particular family but generally does not have a wide enough focus to help the therapist fully understand the complex and circular interactions that serve to generate and maintain problems. As the focus for family therapy is to promote change in these patterns, good research in this area is essential in order to formulate intervention strategies and assess the effectiveness of help.

As well as the tension between the linear nature of the research process and the circularity of the theories underpinning family therapy (Goldberg & David, 1991), there is also a tension between the individual focus of diagnosis and the family therapist's formulation of the presenting symptom as one part of a wider family interaction – just one piece of the jigsaw.

Within the family therapy field attempts to equate particular, detailed patterns of family interaction with particular presenting problems have not been very successful. The description of the 'psychosomatic family' put forward by Minuchin *et al* (1978) has been criticised (Coyne & Anderson, 1989; Wood, 1993) and it is generally agreed that a range of family patterns can be found applying to a range of presenting problems. Perhaps more successful have been the attempts to isolate particular dimensions of family relationships and relate them to the notion of functional and dysfunctional families (Olsen *et al*, 1983). The most useful of these dimensions seem to be those of adaptability and cohesiveness with the most dysfunctional families lying to the extremes of the continuum. Evidence relating to the families of school phobics and truants would suggest that the families of school phobics may be characterised by high cohesive or 'enmeshed' relationships and those of truants by low cohesion or 'disengagement'. It is interesting to note that in their small study of adolescent school phobics Huffington & Sevitt (1989) suggested that over time relationships in the families of more chronic school phobics had changed to become 'disengaged' and suggest the importance of considering a two-way interaction between symptom and family relationships. Many questions remain to be answered more fully including why do children present with one problem rather than another, what are the early indications that a family (and its wider relationships) will not be able successfully to support children in their school attendance and what are the most effective ways of intervening into family relationships?

Although family therapy is a frequently used intervention, there have been no controlled studies of its effectiveness in addressing problems of non-school attendance. However, reviews of studies of family therapy in general indicate that as a form of treatment it is at least as effective as other kinds of interventions over a range of problems and treatment settings (Hazelrigg *et al*, 1987; Markus *et al*, 1990). However, despite the methodological problems of researching into psychotherapy in general and family therapy in particular (Gale, 1979; Frude, 1980), there are many questions that need to be addressed. As well as asking whether or not family therapy is a useful intervention we also need to know the effects of combining it with other approaches and what it is about the therapy that makes the difference and leads to positive change. In this way successful treatment combinations can be developed and refined.

Systems theory

Systems theory provides the framework for the practice of family therapy and although most readers will have some familiarity with the main ideas it may be helpful to reiterate some of the basic concepts. For more detailed discussion I refer readers to other texts (Hoffman, 1981; Burnham, 1986; Barker, 1992).

Circularity

Although it is easy to slip into linear explanations of particular behaviours and make statements such as "the mother's anxiety caused her son to stay home from school", most child psychiatry professionals would acknowledge that what is being described is just one part of a wider pattern of behaviour and will seek to reveal a broader picture. The family therapist has a particular interest in the way in which the behaviour of different family members connect and interact with one another and will seek to move the spotlight from one narrow presenting problem (e.g. fear of school) to illuminate these wider patterns of relationships, often presenting an alternative definition of the problem suggesting alternative or additional interventions.

The whole is greater than the sum of the parts

These ideas about circularity connect with the notion that the whole system is more than the sum of its parts and there is important information to be gained from looking at the relationships between different entities. Not only do individuals affect one another but sets of relationships can affect other sets of relationships. For example, a conflictual relationship between father and son may lead to a greater closeness between mother and son.

At times the preservation of the family system appears to have precedence over individual needs. For instance, in a family that fears the results of serious argument subtle and complex moves might be made to avoid confrontation and the feared breakdown of the family.

Context

The individual, family, community and school can all be thought of as individual systems that operate within particular contexts. It is those contexts that give meaning to particular behaviour. For example, the reluctance of a mother to demand her son's return to school in the early days of school refusal might make more sense when viewed in the context of the father's violence, which has thrust the mother into a protective role towards her son. Failed attempts to reintegrate a child into school need to be viewed not only in the context of the family but also in the context of the school/family system. It is the context that keeps the problem alive so that by successfully intervening in that context, e.g. family relationships, the presenting problem should diminish.

Beliefs, behaviour and relationships

The importance of beliefs in determining behaviour and relationships has been widely discussed and family therapists are concerned to know about important beliefs in families in order to understand behaviour and also to help formulate interventions that will be acceptable and useful to families. An intervention that contradicts a strong belief is likely to be rejected. With problems of school attendance it is particularly important to understand beliefs around education, schools and teachers. Beliefs give rise to rules in families and again these can at times be unhelpful. Although family therapists may have a particular focus on behaviour, beliefs or relationships, most are concerned with all three and the relationship between them. For example a child's reluctance to involve teachers in difficulties might be traced back to a family rule about coping with one's own problems, which may prevent the development of supportive relationships within school so that there is no easy way of dealing with day-to-day school problems.

Recently there has been a renewed interest in the way in which beliefs and behaviours act as constraints and limit the options for change (White, 1986). They can act as blinkers and prevent the discovery of new options and new patterns.

Stability and change

The main concern of the therapist is not the epidemiology or even causation of difficulties. These aspects are adjuncts to the main task of helping individuals and families make positive changes in their lives. It is the present and future that are of most importance. Family therapists describe the continuous tension between stability and change and the need for families to be both flexible and ordered (Watzlawick *et al*, 1974). The demand for change on all families and individuals is great. We all have to make continuous adjustments in response to the changing needs of family members and changing external circumstances. At certain key stages in the life cycle the need for change both in the individual and the family becomes more crucial and it is at these times that there is a particular risk that problems will develop (Carter & McGoldrick, 1989). The child's own individual development is inextricably linked with the development of the family. For example, when a child moves to secondary school relationships within families change and the child becomes more independent, investing more energy in relationships outside the family. In situations in which these changes are experienced as threatening, actions may be taken to stabilise by returning to old patterns. Thus a child could develop physical symptoms and a fear of going to school in part to support a parent who is feeling upset by the change in relationships demanded by the growing child. This is not to imply that the child makes a conscious decision to make this sacrifice but a system of subtle responses to quite normal reluctance could mould and intensify the symptom. The mother may add to it because it feels more comfortable to have the child at home, the father because it is helpful to him to have the mother involved with the child, and other children because it gives them a chance to get on with their lives.

Assessment

During the treatment phase, the family therapist might do work that focuses mainly on family relationships or relationships with wider systems but at first contact it is important to take a broader view of the assessment process so that the most effective intervention strategies can be formulated. However, family therapists using systems theory as a major framework for understanding problems and formulating interventions will inevitably emphasise different aspects of the assessment from someone taking a more individual, behavioural or developmental perspective.

This section concentrates on the assessment of the family including the relationship with wider systems, although it is of course also important to gather detailed information about the development of the problem, the development of the child and important family history.

Referral

Family therapy has taken particular account of the process surrounding referral (Reder & Kraemer, 1980; Crowther *et al*, 1990; Dare *et al*, 1990). There is an acceptance that referrers are often an important part of the system to be addressed. One of the basic tasks is to identify the person who is asking for help. As clinicians we can all think of cases where we have worked very hard to effect a change in the family and later realised that they are not wanting help for the problem referred. In school-related problems this is an issue of particular interest as on occasions the most concerned parties appear to be the school, psychologist or education social worker rather than the child or family. Those who draw on a 'solution-based' brief therapy have delineated three kinds of referral: those where the client is the customer and really wants help for a problem; those who are complainants and although acknowledge a problem are not in the market for help, and thirdly those who are merely visitors and have been sent by someone else (Berg, 1991; Durrant, 1993). When the referrer and the family do not agree about the request for help it may be useful to hold a joint meeting to promote a discussion between referrer and client in the hope that they can come to some agreement (Aponte, 1976). Alternatively it may be possible to make a different contract with the family that better reflects their perception of their problem. It is important to avoid being caught up in the conflict between other professionals and the family without being in a position to promote change.

Often there are already a large number of professionals involved in serious school attendance problems. The referral to a specialist agency can reflect a lack of specialist skill in the other professionals but it might also reflect particular issues within the professional system or in their relationship with the family. I will outline a few of the more common scenarios.

Relationship between client and professional

Sometimes professionals can become stuck in too close, too distant or even conflictual relationships with clients. Therapy demands a degree of manoeuvrability if new interventions are to be tried. An education social worker may have become too close and sympathetic with a family or an individual family member and find it difficult to see any negative contribution, or perhaps have lost the ability to be challenging when necessary. On the other hand, a teacher may have been caught up in a fierce conflict about the need for attendance and lost any possibility of further co-operation.

On occasions the contribution of professionals can make it less likely that families will be able to solve their own problems. One way is to be so helpful that the family experience of being helpless and incompetent is reinforced. Another is to continue to support an unhelpful view of the problem. For example, a paediatrician may continue to carry out physical investigations at the request of parents when it is reasonably clear that there is no physical basis to a child's complaints.

Issues within the professional system

Sometimes the professional systems themselves can become dysfunctional leading to less effective work with clients. A referral to another agency may be one strategy to resolve professional differences, to compensate for failures in service such as a depleted education support service or a school that has been unable to control bullying, or provide a good degree of contact and co-operation with parents. On occasions breakdowns in service can engender a sense of guilt, which again can be an important factor in the decision to refer.

An understanding of the referral process can be crucial in making an effective contract with the family and ensuring that everyone works together to promote and support change. The therapist might well find it helpful to hold professional meetings to formally agree co-operation with treatment plans.

The family assessment interview

There is of course no clear division between assessment and therapy. Just as new information is gained throughout contact with a client, patient or family so the assessment interview has an impact on the family. There are usually two broad aims in an assessment interview:

(a) to gather as much useful information as possible
(b) to begin to set up a relationship and structure that will support further interventions.

Within family therapy the assessment process will vary depending on the particular model or focus that is used. Here I will outline a broad approach to family assessment that leaves the therapist with some flexibility of approach.

Who to invite?

There is some debate among family therapists about what constitutes the 'meaningful system' in relation to therapy. Some therapists will insist that it is necessary to work with the whole family living at home and may refuse to meet with the family if important members are missing. Skynner (1974) points out that in working with the families of school phobics without the father present the therapy may be replicating fundamental family problems. However, refusing therapy in the absence of fathers might be discriminatory towards women who often bear the main burden of family difficulties and pressures from outside agencies. In addition, many families are separated and/or reconstituted and often relatives, friends and others can play a significant role in family life in general and the presenting problem in particular. In these situations it would seem most helpful to think in terms of the 'problem-oriented system' and attempt, at least initially, to convene as many members of this system as possible. Some therapists prefer to leave the decision about who attends to the parents and indeed this can reveal important information. However, it is important to be mindful of family members or significant others who are absent and to enquire about the reasons for their absence, what their views would be and what efforts should be made to encourage them to attend.

Setting up the interview

Although the family therapist may, for a particular reason, choose to interview individuals or subgroups, the main assessment will take place by meeting the whole family group affording the opportunity to observe patterns of relationships at first hand. If the interview can be observed by other members of the team this will be of great advantage (see below). The room should be large enough to accommodate the family and allow the therapist to observe the whole picture. Age-appropriate toys and drawing materials should be available and adolescents and even adults can feel more comfortable if they have something to 'fiddle with'. The family should decide its own seating arrangements as this can provide important information. A clear introduction about the assessment procedure and timing is important both for ethical and clinical reasons. It is useful at the beginning to explain the reasons for meeting with the whole family and to set some simple rules for the session, such as everyone staying in the room. Parents often need permission to be in charge of their own children and clarifying this helps promote usual patterns of behaviour as well as giving more control of the process to the parents.

Joining

Although structural family therapists have written most about this phase (Minuchin, 1974), all family therapists would see it as very important. The kind of relationship formed will again depend on approach but a degree of flexibility is always important. In family therapy where the client is the system rather than individuals it is especially important to join with all family members, and time spent at the beginning of an interview making positive contact is crucial if all family members are to work towards resolving difficulties. Particular skills are used to communicate with children taking account of their developmental level. The referred child may be particularly uncomfortable and care is taken initially to discuss positive topics and to avoid increasing discomfort by only talking about school.

Family definition of problem and goals

One very important task in the assessment process is to gain a clear idea of the views of family members about the 'problem'. Sometimes there is a shared view but often there will be differences. The challenge is to find a definition of the problem that can be agreed by everyone and is also acceptable to the therapist and agency. Another important aim is to help family members formulate concrete measures of success. These may relate to a complete resolution of the difficulties but should also include small indications of improvement. For instance, returning happily to school may be the ultimate aim but walking to the local shop may be a smaller agreed goal.

Finding connections through circular questioning

Both clinicians and researchers know the importance of devising a good question. In order to formulate interventions family therapists need to gather systemic information about beliefs, behaviours and relationships and how they connect to the presenting problem. A particular kind of questioning technique called 'circular' or 'reflexive' questioning has been developed to gather this information. There are many useful descriptions of this kind of questioning and its use both to gather information and as an interventive technique (Penn, 1985; Tomm, 1987). The main aim of using these questions is to reveal (for the benefit of therapist and client) new information and new connections that go beyond the set story that clients usually tell about the problem and to show the way in which other family members contribute towards the problem and can also contribute towards the solution.

Observing pattern and process

It will already be clear that in addition to the content of what is said and done during the assessment the family therapist closely observes the repetitive patterns and process of interaction within the family. This includes verbal, non-verbal and relationship patterns and repetitive behavioural sequences and patterns of communication. Children's play and drawing should be included. This information will develop a fuller picture of family life and relationships and provide a focus for future interventions.

Family structure

Even if a family therapist does not work primarily in a structural mode the examination of family organisational patterns can be an important source of information. This involves not only the observation of individual relationships but also those between subgroups within the family. Structural family therapists are clear that some organisational patterns meet the needs of family members better than others but there is wide recognition that the kind of family structure that is most functional will depend on a number of factors, including life cycle stage and cultural context. They would argue that all families benefit from clear and moderately flexible boundaries between individuals and subsystems and a clear hierarchy in which adults have more power than children (Minuchin, 1974). The ability of the organisational pattern to deal with and resolve conflict is also an important consideration. Some common dysfunctional patterns are:

(a) overclose or 'enmeshed' relationships that make individuation and independence difficult to achieve

(b) 'disengaged' relationships in which basic needs for intimacy and care are not met

(c) inverted, collapsed or unclear hierarchy that interferes with the need for decision-making and clear leadership and discipline

(d) boundaries that are either too rigid or too permeable and do not provide an appropriate degree of flexibility or stability

(e) triangular patterns of relationships in which there is either a cross-generational alliance that is stronger than the parental alliance or coalitions between two family members against another

(f) conflict avoidance: all of these patterns can work to avoid conflict being addressed and resolved.

Structural therapists argue that symptoms such as school refusal and other school-related problems arise out of, and are maintained by, dysfunctional patterns.

The therapist will test out the flexibility of these organisational arrangements by, for example, asking distant parents to enter into a discussion.

Strength, exceptions and attempted solutions

Often when families come for help they are feeling defeated and have stopped noticing the times when things are going better or they are successfully dealing with their problems (George *et al*, 1990). By uncovering exceptions to problem behaviour or identifying times when life is a little less difficult the therapist and family can identify a base on which to build and hopefully challenge the perceived hopelessness of the situation.

Usually families have attempted solutions to their difficulties and it is useful to ask about and identify these for four reasons. Firstly, they give a clue to the families preferred mode of tackling problems; secondly, it may be possible to identify why these often very good solutions have not been successful (perhaps because they have not been tried for long enough or too rapid change was attempted); thirdly, the discussion contributes towards the important process of empowering families; and, fourthly, it avoids the trap of suggesting interventions that have already been unsuccessfully tried.

Relationship between family and wider system

Although the role of other professionals will probably have been evaluated at the point of referral it is important to spend some time during the initial interview assessing the relationship between the family members and those wider systems. This is helpful both in order to assess the role of such interactions in the genesis and maintenance of problem behaviour as well as to help predict the likely pattern of co-operation with further interventions. Taylor (1986) discusses the role of the child as a go-between in relation to the school and family. She suggests that this is a difficult role for every child and in situations where the school and parents are not working well together the task for the child of holding school and home together can be impossible and problems arise. This is a form of triangulation as described above. One solution for the child can be to side with one against the other, perhaps leading to disengagement from home or refusal to go to school. Cultural, racial and gender issues will all play a part in the relationships between home and school as will the parents' own experience of education and the teacher's own experience of family life.

Formulation

The family therapist is less interested in giving a diagnosis to a particular child than in formulating a multilevel picture of family relationships (including those with wider systems) and how these relate to the presenting problem. From this, decisions will be made about a way forward to help the family bearing in mind their view of the problem and their commitment to particular kinds of change. Family therapists generally avoid a firm diagnosis because of the risk that it can shut down curiosity and limit approaches to help.

Family therapy approaches to treatment

Following the assessment and formulation of agreed goals therapists will vary in their specific approach. This will be influenced by a number of factors including experience, personality of the therapist, preferred model, time, resources and agency policy. Some approaches are more problem-focused than others but most therapists would share the view that the longer problems exist the harder they are to overcome and would prefer to move towards an early return to school in order to limit the damage to peer relationships and educational attainment.

Reframing

Basic to all family therapy approaches is the concept of reframing (Watzlawick *et al*, 1974). This is the process of giving an alternative meaning to a set of circumstances, and allows for the development of new perceptions and actions. For example, a young boy who complains of physical symptoms in order to avoid school may be thought of as 'sick and vulnerable' by his parents. It may be helpful to them to reframe his behaviour as 'challenging to their authority' in order to free them to be firmer in their handling of the situation. The challenge to the therapist is to find reframes that introduce sufficient difference but are also acceptable to the recipient and hold possibility for positive change. These may be introduced through the use of language, descriptions and interpretations or enactments within the session. Fundamental to the concept of reframing is the idea that we construct rather than discover reality (Efran *et al*, 1988).

A team approach

Most family therapists find it very helpful to work with colleagues either as a pair or in teams. It is an almost impossible task for one person to observe and think about all the different levels of information that are being sought, and the task of remaining sufficiently outside the family system to introduce new ideas can be difficult when there may be strong pulls from the family to side with their view of the problem or even to pull the therapist into the pattern of family relationships. Team members, who will often be viewing the session from behind a one-way screen, can provide alternative views and be watchful of the therapist/family system. Teams can be used in more creative ways, such as to debate the issues raised in the session in front of the family or to present both sides of the dilemmas that families often face when there is a demand for change (Papp, 1980; Anderson, 1987). In most approaches the therapist will take one or more breaks during the session to talk with colleagues and end with a forceful message to the family, the aim of which is to help them towards change and to promote between-session work. Where the technology of video and screens do not exist other perspectives can be introduced by a colleague sitting in during the interview or by appropriate supervision.

Different approaches to therapy

It is not possible in a chapter of this size to do justice to the wide variety of approaches and techniques that have been developed by family therapists. I will mention some of the main models giving examples of techniques that I hope will give a flavour of that approach.

Structural therapy

The aim of this approach is to change the family's dysfunctional organisational patterns, which are thought to support the presenting symptom. The main work is done within the session, the therapist often physically repositioning family members to enable them to carry out interactions in a different way. The following case example will be used in discussions of this and the other approaches.

Robert, aged 13, was referred by the educational psychologist. He had a long history of school problems and had only attended his secondary school for a few weeks, remaining at home for the previous 18 months. He had a number of physical symptoms including headaches, but investigations had shown no physical cause. His mother sat close to him in the interview and was frequently in tears, often when Robert challenged her or was disrespectful. At the specific request of the therapist the father attended the session though he was uncomfortable and was clearly unused to being involved in discussions about his son. Robert's brother Carl (aged 17) also attended the session. He was successfully working but had experienced a period of social phobia in his early teens. He had always attended school, though with some absences. The mother was very anxious about Robert but also had a number of health problems herself, including a history of depression. The father was co-operative but had a rather gruff and challenging style. He rarely looked or spoke to the other two members of the family who tended to speak for him and correct any mistakes he made. He worked long hours as a lorry driver and there were indications that he had a drink problem.

This brief case description raises many issues that suggest various approaches but the structural family therapist would focus on the collapsed hierarchy (the way in which the parents lack authority and confidence), the poor parental alliance, the close alliance between mother and son, which sometimes took the form of a coalition against father, and the disengaged and peripheral position of father. If the therapist thought that the family were feeling defeated and had lost motivation to change the first move might be to intensify parental concern about the problem, perhaps by asking them what life would be like when their son was 35 and still at home in the armchair, or discussing legal action that might be taken if they did not attend to their son's education. The next step might be to encourage the parents to discuss together how they might help each other to handle the situation, making a special effort to join with and support father in his contributions to the discussion. This is in order to 'unbalance' or change the usual pattern in which all the worrying and planning is left to the mother. The aim is not only to generate new ideas but also to strengthen the parental alliance and in so doing encourage the development of a more appropriate hierarchy and firmer boundaries between the parental and child subsystems. The parents may be placed in chairs facing one another leaving Robert on the edge, perhaps engaged in discussion with his brother about strategies to overcome fears. The function of this is to strengthen the sibling subsystem. If Robert seeks to interrupt the parental discussion the therapist will gently ask him to stop. The therapist might also spend time talking about Robert's attempts to control his parents or his disrespect for them as a way of reframing his behaviour in order to mobilise energy for change. The hope is that if the family can find alternative patterns of interaction and relationships the problem will become less entrenched and other resources to tackle the problem will be released. Minuchin (1974) and Minuchin & Fishman (1981) give full accounts of this approach.

Milan systemic therapy

Milan systemic therapy continues to evolve and it is impossible to encapsulate these developments in a short account. However, I will outline some of the basic characteristics. The therapist begins by forming one or more hypotheses about the way in which the presenting symptom connects with the experience, behaviour and beliefs of other family members. One hypothesis relating to Robert's family would be that his refusal to go to school enabled his mother to remain home based and thus avoid the stress of making new relationships in the outside world. It also keeps his mother involved with him in such a way that she does not make emotional demands on his father. This could be linked with the parents' experience in their own families of origin. This formulation is regarded as a working hypothesis to be tested out by questioning and disregarded for another if it ceases to be useful. Interventions are linked to a hypothesis and are designed to challenge belief systems. The assumption is that all behaviour and relationships arise out of systems of belief. These challenges to belief can come through circular questioning and the revealing of new information, or through powerful messages delivered by the therapist outlining the hypothesis that has been formulated and sometimes prescribing the symptom behaviour as the only way the family knows to manage their relationships, while also highlighting the sacrifices that are being made. In this case those could include the son's chance of education, the possibility of mother having her own life and the father's experience of being close to his son. Circular questioning might explore relationships and beliefs in the wider family and over time, and promote the family to think about and explore differences. The stance of the therapist is one of 'neutral curiosity' (Cecchin, 1988) and this approach is less committed to an early return to school or other specific outcomes, leaving the family to determine the pace and direction of change. Campbell & Draper (1985) and Boscolo *et al* (1987) give full accounts of this approach.

Strategy therapy

There are a whole range of strategic approaches that lie on a continuum, which runs from narrow problem-focused approaches such as the brief therapy of the Mental Research Institute in California (Fisch *et al*, 1982) through to the strategic/systemic therapies that are less narrowly focused and are concerned with exploring dilemmas about and constraints on change (Papp, 1980; White, 1986). These approaches can be very different in practice but share the understanding that the therapist is responsible for designing strategies that will help particular families to make positive changes in their lives. At the problem-focused end of the continuum the therapist concentrates on identifying the solution that families have applied to their problems on the basis that very often presenting problems can be seen as failed solutions. In Robert's family, the school phobia could be viewed as a failed solution to the challenge of life cycle changes, or the protection of Robert as the family's way of cushioning him from the stresses of life. In this way the therapist reframes the problem in a way that 'positively connotes' the motives and behaviour of the parents and so lessens resistance to alternative suggestions. The therapist will then design an alternative and very different way of tackling the problem, which will be presented to the family in the form of a task to be reported on in subsequent sessions. In Robert's family the task might be to 'baby' Robert to an intense degree in the hope that he and the family could not tolerate this, or to limit the protective behaviour to certain times of the day while 'practising independence' at others. The list of possibilities is endless but they are all problem-focused and designed to break into the stuck patterns of unsuccessful problem resolution. The therapist has to skilfully engender enough co-operation to carry these interventions forward. This is a brief minimalist approach which assumes that small changes can have a knock-on effect leading to more profound change.

Brief solution-based therapy

Brief solution-based therapy has developed over the past 10 years and although it may be considered to be a strategic therapy it has a very particular approach that is worth considering separately. This approach is solution-focused rather than problem-focused. Although some time is spent helping the client to define and describe what they consider to be their problem, the main thrust of the initial session is to identify any exceptions to problem behaviour and to track solutions that have been tried. The route of the therapy is carefully worked out so that if the therapist cannot identify any exceptions the next step is clear (in this case an observational task or identification of solutions to other similar problems, such as the way they overcame problems with the older son). If exceptions are discovered these and the circumstances around them are explored in detail and tasks devised to build on these. Time is spent helping clients define clearly the improvements they would like to make in their lives, often asking what their life would look like if a miracle happened and their problem disappeared. Goals are broken down into small steps with questions such as "what would be the first sign that

Robert was getting nearer to a return to school." There is an emphasis on empowering family members and rekindling hope that improvements can be achieved. Avoidance of talk about problems or failure is part of this process. The focus is on helping clients to do more of what works.

Narrative approaches

This is a new approach in family therapy mainly developed by Michael White, David Epston and other Australian and New Zealand family therapists (White, 1988/89). They observed the way in which negative 'stories' developed about individuals and how these stories influenced the way in which individuals viewed the world leading them to sift out information that did not fit that 'story'. In this way Robert had come to think of himself as an anxious sickly boy who could not survive the rigours of school. His family and others were part of the weaving of this story, which they also believed. They all stopped noticing those occasions when Robert could face social situations or seemed robust and well. The aim of therapy is to challenge this dominant story and build up a more positive and helpful view of Robert, which in turn would influence the way he lived his life and the expectations others had of him. Another prevalent negative view in the family is that the parents cannot persuade their son to do as they wish. The therapist may choose to make this story the focus for work. One of the strategies used is to have conversations that work to 'externalise the problem' so that Robert would be described as a boy with an anxiety problem rather than an anxious or phobic boy. There would follow an exploration of the ways in which this problem influences his life and the ways in which he can influence the problem. Once the problem is seen to be outside Robert the therapist can work with him and his family to devise strategies that further defeat the power of the problem. This could include involvement in other therapies such as social skills training or joining a sports club. The approach in general is described by White (1988/89) and in relation to school problems by Epston (1989) and Durrant (1993).

Combining family therapy and other interventions

Family therapy is based on the assumption that most families, if they are helped sufficiently to break out of stuck and unhelpful patterns, contain the required skills to overcome their problems. Each of the approaches described focuses on a particular aspect of family functioning rather than being mutually exclusive. Sometimes one or other of these family therapy approaches is enough to promote change but the family therapist must also be alert to those occasions when the family is not able to meet the needs of a child and issues of child protection must take precedence. Sometimes it is helpful for family therapy to be combined with additional treatment approaches (Skynner, 1974), which may be targeted at the family, individual or other systems such as the school. Although the family will often be able to help their child to develop strategies to overcome anxiety or to set up a graded reintegration into school, there are occasions when it is more effective for others to take on these tasks. Time is a very important factor in school attendance problems and it is important to include other strategies at an early stage. There is a need for more information about the effectiveness of these different combinations and care should always be taken to ensure that professionals are working together in a helpful way.

Implications for service provision

There is no doubt that problems of school attendance are serious in themselves and give rise to other serious consequences. Although child psychiatric clinics are familiar with children who show phobic symptoms as well as those who truant and also become involved in crime and delinquency, there are many more children for whom avoidance of school for one reason or another is part of life. This may be coupled with other emotional, learning or conduct disorders, which are less likely to be attended to because of their absence from school. The consequences of absence or infrequent attendance can also be great not only in terms of school attainment but also in the development of social skills, discipline and good peer relationships. For most children the family remains the major influence in their lives and it is important that attention is given to maximise the capacity of parents and other family members to support their children's education as well as giving due attention to schools and the education system.

Despite the lack of hard research data to support the effectiveness of family therapy with school attendance problems, clinical practice indicates that it is a valued intervention. Systems theory provides a broad framework for assessing difficulties and planning help and has the advantage of taking account of other professional systems, and contexts such as culture and the legal system. In addition this framework does not exclude the use of other individual or group-based interventions.

The practice of family therapy is greatly enhanced by the availability of resources, such as one-way screens and telephones or ear bugs for supervisions and the possibility of working in pairs or teams. Often children are referred to clinics only when the problems are entrenched and, developing from an interest in wider systems, some family therapists have successfully set up clinics and consultation services within schools with the advantage of identifying problems at an earlier stage and helping to develop skills within school (Taylor & Dowling, 1986).

There is a need for more research in a number of areas including the identification of risk and protective factors and this has been addressed throughout the chapter. Perhaps more than any other child psychiatric problem school attendance problems concern many agencies and any service will need to pay due regard to the setting up of good multidisciplinary and multi-agency teamwork to avoid the professional systems becoming a problem in themselves and in order to maximise the effectiveness of interventions.

References

ANDERSON, T. (1987) The reflecting team: dialogue and metadialogue in clinical work. *Family Process*, **26**, 415–428.

APONTE, H. (1976) The family school interview: an eco-structural approach. *Family Process*, **15**, 303–313.

BARKER, P. (1992) *Basic Family Therapy* (3rd edn). Oxford: Blackwell.

BERG, I. (1980) School refusal in early adolescence. In *Out of School. Modern Perspectives in Truancy and School Refusal* (eds L. Hersov & I. Berg) pp. 231–250. Chichester: John Wiley.

—— (1991) *Family Preservation: A Brief Therapy Workbook*. London: B.T. Press.

—— (1992) Absence from school and mental health. *British Journal of Psychiatry*, **161**, 154–166.

——, BUTLER, I. & McGUIRE, R. (1972) British order and family size of school phobic adolescents. *British Journal of Psychiatry*, **121**, 509–514.

BOSCOLO, L., CECCHIN, G., HOFFMAN, L., *et al* (1987) *Milan Systemic Family Therapy*. New York: Basic Books.

BOWERS, L., SMITH, P. & BINNEY, V. (1992) Cohesion and power in the families of children involved in bully/victim problems at school. *Journal of Child Psychology and Psychiatry*, **14**, 371–388.

BOWLBY, J. (1973) *Attachment and Loss, Volume 2: Separation, Anxiety and Anger*. London: Hogarth Press.

CAMPBELL, D. & DRAPER, R. (eds) (1985) *Application of Systemic Family Therapy: The Milan Approach*. London: Grune and Stratton.

CARTER, B. & McGOLDRICK, M. (1989) Overview: the changing family life cycle – a framework for family therapy. In *The Changing Family Life Cycle: A Framework for Therapy* (2nd edn) (eds B. Carter & M. McGoldrick), pp. 3–29. Boston: Allyn and Bacon.

CECCHIN, G. (1988) Hypothesising, circularity and neutrality revisited: an invitation to curiosity. *Family Process*, **27**, 405–413.

COYNE, J. C. & ANDERSON, B. J. (1989) The 'psychosomatic family reconsidered' II: recalling a defective model and looking ahead. *Journal of Marital and Family Therapy*, **15**, 139–148.

CROWTHER, C., DARE, C. & WILSON, J. (1990) Why should we talk to you? You'll only tell the court: on being an informer and family therapist. *Journal of Family Therapy*, **13**, 105–123.

CRUMLEY, F. E. (1974) A school phobia in a three generational family conflict. *Journal of the American Academy of Child Psychiatry*, **13**, 536–550.

DARE, J., GOLDBERG, D. & WALINETS, R. (1990) What is the question you need to answer? How consultation can prevent professional systems immobilising families. *Journal of Family Therapy*, **12**, 355–366.

DOWLING, E., BARRETT, M., GOLDING, V., *et al* (1985) Patterns of interaction in families presenting a child with an educational problem: a clinical research development. In *The Family and the School: A Joint Systems Approach to Families with Children* (eds E. Dowling & E. Osborne), pp. 40–62. London: Routledge and Kegan Paul.

DURRANT, M. (1993) *Creative Strategies for School Problems*. Epping: Eastwood Family Centre.

EFRAN, J., LUKENS, R. & LUKENS, M. (1988) Constructivism: what's in it for you? *Family Therapy Networker*, Sept/Oct, 25–32.

EPSTON, D. (1989) *Collected Papers*. Adelaide: Dulwich Centre Publications.

FARRINGTON, D. (1980) Truancy, delinquency, the home and the school. In *Out of School. Modern Perspectives in Truancy and School Refusal* (eds L. Hersov & I. Berg), pp. 49–64. Chichester: John Wiley.

FISCH, R., WEAKLAND, J. & SEGAL, L. (1982) *The Tactics of Change: Doing Therapy Briefly.* San Francisco.

FOGELMAN, K. & RICHARDSON, K. (1974) Some findings from the National Child Development Study. In *Truancy* (ed. B. Turner). London: Ward Lock Educational.

———, TIBBENHAM, A. & LAMBERT, L. (1980) Absence from school: findings from the National Child Development Study. In *Out of School. Modern Perspectives in School Refusal and Truancy* (eds L. Hersov & I. Berg), pp. 25–28. Chichester: John Wiley.

FRUDE, N. (1980) Methodological problems in the evaluation of family therapy. *Journal of Family Therapy*, **21**, 29–44.

GALE, A. (1979) Problems of outcome research in family therapy. In *Family and Marital Psychotherapy: A Critical Approach* (ed. S. Waldron-Skinner), pp. 62–74. London: Routledge and Kegan Paul.

GEORGE, E., IVESON, C. & RATNER, H. (1990) *Problem to Solution. Brief Therapy with Individuals and Families.* London: B. T. Press.

GOLDENBERG, C. D. S. & DAVID, A. S. (1991) Family therapy and the glamour of science. *Journal of Family Therapy*, **13**, 17–30.

HAZELRIGG, M. D., COOPER, H. M. & BORDUIN, C. M. (1987) Evaluating the effectiveness of family therapies: an integrative review and analysis. *Psychological Bulletin*, **101**, 428–442.

HERSOV, L. A. (1960) Persistent non-attendance at school. *Journal of Child Psychology and Psychiatry*, **1**, 130–136.

——— (1985) School refusal. In *Child and Adolescent Psychiatry: Modern Approaches* (2nd edn) (eds M. Rutter & L. Hersov), pp. 382–399. Oxford: Blackwell.

HETHERINGTON, E. M. & MARTIN, B. (1972) Family interaction and psychopathology in children. In *Psychopathological Disorders of Childhood* (eds H. C. Quay & J. S. Werry). New York: John Wiley.

HOFFMAN, L. (1981) *Foundations of Family Therapy.* New York: Basic Books.

HUFFINGTON, C. M. & SEVITT, M. A. (1989) Family interaction in adolescent school phobia. *Journal of Family Therapy*, **11**, 353–376.

IMBER BLACK, E. (1988) *Families and Larger Systems: A Family Therapist's Guide Through the Labyrinth.* New York: Guilford Press.

JOHNSON, A. M., FALSTEIN, E. I., SZUREK, S. A., *et al* (1941) School phobia. *American Journal of Orthopsychiatry*, **27**, 307–309.

KAHN, J. H. & NURSTEN, J. P. (1962) School refusal: a comprehensive view of school phobia and other failures of school attendance. *American Journal of Orthopsychiatry*, **32**, 707–718.

KINSTON, W. & LOADER, P. (1984) Eliciting whole family interaction with a standardised clinical interview. *Journal of Family Therapy*, **6**, 347–363.

LEVENTHAL, T., WEINBERGER, G., STANDER, R. J., *et al* (1967) Therapeutic strategies in school phobics. *American Journal of Orthopsychiatry*, **37**, 64–70.

LOADER, P., BURKE, C., KINSTON, W., *et al* (1981) A method for organising the clinical description of family interaction. 'The Family Interaction Summary Format'. *Australian Journal of Family Therapy*, **2**, 131–141.

MALMQUIST, C. P. (1965) School phobia; A problem in family neurosis. *Journal of the American Academy of Child Psychiatry*, **4**, 293–319.

MARKUS, E., LANGE, A. & PETTIGREW, T. F. (1990) Effectiveness of family therapy: a meta analysis. *Journal of Family Therapy*, **12**, 205–222.

MINUCHIN, S. (1974) *Families and Family Therapy.* London: Tavistock.

———, ROSMAN, B. L. & BAKER, L. (1978) *Psychosomatic Families: Anorexia Nervosa in Context.* Cambridge: Harvard University Press.

——— & FISHMAN, H. C. (1981) *Family Therapy Techniques.* Cambridge: Harvard University Press.

MOORE, T. (1966) Difficulties of the ordinary child in adjusting to primary school. *Journal of Child Psychology and Psychiatry*, **7**, 17–38.

NEWSON, J. & NEWSON, E. (1977) *Perspectives on School at 7yrs Old.* London: Allen and Unwin.

OLSEN, D. H. (1986) Circumplex model vii: validation model and Faces iii. *Family Process*, **25**, 337–351.

———, RUSSELL, C. S. & SPRENKLE, D. H. (1983) Circumplex model of marital and family systems: VI, Theoretical update. *Family Process*, **22**, 69–83.

OLWEUS, D. (1980) Familial and temperamental determinants of aggressive behaviour in adolescent boys: a causal analysis. *Developmental Psychology*, **16**, 644–660.

PAPP, P. (1980) The Greek chorus and other techniques of family therapy. *Family Process*, **19**, 45–57.

PENN, P. (1985) Feed forward: future questions, future maps. *Family Process*, **24**, 299–310.

REDER, R. & KRAEMER, S. (1980) Dynamic aspects of professional collaboration in child guidance. *Journal of Adolescence*, **3**, 165–173.

REID, K. (1983) Retrospection and persistent school absenteeism. *Education Research*, **25**, 110–115.

SKYNNER, R. (1974) School phobia: a reappraisal. *British Journal of Medical Psychology*, **47**, 1–16.

TAYLOR, D. (1986) The child as go-between: consulting with parents and teachers. *Journal of Family Therapy*, **8**, 79–90.

———, & DOWLING, E. (1986) The clinic goes to school: setting up an outreach service. *Maladjustment and Therapeutic Education*, **4**, 12–29.

TOMM, K. (1987) Interventive interviewing: Part 2. *Family Process*, **26**, 3–14.

WATZLAWICK, P., WEAKLAND, J. & FISCH, R. (1974) *Change: Principles of Problem Formation and Problem Resolution*. New York: Norton.

WHITE, M. (1986) Negative explanation, restraint and double description. *Family Process*, **25**, 169–184.

——— (1988/89) The externalising of the problem and the restructuring of lives and relationships. Dulwich Centre Newsletter Summer 1988/1989.

WOOD, B. L. (1993) Beyond the 'psychosomatic family': a biobehavioural family model of pediatric illness. *Family Process*, **32**, 261–278.

18 Working through parents: a social worker's approach

JEAN NURSTEN

This chapter gives an example of work in a child and adolescent psychiatric clinic within a general hospital where the social worker undertakes the treatment of parents of school-refusal children (Kahn *et al*, 1981). However, social workers in different settings, such as education, health, probation and social service departments, meet children who are absent from school for a variety of reasons and causes. School refusers will be among this larger number and social workers may become the agent who refers the child and family to an appropriate service, or who addresses the problem more directly within their own setting.

It is the Education Act of 1944 that imposes on the local authority the responsibility for ensuring that parents and children take full advantage of the education system. To this end, the education welfare officer (sometimes named as the education social worker) provides a social work service to pupils, parents and teachers while ensuring that regular attendance is of paramount importance. Non-attendance leads to an assessment of circumstances at home and at school, which may go towards resolving the problem. Should the issue not be resolved, a plan of action may be to start off court action in order to carry out statutory duties, on behalf of the local education authority, either in the Magistrates or Family Proceedings Court. Previously, a Supervision Order for non-attendance at school could only be brought by a social services department but since the Children Act of 1989, an Education Supervision Order granted by the court gives authority for an education welfare officer to work more closely with a child and family. This may include meetings with teachers, or group work and counselling for the child seen as a truant, who is characteristically away from home as much as from school. The child seen as refusing school and reluctant to leave home may be referred to the School Psychological Service or, with consultation with the family doctor, to the Child and Family Psychiatric Services.

Social workers in such psychiatric settings have a function as a member of a team working together to assess and treat children's emotional, behavioural and cognitive problems. The specific role within the team is, most often, to work with parents or carers, but joint work with the child psychiatrist, or clinical or educational psychologist or remedial teacher, may play a relevant part. Parents' problems may sometimes be partially expressed, even 'owned', by their child and this may disturb the child's development and relationship with both the family and outside world. Unless parents are helped in their own right, it may be hard for a child to change, even to the extent of going to school.

In the case presented, which was referred to a child and adolescent psychiatric clinic, school refusal may be seen as a manifestation of a problem that is wider than school alone. It opens the door for us to see how the family members relate to each other, and the meaning the issues hold for them. The present problem of refusing school is a repetition of Laura's father's school refusal a generation back and her older brother's earlier refusal. In relation to herself, it is a fall-back position to her own fear of going to school and wish to be at home during her first years at school. The case also shows the problem displayed strongly, but characteristically, in adolescence of the individual attempting to establish autonomy and cope with the conflicting need for dependence and independence. The case is disguised.

Recordings of interviews with both the father and the mother are given and discussion of these gives consideration to the social worker's approach, which draws on concepts from cognitive therapy in this instance, although other social workers have chosen to work with other ways of problem-solving. Each of Laura's parents needed help with negative thinking and space to disclose the loss each had sustained – of their own mothers, his job, her health and both losing their three sons who had left home.

Cognitive therapy

Cognitive therapy has been shown to be a useful technique in relation to helping adults who are anxious and depressed (Beck, 1987 summarises the position) and to helping children and adolescents (McAdam & Gilbert, 1985). A constituent part of the cognitive approach is that people are held to interpret their world as coloured by their own sets of values, beliefs, expectations and attitudes. Cognitive therapy begins then by identifying and questioning such sets that make up the schemata, that is, the styles of thinking. Such styles of thinking about the self, the world, the interpersonal relationships and the future lead to specific behaviour and feelings. When a person is anxious or depressed the styles of thinking incline to be negative, which is further upsetting. The aim of therapy is to pave the way for the cognitive constructs to be accessible to discussion and to change.

The cognitive constructs in relation to school refusal may be apparent in the parent(s) or child's view of themselves and of their world. For instance, particular ways of thinking, known as cognitive error, become apparent when a parent like Laura's father claims that, "The fact that she doesn't go to school proves that I'm no good as a parent". He is making an arbitrary inference and allowing one fact, although important, to affect the whole view of his parental role. Similarly, a child like Laura may over-generalise in saying, "No one misses me at school, so what's the point; I've fallen behind so I'm no good". A parent may minimise relative success: "He/she is going but not on the days of PE, so I've got nowhere". A child may think in absolute terms: "I've lost ten weeks of schooling. I will never catch up and be any good". And a parent may personalise the school absence − "It's all my fault. I'm not firm enough" − discounting the conjunction of factors such as change of school, push of adolescence and a child's partial wish to be at home.

Laura's case is now presented, with extracts of early interviews following the initial assessment of the problem by the team. The intention of the assessment was to develop the relationship between the family members and the professional workers and clarify that the goal was to help the family see that school refusal was part of the family's problems.

The recordings of interviews are offered as few are presented between a social worker and the client. Conversations of this nature are seldom recorded (see comment in Skynner, 1974). The social worker's place in the team has few mentions in the literature, yet has a place in addressing school refusal. Unfortunately, many psychiatric social workers are being withdrawn from multidisciplinary teams both in the UK and USA as the employing authority sees the need to deploy their services elsewhere in the field of mental health or generic social work.

Laura MacLeod's case

Laura is 15 years old and the youngest of four children. At the time of referral her three older brothers were away from home and she lived alone with her mother and father, Mr and Mrs MacLeod. The father is a manager of a large office and has a good income. The family is intelligent and strong willed. Father has a phrase: "The Mac's never break", but as we shall see, he could have added "They only break away". Any member wanting to live his own life, even if this only means starting the pattern over again, has to act violently to get out of the system.

Mrs MacLeod brought Laura to see a child psychiatrist one March, as Laura had not been in school since Christmas. She herself was seen by the social worker. The problem of refusing school had been apparent for the whole of the previous year, but despite attendances being sporadic Laura had not totally refused to go. She would cry and feel unwell before school time. This dated from the previous January just after the family had moved from one district to another. Laura was a week late starting in school because of the family's move, and she found it uncomfortable to mix with 1000 pupils, having previously been to a smaller school. In her second week of school, she was involved in a car accident when she was out alone with her father and, although unhurt, she was shaken and had a few days off school. When she did attend, she felt unable to concentrate and obtained poor marks in comparison with the standard she had formerly achieved. She would complain about being unaccepted and having to walk to lunch alone, and the other girls were said to have made derogatory remarks about her clothes.

Mrs MacLeod further related that Laura was finally upset when the other girls accused her of being pregnant. This led Mrs MacLeod to talk about Laura's involvement with a 19-year-old boyfriend called Tom. Laura had known him for over a year, but Mrs MacLeod disapproved very much, as she described him as uncouth and of being born "on the wrong side of the tracks". Mrs MacLeod had discouraged Laura from seeing Tom, but she had since discovered that they had been meeting on the quiet all summer. Laura had made a stand and said that if she were forbidden to see Tom she certainly would not go to school. Mrs MacLeod gave in and by Christmas time she was having him to dinner every Sunday, although the atmosphere was very strained when he was in the home.

Mrs MacLeod used the same adjectives to describe Tom that she later used to describe her husband, saying that Tom is domineering, possessive, single-minded and driving. Laura would like to leave school and marry Tom, but Mrs MacLeod thinks that she is too young even for a steady boyfriend, and she only wishes that Laura would think instead of church and school attendance. However, she very much fears that Laura, having already packed her bags twice and threatened to leave home, will one day put this into practice.

Mrs MacLeod gave the following history of Laura's early childhood. She related the events that had led up to Laura's present difficulties, but it will be seen later that the family's main problem lies within the area of their interpersonal relationships, and the multiple losses experienced.

The first upset came when she was $3\frac{1}{2}$ years old. Mrs MacLeod was taken ill and it was a shock for Laura when her mother was removed to hospital. Laura was not clearly told why or where her mother was going. For the next 16 months, Mrs MacLeod was backwards and forwards (Laura $3\frac{1}{2}$–$4\frac{3}{4}$) between the hospital and home as she was having severe haemorrhages. During this time, she had a gall-bladder operation that involved many blood transfusions. When she was in hospital, she got hepatitis and later had to have a gastrectomy. She also had some of her bowel removed. She had a really rough time for 4 or 5 years, and she was given a 50:50 chance of living.

Around this time a series of losses occurred that affected the family. The oldest son went into the Services, her husband's mother died, a nephew died in a car crash and a niece was drowned; and then Mrs MacLeod added with much hesitation that her own mother died too. In addition, Mr MacLeod had to go into hospital because of a hernia, and during this time his company moved to another part of the country and he lost his job. He had to start in the insurance office at a clerk's wage, which he viewed as starting at the bottom.

When Laura started school she was terrified lest her mother would not be at home when she returned. Mrs MacLeod had to escort Laura until she was 7 years of age and then, temporarily, they had no difficulty. However, Laura did not do well with lessons and was kept down a term. Since then, she had always been bigger than the other children and had felt self-conscious about this. Laura made friends in the area (where they lived next to a funeral director's office), but Mrs MacLeod disapproved of her type of friends. The family moved, partly to give Laura a so-called choice of friends, but also so that Mr MacLeod was near to his work.

Family history

Mrs MacLeod

Mrs MacLeod, on most occasions that she attended the clinic, looked a neat, subdued, but well-dressed woman of 57. From the first interview she showed that she desperately needed to talk to someone about all the family difficulties. She was so anxious in her first interview that she could not listen. It seemed as though she wanted to rush into self-accusations before anyone else could do it for her. She was a frightened and lonely person, and needed to talk about her illnesses as she had never been able to go over them fully with her own mother, and her husband in her view had never listened. She attended the clinic as though it was inevitable that she had to add to her burdens. Mrs MacLeod still sees neighbours from the original home, but seemed to find it impossible to make contact with people in the districts they have lived in more recently. She did not join in the social life.

Mrs MacLeod was the only girl with three brothers, just as Laura, though the order is not quite the same, Mrs MacLeod having an older brother and two younger ones. She looks back on her childhood as "peaceful". She went away to boarding school and in the holidays there were games of tennis, beach parties and pony riding. Her mother was considered a very gracious lady by her father and the whole house revolved around keeping things pleasant for her. Mrs MacLeod recalled two episodes. She remembered banging a door when she was 10 years old and her father making her apologise to her mother for causing a disturbance. She also recalled visiting her parents for the first time with her two oldest children as toddlers. The first thing she was told when she went back home was that she must remember that her mother needed peace and quiet, and there must be no disruptive behaviour. She was hurt as she proudly wanted to show off her children, and she felt that she was only met with rebuff.

Mrs MacLeod's present relationships can be summed up in the following way. Both her parents are now dead. She views her husband as hard-headed, unsympathetic and unloving. She would like more from him than she gets. With Laura she had had a very difficult relationship for the past year as Laura has shown her no affection and has openly said that she hates her. With Tom, Laura's boyfriend, Mrs MacLeod's relationship is very ambivalent. When Tom is around, she worries about her daughter's behaviour. When Laura temporarily breaks off with Tom, it is Mrs MacLeod who acts in a bereft way and feels deserted. She can in the same interview blame Tom for Laura's absence from school, and yet pin her hopes on the possibility that Tom might help her to return.

Mr MacLeod

Mr MacLeod is aged 52. He is a small, immaculate looking businessman who is very ambitious, hard working and proud of his success. He chooses his words carefully during interviews and tends to talk in clichés. He was brought up in a small town on a bleak coastline. He is the youngest of five children, having two older brothers and two older sisters. He too had had a problem over attending school, which was solved by his mother employing a local teacher to tutor him. He refused to attend school at 15, the same age that Laura refused. Mr MacLeod built up strong resentment towards his teacher, and even though a change of school was tried the resentment soon began to build up towards the new teacher. He found that his "solution" was to run away from home, which he did when he was 17. He was very homesick, and remembers crying and longing to return, but not giving in to it. He knew that his mother wanted him to, but he stuck it out. Another way in which he solved his problems was to become a "joiner" of various groups such as the Church, the Masons, the school committee. At first, with his frequent mention of his group activities, it seemed as though he might be a sociable person, but it became apparent that he had few relationships within these groups, as none of the other people are described by him, or come to life, when he talks about his activities.

In his family relationships, he views his wife as a nagger. He refers to her all the time as "mother". He thinks that she is too soft with the children and too demanding of his time. He makes attempts to form a relationship with Laura but it is noticeable that his way of doing this is only to give her money to spend, or to offer to show her around the office where he works; he finds it difficult to enter into her world. With his sons, he has been very ambitious and bitterly disappointed that they have not wanted further education. He has driven them to school in a Bentley, but somehow given them little on which to build when it came to selecting a career. He views Tom, Laura's boyfriend, as a rival and vacillates between trying to forbid him to come to the house and saying nothing when he is present, despite instructing him not to appear.

The three sons tried to solve their problems by leaving home, in the same way that the father did in his day. The oldest boy went abroad with no job to go to; the middle son married a girl of a different religion, much in the same way that one of the mother's brothers did some years ago; the younger boy, who was a case of school refusal himself, is now in the Services and refuses to visit home.

Casework

The case of Laura MacLeod's school refusal illustrates the many factors that usually coincide before the syndrome is fully developed. The interpersonal factors between the family members become apparent; the members are engaged in battle. Laura is the last child still at home and the lack of sibling support, the threat of mother's ill health and the cosy bedroom chats with father have aroused Laura's fears. Laura's relationship with Tom arouses the mother's fantasies and the father's rivalry.

On the intrapersonal level, the push of adolescent urges can be seen as an additional stress. On the socio-cultural level the disturbance is increased by the change of district and school, when powers of adaptation are already strained. There is lack of success and lack of peer group support too.

The current difficulty can be viewed, too, as a resurgence in Laura herself of problems originally experienced around the age of $3\frac{1}{2}$ years. Possibly it was at the height of Laura's infantile wishes to have her father to herself that she found that her mother does in fact, as well as in fantasy, disappear from home. No reason was given to her at the time and she may have felt that her thoughts and wishes were indeed dangerous. She had only to think that she would like her mother out of the way and lo! it happened. Later, with the pressure of adolescence re-creating the difficulty that she had not fully worked through in the past, she found that it seemed safer to keep her mother within sight. Should they be apart and Laura at school, maybe her destructive thoughts would again be powerful enough to hurt her mother.

In an examination of the parents' own history, a continuation of old patterns can be seen in the parent–child relationship. Father refused school; mother's relationship with a boyfriend was jeopardised by her father; and now Laura refuses school and chooses a boyfriend (in her father's image) who is criticised by her parents.

The treatment plan included psychotherapy with Laura and casework with the parents. Both parents were brought in to the situation, as Mr MacLeod was tending to disagree with and undermine treatment, while at the same time feeling rather left out of the process. Both parents were seen alone, and a few weeks later there was a joint interview between the parents, the psychiatrist and the social worker. The aim of this was to get the parents to start working together. Mr MacLeod had tried to split off Mrs MacLeod from treatment and, in much the same way, Mrs MacLeod had herself tried to come between the psychiatrist and Laura, and between the psychiatrist and the social worker. One of the results of the joint interview was that the psychiatrist and social worker could be seen working together.

Both parents needed to understand that Laura had more problems than school attendance; because otherwise, if Laura had returned to school within 2 or 3 weeks of the start of treatment, it would have been likely that the parents would have broken off their attendance. In the first interviews with the social worker they were helped to see, even if somewhat intellectually, that Laura's problems were wider than this and that school was focusing attention on only part of her problems. It was pointed out to her parents that some of Laura's difficulties were enactments of their own earlier ones. They too had had battles with their parents, which were resolved in the ways that their sons have repeated and which Laura perhaps might repeat as well. Apart from having the aim of keeping Laura in treatment should she return to school, it was also necessary to help the parents to see that an environmental change was not the only answer. Mr MacLeod recalled that this had been tried in his case and had not been a success, as he had carried problems through to the new teacher. Mrs MacLeod did, however, try to arrange for Laura to go to another school; she was disappointed when this failed. She had to be supported through this and helped to face that some of Laura's problems were other than in the school itself.

Another part of the inital stage of treatment was to help Mrs MacLeod tolerate the process, as she tended to sexualise every situation and could easily have fled from treatment because of this. Part of her was wanting to limit Laura's social relations with Tom, because she found her imagination running riot. This was carried over to a concern about Laura and the psychiatrist being alone together. One time she brought a magazine found in Laura's room, picturing a naked girl lying on a psychiatrist's couch; another time she brought a newspaper clipping about a local psychiatrist in personal difficulties. Both articles were colouring her attitude to Laura's own, current psychiatrist.

The following extracts from interviews with the parents illustrate some of these points. The extracts are subsequent upon the full social, personal and family histories that are part of the diagnostic study and the development of a professional relationship, but further aspects are revealed, of course, in later sessions. The interview with the father aimed at helping him to accept treatment, and to see that treatment itself needed to be directed not only towards Laura's return to school but also towards showing her a way to come to terms with herself, within the family situation. Interviews with fathers of school refusers are rarely undertaken and recorded.

Report of father's session with the social worker

Mr MacLeod was seen today. He came well before time and carefully chose his words during the interview. He said he thought Laura was having things too easy in the way that he did when he was the same age. He recalled that at 15 he refused to go to school himself and ran home to his mother. He thought the teacher was picking on him, and as a form of rebellion, he decided to stay at home. If his father had been at home, this would not have been allowed. I asked him what things he felt had contributed to Laura's similar problem and he immediately began blaming his wife's age, then her illness and, thirdly, his work, and added that with moving so many times, Laura had had readjustments to make. He himself had always been able to adapt, as he has soon joined the local church or a committee in a new district and found a place for himself in a group. He is surprised that none of his children have taken part in organising groups as he has, but have gone just to join in as "members".

He went on to wonder if he were partly to blame? He said he now handles 42 people at the office, but he notices that he is not firm when he gives an order and often over-sympathetic. He felt that perhaps this happens also in his relationship with Laura, although he added that initially he was not told of her absence and it was some weeks before he found out. He wonders if he would have been able to be as strong as his own father would have been. His own father might have thrown him out if he had realised there was trouble.

I asked him what such an action would achieve for Laura, and he said that it would only make her rebellion worse; it is difficult to tell what would have happened if he had taken a stand. His friends even tell him to throw Tom out of the house, but he has not done this. He has talked to Tom, and although he partially accepts him he criticises him for having no job and for having some of the same qualities that he has just told me he had observed in himself. For instance, Tom is very sensitive and feels unwanted by people who are greater in authority, rather in the way Mr MacLeod felt when he was at school.

I asked him to tell me more about how he was himself at a similar age to Tom. He again said that he refused to go to school; his problem of school refusal was solved by his mother employing a local teacher, who lived only two houses away. Mr MacLeod went on to say that he was the youngest of five children; he was his mother's favourite and it was he who always got the new suit and the new bike. His father was mostly out of the house at sea, but, as a 'contribution' to her religion, mother would have ministers staying in the house. He remembers two of them, even as students, giving him the strap. After having the private teacher for about a year, the family moved to a new house about 20 miles away and he thought this was a chance to start all over again. He did go to school, but he soon saw himself resenting the new teacher all over again.

Suddenly, at 17, he made the decision to leave school completely and, in addition, he left home for London. This was in spite of an uncle planning to send him into the Church, and an old friend wanting to have him in the Civil Service. I asked him what he was going "towards" and he replied that he thought of London as being a new life where money grew on trees and where living was easy. He went to live with one of his older brothers for about 2 months, but just remembers that as a continuous battle. I asked him what helped him at this stage. He tells me that being away from home was a solution and having nowhere to turn made him look at himself. He recalls crying and being homesick, but he stuck it out, although he knew his mother would want him back.

Another way in which he solved his problem was to become a "joiner" of various groups such as the Church and the Masons. As he mentioned no specific person, I asked him about this and he said no particular individual was important. It was being a member of a committee that did things for him.

I wondered what solutions he has for Laura? He thought her problems could be solved in the same terms as his own; that is he felt she should join some groups. As another possibility, he suggested that she should perhaps change schools. I reminded him that changing schools had been no solution for him, as he had told me himself that he had started to resent the next teacher after he had made a change. He saw this was true, and he did not really believe in the change of school. He drew up to me closely, and began to tell me in a confidential way that he had even put this to Laura when he took her into his bedroom and closed the door, making the offer to let her go to another school, and confessing that he himself did not like school in his own days. Laura then told him that she did not want to go to any school.

Mr MacLeod went on to reminisce about his second son's dislike of school, when the family moved. The new teacher found the boy so bright that they had him transferred to a high school. He refused the chance, but eventually was able to go to another school where there was less pressure. As this worked for his sons, Mr MacLeod had half-hoped, even against his better judgement and in the view of his own experience that it would work with Laura. He thought the over-sympathetic atmosphere at home was no help. Mrs MacLeod was evidently letting Laura get up at any time of the morning, and routine seemed to have gone by the board.

Mr MacLeod began to try to get me to side with him against his wife, as he said no doubt she had "droned" on to me about all her operations and this chatter was a nuisance wasn't it? I said that the operations must have been a great threat in Mrs MacLeod's life and that it often takes a person a long time to get over this. He went on to say how possessive she was, and even now when his second son and his wife have a baby, Mrs MacLeod thinks it is her right to care for the baby for quite a part of each week. However, his daughter-in-law won't allow this and Mr MacLeod, even though saying she wasn't quite the sort of girl for the family, goes on to say that this girl was quite right in refusing to part with her baby. Mrs MacLeod clings on like his mother did. He and his sons have tended to break completely away, and he wonders what there is in store now for Laura.

I said treatment would be directed not only at her refusal to go to school. We would all be working also on a way for her to emancipate herself from the family more successfully than the way he had told me he had done, or that his sons had done. I went on to say that their break had been so complete, it seemed as though it had to be this way or not at all. Perhaps there was a middle way for Laura? He ended by stating that although he hadn't been told what to do, which he had expected, he did feel he could see what we were aiming at in treatment, and he agreed with this.

Discussion of father's interview

Mr MacLeod was puzzled and worried by his daughter's behaviour and, while feeling powerless to alter the situation alone, he was equally puzzled about psychiatric treatment. The focus of the interview had therefore to be twofold. First, Mr MacLeod needed to see himself as part of the treatment plan and, secondly, the aim of treatment had to be explained, otherwise a return to school although important would have remained as the limited goal.

The caseworker relates his past to the current situation, in the context of Laura's problem. Mr MacLeod's solutions to his adolescent difficulty were not judged as good or bad, but instead he was helped to think whether his solutions would be of actual assistance to Laura. He tended to have 'either/or' solutions to problems – one escapes from control by changing the environment or submits to control. By the end of the interview, he was at least ceasing to apply this formula and was instead "wondering" about Laura's future and so could accept, admittedly on an intellectual level, that she might be able to achieve independence and continue to have a place in the family.

He himself needed help with the feeling that he was to blame in not being firm, neither in his office, nor strong like his own father with his children. This is not directly explored as guilt (should it amount to this) is difficult to alleviate by cognitive restructuring. However, Mr MacLeod may be helped in his current situation by addressing his tendency to be self-critical. Should he be blamed, and his opinion of himself confirmed, he would hold himself in less worth, and/or likely to over-react by being firm in the image he has of his father in throwing his child or her boyfriend out. He is helped to find his own answer in responding to the questions relating to the present situation. Would blaming himself really get Laura back to school? What would such an action as throwing her out of the home achieve? He is able to say that her rebellion would only be all the worse. This counters his tendency to select an abstraction, which is only one of several that are likely to be relevant to Laura's situation. Had his tendency to self-blame not been taken up he may have felt worse and attempted less than appropriate ways to deal with Laura's place in the family and at school.

Realistic thinking is addressed, too, when Mr MacLeod suggests a change of school as a remedy. He is helped to think around this, and is then able to say that he realises that this would not be effective as Laura has indeed told him that she does not want to go to any school.

Report of mother's session with the social worker

The following extract is from an interview with Mrs MacLeod, subsequent to the history but during the initial stages of the treatment process. In this interview an attempt was made to help Mrs MacLeod face the larger problems behind the refusal of school and cope with anxiety about treatment.

Mrs MacLeod came in today and brought out a comic saying that she had found this in Laura's bedroom. She didn't want me to think that she was snooping, but as there was an article on psychiatry in it, she thought that she would bring it along for me to see. The article showed a naked girl lying on a couch. I asked Mrs MacLeod why this should worry her, as the reality of Laura's visits would show Laura that her interviews were not like this. Perhaps it was that she herself worried about the interviews? She replied that she knew her doctor would not have sent her to this clinic unless everything was in order. I asked her what in particular had raised her fears and she told me that in today's paper there was a discussion of a local doctor's seduction of a patient. She said that part of her worried, although the other part had been reassured by actually seeing the psychiatrist.

She went on to show me Laura's report card. During her early school days Laura had nearly always had good marks, but after moving these went down. Mrs MacLeod said that even now Laura herself is pleased she is coming, and sees that she needs some help. Mrs MacLeod went on to say that there is even a slight change of heart towards Tom, and Laura is away staying with a friend at the moment and when she is parted from Tom everything seems all right. Laura is going bowling tonight with two other boys and is going to be back home at 11 o'clock. When she is at home, she just hangs back and won't have any friends in, but she still asks her mother if she can get married. Mrs MacLeod says that their former home had not been a nice place for her, as their flat had been next door to an undertaker's office. They had had to move there when money had become short. She went on again to blame Tom for Laura's condition.

I reminded her that Laura's problem had begun before she met Tom. It therefore seemed that there were other factors at work and I said that, for instance, Laura had had to change districts and get used to new people, change from a small school to a larger one and, in addition, enter adolescence. Mrs MacLeod was able to agree with this and said that, indeed Laura had had a difficult time because of meeting different types of girls at the new school. Laura was criticised for wearing too much make-up and for wearing her skirts too short. The other girls were dressed differently and Laura was ridiculed and ostracised. As a consequence, Laura began crying and finding it difficult to go to school. Mrs MacLeod admitted difficulties did begin before Tom.

I said that even if Tom and Laura were to break up, many problems would still be left, as we have just found that more than Tom alone contributed to Laura's difficulties. Once again, Mrs MacLeod was able to agree and said that Laura was actually better now staying with a friend, since she would go to church from her friend's house, but not from home. I said that this sounded as though she were saying that some of the trouble lay between Laura and her parents. Mrs MacLeod said yes, it seemed so . . . it had been easy to send her away and so avoid difficulties, although she missed her. I added that perhaps there was some relief too. Mrs MacLeod again agreed and said that even Laura herself doesn't know what got into her.

Mrs MacLeod brought Tom's name in again, and said that Tom should get her back to school. I commented that she was expecting more of Tom than from herself or her husband; they had not been able to get Laura back to school. Mrs

MacLeod looked a little surprised and didn't say anything, but went on after a little time to say that Tom was working now and Laura would not be able to spend all her afternoons with him, and might actually have some incentive to return to school . . . however, she pondered on this, and added that she was not at all convinced that this would really make any difference . . . there would still be a lot of trouble left, and Laura would remain rebellious.

I said that as a family they had had difficulties over dependence and independence, and I then went over some of the same issues that I had gone over with her husband in the morning. I added that Laura was having difficulty growing away from the family while still allowing herself to be close to them; the boys had found it necessary to separate themselves completely from the family.

Mrs MacLeod went on to try to blame her husband, saying that he only wants achievement. I acknowledged that it was difficult for her husband to stand failure, when achievement means so much to him. Once again she tried to blame her husband, but on going over Laura's problem again, she began to accept her own involvement and her own difficulty in dealing with angry feelings.

Discussion of mother's interview

Mrs MacLeod is a person who has suffered many losses. Her own loss of health, her mother's death and son's absence from home between the ages of 47 and 52 years of age coincided with both the start and the early years of Laura's schooling. Such a theme was relevant to Mrs MacLeod's own recent past but it also hinged on the anticipated change that would come about should Laura, her only daughter and the only remaining child at home, return to school, and eventually leave home. Help around this theme related to her negative predictions that it was inevitable that she would be more lonely and unhappy.

However, the interview under discussion brings in another theme that reveals her mixed feelings about those who are helping towards resolving the problems in the family's situation. Mrs MacLeod shows that she is suspicious of others' behaviour and does not readily see herself, in the constellation around Laura, as someone who may have a place in the presenting problem. Her husband had managed to attribute blame to himself but his wife sees the fault of absence from school as lying in Laura's boyfriend Tom and in her husband. She, like her husband, needed help in more realistic thinking. The direction of the move varied – Mr MacLeod needed help to ameliorate his self-blame by seeing multiple factors at work, whereas Mrs MacLeod needed help to see her own self as part of the scene rather than be hostile and see others as wrong. Issues were present even before Tom came on the scene during the past year, and difficulties continue now even though she was instrumental in arranging a change of school, which failed. However, she begins to accept her own involvement.

Reality needed to be presented, too, in relation to Laura's contract with her child psychiatrist. Mrs MacLeod's sexual fantasies had been stimulated by Laura's supposed behaviour with Tom (school mates saying she was pregnant), which was discussed in another session. Fantasies surfaced again when she saw the nature of an article on psychiatry that she found in Laura's room. She had over-generalised from this and had become anxious about treatment and the relationship that a young girl may have with a psychiatrist. This reflected her resistance to treatment.

By end of the session, Mrs MacLeod accepted that should Laura return to school "there would still be a lot of trouble left", and she began to see that the problem also lay between Laura, her husband and herself. When Mrs MacLeod reverted to blaming Tom, she was able to think through this herself and face that a change in Laura's friendship with Tom would not really solve the basic problem of the way in which she and her husband, and Laura, found difficulty in getting on with each other.

Summary

Aspects of cognitive therapy were drawn upon in the sessions with Laura's parents. A professional relationship had already been developed in earlier sessions that enabled both parents to continue coming to the clinic and it underpinned the likelihood of reaching a shared agenda. The agenda was taken to be that Laura's school refusal was an aspect, albeit important, of wider issues concerning the interpersonal relationships within the family and in the outside world of school. To this end, Mr and Mrs MacLeod need help to explore their understanding of themselves and each other through putting their readily available thoughts about attitudes, beliefs and values into words. For instance, Mr MacLeod needed to talk about the uncertainty that he had about his parental role, and Mrs MacLeod about the attrition experienced in her life through multiple losses. In addition, attempts were made to help them see each other from another point of view – this led to Mr MacLeod hearing that Mrs MacLeod's surgery "must have been a great threat . . . it often takes a person a long time to get over this"; and it led to Mrs MacLeod hearing that, for Mr MacLeod, "it was difficult for her husband to stand failure when achievement means so much to him".

The sessions were also used to show that each parent had a part to play. Alternative ways for them to view and approach the problem were sought. Mrs MacLeod tended towards being a hostile, angry person who ascribed fault and 'wrongness' to others, such as her husband and Laura's boyfriend, and to the teachers and the child psychiatrist. Mr MacLeod showed features of a more depressive nature as he homed in on self-criticism and blame. Realistic thinking was put forward with the intention that Mrs MacLeod be helped to be less stringent in placing 'wrongness' on others; and that Mr MacLeod reach the conclusion himself that self-criticism, leading to firmness as a parent like his own father, would ultimately make Laura dig her toes in all the more. After weekly hour-long sessions over 3 months with the child psychiatrist Laura was able to return to school. During this period Mr and Mrs MacLeod were seen either together or on their own by the social worker. Family relationships improved.

The casework focused on mental events that readily surfaced in both parents. Discussion then began to lessen the anxiety and hostility, the uncertainty and low spirits, which featured in Mr and Mrs MacLeod's relationship with each other and with Laura.

References

BECK, A. T. (1987) Cognitive models of depression. *Journal of Cognitive Psychotherapy,* **1**, 1.

KAHN, J., NURSTEN, J. & CARROLL, H. M. C. (1981) *Unwillingly to School* (3rd edn). Oxford: Pergamon.

McADAM, E. & GILBERT, P. (1985) Cognitive behavioural therapy as a psychotherapy for mood disturbance in child, adolescent and family psychiatry. *Newsletter of the Association for Child Psychology and Psychiatry,* **7**, 1.

SKYNNER, A. C. R. (1974) School phobia: a reappraisal. *British Journal of Medical Psychology,* **47**, 1.

19 Psychotherapy for school-refusing children with separation anxiety

JUDITH EDWARDS and DILYS DAWS

The two authors of this chapter are child psychotherapists trained at different periods, at the Tavistock Clinic. One of us (D.D.) is also the daughter of Jack Kahn, and grew up hearing his ideas develop in his years in general practice. He started to speculate and comment on the processes going on in the families who were his patients. He took a wry interest in those patients who needed visits because they were housebound, and thought about what had led them towards psychosomatic conditions of all kinds and the tyranny that could extend to the lives of the family. This was in the forties and early fifties before there was popular knowledge of the psychological aspects of illnesses, and of the relation between symptoms and family dynamics.

Jack Kahn's work on school refusal developed with Jean Nursten in a later period of his life, after he had trained and was working as a child psychiatrist. However, one of his major hypotheses, that school-refusing children had difficulty in leaving home, rather than in going to school, was based on his vivid memories of homes that revolved round sick members of the family. In most of the actual cases that he saw, and all of us as clinicians today see, the illness in the family is presented in a much more subtle way, as an emotional fragility, but those extreme cases in general practice helped draw his attention to them in the first place. Although we quote only occasionally from Kahn & Nursten, many of our ideas are naturally based on theirs.

Following Kahn & Nursten's work, and other writers on the subject, school refusal is almost always thought of as a family problem, and we will return to this issue later in the chapter. The work can be likened to a series of concentric circles: first, family work will explore the problem, and the family's anxiety will hopefully be contained and be able to be thought about in a new way. If individual treatment of a child is considered to be helpful, then sessions will be offered in either a time-limited or an open-ended way, and the child will meet regularly with a child psychotherapist to explore what may be going on in her/his mind that has produced the symptom of not being able to go to school. Then it may be possible to sort out external factors (such as bullying) from internal difficulties to do with self-esteem, or the lack of it, which may overwhelm and depress a child to the extent that she/he lacks the energy to mobilise hope. Gradually as a child is able to experience a sense of hope and a sense of self, the areas that were stuck and immobilised can come alive. The sessions and the gaps between them rehearse hellos and goodbyes in a new context, and the impact of separation can be thought about and then reworked so that it becomes more possible, and is allowed by the child and by the family.

Psychotherapy

A psychotherapist will work with a child in a protected setting, using in most cases a box of toys and drawing materials. Melanie Klein discovered that a child's drawings and playing with small toys had parallels with an adult's free associations and dreams; they are a working through in symbolic form of an unconscious process. Play can express feelings and emotions before words are available for them, or as an elaboration of them. The way a child sets out the figures in the doll's house, for instance, may be an illustration of an internal drama. When the fear underlying the dread of going to school can be spoken about, misperceptions can begin to be understood, fears become more manageable. When a child talks to a therapist about panic he may well experience the panic as he describes it. By talking with a child in the context of the to-and-fro relationship in the therapy room, rather than by historical reconstruction, the therapist may be able to make sense of the internal struggles that have resulted in the impasse of school refusal.

As the relationship between child and therapist develops, so it will become increasingly coloured by past relationships. It is through this 'transference' relationship that difficulties can be thought about and overcome. In a new situation, we all have our own particular way of behaving, and this indicates what our expectations, hopes and fears of this meeting are, based on our thoughts about what has happened in the past. As Heinrich Racker (1968) said in his book *Transference and Countertransference*, "every person acquires in childhood [and we would like to add, in infancy] certain characteristic ways of living his love". As the therapy proceeds the therapist will represent in the child's mind at different times both mother and father. The interplay of these evoked parental figures will give the child the opportunity to re-experience with the therapist the areas of difficulty. Sometimes the therapist can represent what may have been lacking in the parents: a vital combination of understanding and authority.

It is also worth noting that generally in work with children, the outcome is more hopeful if the symptom is picked up and worked with at an early stage. By adolescence family patterns and individual's responses to them are firmly established, and become further complicated by the adolescent's task of separating out from the family in an age-appropriate way. The difficulties posed by the transition through puberty and problems about sexual identity and relationships serve to exacerbate earlier unresolved issues about separation.

To build on Kahn & Nursten's original title, Shakespeare's picture of the reluctant schoolboy "creeping like snail unwillingly to school" seems to describe very well the heavy burden that makes life for a school-refusing child feel so intolerable. Like the snail, the child carries on his/her back the pain and worries from home, and cannot get away from all this to learn and develop. We think of snails as slow moving and unable to change; the school-refusing child is stuck in a vulnerable state, inadequately protected by a fragile shell of coping.

When Freud (1920) saw his grandson playing a repetitive game with a cotton reel, where he threw it away and then 'found' it, he recognised this game of 'playing gone' as being to do with the first of many developmental steps along the pathway of managing separations: "The game was related to the child's cultural achievement – the instinctual renunciation which he made in allowing his mother to go away without protesting".

While Freud emphasised the renunciation needed in order for a child to grow and develop, we also see that the loss is paralleled by a gain, an entry into a wider world and the growth of individuality. The first separation from mother and how it is managed prefigures the introduction of the baby-sitter, the play group, the nursery, primary school, secondary school and onwards. At any transitional stage there are no set of givens to show mother and child how to do it, but rather a complex of internal and external forces in play.

Paradoxically, in a chapter about child psychotherapy, we write a great deal about families. School refusal is a *separation* issue, and it is crucial to think about the dynamics of the family that the child has so much difficulty in leaving, even for the length of a school day. However, each school-refusing child is different. The content of their fears about going to school, the shape of their fantasies of what will happen if they leave parents and home, are theirs and theirs alone. Child psychotherapists, with their interest in the details of a child's internal world, can help the child communicate some of this to their parents in family meetings.

We discuss how school refusal can arise from difficulties around separation that may have been present in the family for years. The result may be a child unconsciously 'electing' or being elected to stay at home rather than conform to the cultural norm of going to school. It is often a complicated knot to untie. There will almost always be reality factors at school such as bullying or anxieties stirred up by a particular teacher or subject. These external forces (dealt with more fully elsewhere in this book) are complementary to a difficulty that may lie within the family itself. This also leads us on to thinking about the child's own perception and misperception of reality. We describe several case examples where we look at particular children's predicaments

Family dynamics and attachment

In referrals to clinics the whole family will generally be invited, and the difficulty will be initially explored in terms of the family dynamics: the impact of the child on the family and the family on the child, taking into account both past and present external events and the way the family thinks about them. In a recent research paper "Measuring the Ghost in the Nursery", Peter Fonagy and his colleagues (1992) describe how their use of Mary Main's Adult Attachment Interview has led them to discover how much people are still "possessed by their family ghosts" (to quote Selma Fraiberg, 1980), in a measure that relates directly to the individual's capacity to have constructed a coherent account of childhood experiences, however adverse these may have been. People who can talk clearly about their childhood have gone some way towards forgiving their parents, and at being at ease with imperfections both in their parents and themselves. By contrast, those still possessed by their ghosts have not been able to link together their story in a coherent way, and have either blocked out experiences, denied their significance or been unable to relate them in a narrative form. Returning to clinical work, in a series of family sessions a story may emerge, perhaps for the first time, which can help the family begin to integrate previously unthought experiences. This is a relief and a platform for new understanding that the whole family may be able to share.

A social worker in a child and adolescent clinic, Vivien Stringer, recently undertook an informal survey of school refusal cases referred to the clinic over the previous 5 years. In a sample of 22 children, 20 of these, spread in age equally over the primary and secondary school range, presented with psychosomatic symptoms. Further work with the families elicited that separation anxieties played a predominant role in 18 of these cases, linked with depression in one or both parents, and with fears about mother's illness or death in 14 cases. Half the cases involved absent fathers, through divorce or separation, and nearly as many showed evidence of uninvolved fathers, either as a result of long working hours or personal diffidence, or a combination of these. Where the parents were still together, marital discord was almost always present.

In all of these cases, the child's symptom of school refusal was closely linked to what could be described as an experience of insecure or anxious attachment within the family. In this particular sample it was found that 14 cases were resolved during a series of family meetings; three others had both family and individual work concurrently. Four children went on to have psychotherapy after family work, and one became a hospital in-patient. In terms of outcome, 12 children (the majority being pre-adolescent) returned to full-time schooling, four adolescents returned part-time and six adolescents did not return to school. The evident value of this sort of work is that both the family's and the child's experience can be thought about, and treatment can be offered at a level of intensity that is appropriate in that particular case.

John Bowlby (1973), in writing about attachment, very concisely listed how school refusal connected with patterns of family interaction.

Pattern A   Mother, or more rarely father, is a sufferer from chronic anxiety regarding attachment figures and retains the child at home to be a companion.

Pattern B   The child fears that something dreadful may happen to mother, or possibly father, while he/she is at school and so remains at home to prevent it happening.

Pattern C   The child fears that something dreadful may happen to him/her if he/she is away from home and so remains at home to prevent that happening.

Pattern D   Mother, or more rarely father, fears that something dreadful will happen to the child while he/she is at school and so keeps him/her at home.

It is interesting to note now that Jack Kahn and John Bowlby, both occupied with similar issues in the sixties and seventies, seem to have taken little notice of each other's work. For example, the third edition of *Unwillingly to School*, written after Bowlby's *Attachment and Loss* had been published, does not refer to the term 'attachment'.

School refusal and sleep problems

We have noticed how much the separation aspect of school refusal has in common with sleep problems in infants (Daws, 1989). One case, seen by D.D. at a baby clinic, neatly spelled out these connections. At the suggestion of her health visitor, a mother brought her 8-month-old baby, who was waking up frequently during the night. To my surprise she also brought two of her older children, but not with a family meeting in mind. She explained that they were not at school because one was unwell, the other, older one was being bullied at school, and she was keeping her away because the school was not taking this seriously enough. Mother had told the girls to sit quietly at the back of the room, but they seemed very interested in the conversation. I was left with a problem of family dynamics versus ethics. Who had been referred and for what? Was the therapist being asked to take note of the girls' absence from school, or was she meant to ignore them and deal with only one bit of the family interaction, that between mother and baby? These two girls thought they were accompanying their mother while she got a quick cure for the baby's sleep problem.

I decided to go for the reality of their presence and invited them to join the discussion. It seemed to be a much-needed opportunity for them to hear their mother telling a horrendous story of past family disturbance. There was now a fresh start with a new partner, father of the baby, and a new home, but it seemed there was still much to process. Mother told me of violence everywhere, of an attempted break-in to their home, of the bullying at school, of the dangers from traffic if her children went out, of the baby's need to stay close to her at night. She then told me of the tragic deaths of her own parents. People who have had a bereavement, especially losing their parents prematurely, may have great difficulty in allowing their children to separate, either at night in going to sleep or by day in leaving the home to go to school.

It sounded as though this mother did not have enough feeling of safety inside herself to pass on to her children if they went out and left her. Outside, in all its various forms, was dangerous. The new father to this family was going to have to make up for a lot that was missing. I saw this family only once, but things started to get better, the baby slept more, as reported by the health visitor and the older girl returned to school. My understanding of the mother's sense of danger seemed to have lessened its impact.

Fathers

One of the tasks of fathering, as well as having a direct relationship with the baby, is in supporting mother and baby as they get to know each other and in helping them to pull apart as the baby grows. The father can offer the baby the first excitements of the wider world. It is also vital for a baby to experience that part of the relationship between his/her parents that excludes him/her – a baby who grows up without two parents, who are sometimes more interested in each other than they are in the baby, does not have the richness of this example to bring to his/her own marriage. Fathers can help mothers find their own authority and can help keep anxiety in proportion. As Guedeney & Kreisler (1987) say, the father can help by "limiting the influence of mothers' phobias on the child".

Another case showed the connection in a family between a sleep problem and a school-refusal problem as both being facets of separation difficulties. Here the role of the father in the H family turned out to be crucial.

Two-year-old Joe came with his parents Mr and Mrs H about his severe sleep problems. He woke several times in the night, came into his parents' bed and was so restless there that his father ended up sleeping in Joe's bed. As

I (D.D.) asked for some of the family history they told me that 5 years earlier their baby, Tony, had died at a few weeks having been premature. Joe himself had stopped breathing and turned blue at 3 months. I understood how hard it must be for these parents *not* to keep a close eye on Joe through the night. As he moved restlessly round my room, going noisily in and out of the door, it seemed that setting limits was very difficult for these parents. They were glad to tell me of the family tragedy, but did not seem to want to connect their feelings about this with Joe's sleeplessness. They thanked me in a friendly way, mentioned some practical changes they were planning, and said they did not need another meeting. However, they contacted me a few weeks later to say that Elena, their 10-year-old daughter had stopped going to school because she was being bullied. The GP told me that Elena came to the surgery frequently with headaches.

This time I saw all four of the family together, and heard again the tragic story of Tony's death. Tony had never come home after his premature birth and had died in hospital a few weeks later. Elena was 5 at the time; his death, and her own and the family's grief, had clouded her first days at school. If Tony had lived he would now have been 5 and starting school himself.

I saw Elena on her own and made some links about all this. I suggested that she might feel guilty about going to school and enjoying it when Tony was dead, and would never be able to go to school. Elena agreed to this. She told me very movingly of feeling responsible for his death, that she thinks of him every night and cries, and that she thinks of him being one of the stars in the sky.

The next stage was to set up family meetings with a colleague, Dr Gill Stern, and to help Elena tell her parents of some of her feelings, without disclosing what she had told me confidentially. They began to understand that having her mind still full of the family grief for the dead baby was interfering with her life at school. Both parents opened up to talk about their own lives. It was easy to go back to the theme of Joe's problems at night, and to see why it was so difficult for them to be firm and set limits for this precious, second son.

We asked Mr H how his father would have solved the problem, and then discovered that because of the Second World war Mr H had not seen his father for most of his own first 5 years. We could see how he simply did not have an example of how fathers and sons work things out together; but also that his own unsatisfied longing as a little boy for his father was confusing his perception of how close to him his little boy Joe needed to be now.

Mrs H similarly talked about her difficulty in separating from her mother, whom she sees daily, and realised that she was keeping Elena tied to her by allowing her to stay away from school.

As the family started to make all these connections for themselves, they began to be freed from their effects. The parents found themselves able to get together to plan how to help the children, instead of ineffectually arguing with each other. They were able to work with the school to get Elena back, insisting that the headmaster stop the bullying, but equally requiring Elena to attend. When they similarly bounced Joe out of their bed and into his own room, we suspected from their new look of vitality and humour that their own sexual relationship was flourishing again.

Through all this we had acknowledged that Elena needed a chance to talk privately about her own worries and we offered her individual psychotherapy. Although she had started to attend school regularly her headaches persisted, and it seemed that while the enormous changes in the family's thinking had released her to go to school, her physical symptom needed some personal attention. Indeed a large number of school-refusing children also have physical symptoms such as Elena's that can seem to be sufficient reason for not attending school, e.g. stomach aches, feeling sick. Some children also have pains in their legs – the symbolic connection with not being able to walk to school seems inescapable. These are in fact all part of the same syndrome, the same failure to process anxiety and achieve emotional separation from parents. Elena has now started in individual therapy. Having seen that her parents could talk about emotions and get relief from this, she herself was freed to look at the connections between symptoms and her feelings. It seems that change is possible for this family.

Early disturbance

In the case of Mary, who was seen for individual psychotherapy by a colleague for $2\frac{1}{2}$ years, the patterns of eventual school refusal had been well established in primary school. Mary had always been taken to school by mother, came home to lunch and refused to go to school at all if her friend Pamela was absent.

The referral was made in Mary's second term at secondary school. It came firstly from a hospital where Mary had been taken with a back injury after a struggle with her parents, who were trying to dress her to take her to school; and secondly from the school itself, where there was increasing concern about her absences. Mary attributed these to being teased, and to her dislike of PE and French. It gradually became clear in family meetings that Mary and father were in strong competition for mother, and that the family was an isolated and disturbed group who expressed distrust and disdain of outsiders.

In Mary's therapy, what emerged was her angry demand for the exclusive possession of her mother. A stay in hospital for a tonsillectomy had stirred up extreme terrors. She told her therapist about her panic on the ward when she feared she might be abandoned or suffocated.

After therapy began, Mary managed to leave her mother sufficiently to attend a unit for troubled adolescents. She struggled with murderous feelings against her father and siblings, who were competitors for mother. She made cruel attacks on her pets and threatened suicide. What could be seen as normal developmental conflicts had escalated in this troubled family to an extreme point. School refusal can rarely be one of a number of signs that a child is beginning to experience some sort of psychotic breakdown. As Kahn & Nursten (1981) put it there is often a wish to reintegrate a child swiftly so that "acting normal" may reintroduce being normal.

In the sporadic family meetings when the parents could bear to come, what emerged was the parents' unhappy marriage, their lack of personal authority and capacity to parent. Here were a couple who, albeit very reluctantly, did want to be helped with their difficulties. Mary's hostility became lodged in the person of the clinic teacher and she withdrew from the group. Eventually a boarding school placement was arranged, and Mary was able to separate from her family and her therapy to take this up. Towards the time of school-leaving age, she withdrew again and no further push was made. It did seem in this case as if the best efforts were simply too late and that in addition Mary was a particularly disturbed, possibly psychotic girl. Work with separations and transitions much earlier on might well have given her better protection to weather the progress of her disturbance. If we can take this back even further, thinking with parents and their infants about separations is preventative and protective work, which is often vital to ensure later smooth transitions.

Separations and boundaries

A similar story of difficulties in working through separations and the provision of appropriate boundaries can be seen with Peter, who at the age of 13 was referred via his GP. For the preceeding $2\frac{1}{2}$ years of secondary education he had persistently run back home after his parents took him to school. This had resulted in an agreement between school and family that mother spend the whole of the school day in a room with Peter and the special needs teacher, while work was fed into him from subject teachers around the school. Peter was thus at the hub of a system that allowed him to exert unprecedented control over both his parents and the school, rather like a baby in a high-chair, demanding to be fed.

Our colleague worked in interrelated ways to help family and school understand the meaning of this system, and to help something more appropriate develop so that Peter could learn and grow as an ordinary boy in secondary school. She had meetings with the whole family, some meetings with the parents alone and three consecutive individual sessions with Peter. She also met and consulted with the special needs teacher who had been drawn into colluding with Peter's omnipotent wishes because of Peter's suicidal threats. Bringing her in had maintained the problem rather than solving it.

What emerged over time was a history of profound depression in Peter's mother, which she herself attributed to a separation from her grandparents when she was 3. Peter, her youngest child, had carried the greatest weight of her sadness and anxiety. It turned out that separations had been difficult from nursery school onwards, although these problems had been accommodated at primary school. Peter's father seemed, through Peter, to be reliving his own uncontained adolescence, when his parents had not been able to support him in a firm framework to go to school. He repeatedly maintained that he would not make Peter attend school or the clinic. While it is often the case that boys with ineffectual fathers are not able to identify with and use the authority aspect of school in a helpful way, the healthy part of Peter was aware of his profound difficulty and he came regularly to the clinic meetings. He had been involved in smoking marijuana and had to be hospitalised after drinking spirits, but his parents wanted to see this as normal adolescent behaviour. What Peter was able to benefit from was not only understanding but also the exercise of authority: a stance where what might almost be termed a *lack* of empathy with his infantile needs, and an assumption that he *could* go to school normally, was helpful to him.

Over the weeks these issues of exercising appropriate parental authority were thought about, so that the parents were able to understand their role rather than having an attitude of critical superiority to what they saw as the school's failure. Peter's despair, which was overlaid with appearing to be in charge, could be talked about, as could his possessiveness of his mother and his terror of rivals that prevented him from attending lessons with other pupils. Gradually he was able to take himself to school, to be with other children and to fit in with most of the school's requirements.

One-parent families

When school refusal becomes a symptom in a long-term one-parent family, it is very often the missing paternal function that has brought about an inability on the part of both child and parent to separate and grow in a healthy way towards the child's adolescence and eventual leaving home. This difficulty of being in a mother–child couple that is perpetuated beyond the appropriate stage in babyhood is one where both mother and child need the intervention of outside work so that both can be supported: the mother to be able to believe in her child's capacity to grow, and her own capacity to cope with the pain of this when she has no adult partner, and the child to believe that her/his rightful push towards independence will not result in the mother's collapse.

The situation can be complicated in addition by parental illness, where the child has consciously or unconsciously adopted the role of carer.

Bowlby (1973) describes this constellation as "inverted attachment" and adds that the true position is often camouflaged unconsciously with a mother, for instance, asserting that it is the child who is in need of care and protection. What might be seen as over-indulgence is, he maintains "something very different and much sadder . . . such children are chronically frustrated". Thomas's case illustrates this.

Thomas had become increasingly school phobic as he approached secondary transfer and was referred to the clinic because of his anxiety, which also manifested in nightmares and obsessive touching rituals. His mother had lived alone with him all his life and she had been diagnosed as suffering from multiple sclerosis soon after his birth. Thomas's lifelong experience was of a fragile mother, and while consciously he seemed to have accepted the role of being merged with mother in what could be described as symbiotic union (they dressed in a similar way and looked almost like two halves of the same person when I (J.E.) first met them), at an unconscious level he was terrified of this. He showed this when for the first year of his once-weekly therapy he played off-the-ground games and constructed dens in one corner of the room. I understood this as being in order to ward off contact with me as a frightening maternal object. Similarly he asked for "miles of string" and when I gave him a ball of string he spent several sessions constructing huge webs in the room. He explained that he had made webs for as long as he could remember: that at first he made them in order not to get tangled in them, but then he had "given up". He got into his therapy web and deliberately wound its threads around his limbs. An entangling union like that between himself and his mother was all that he could envisage. I saw this as a kind of symbiosis, though not in the scientific terminology where both parties gain by the relationship. Thomas both invited this union and was repelled by it; it haunted his mind and he had dreams and nightmares about it. Bowlby (1973) describes a similar incident with a 9-year-old boy who wound himself up in the window-cord: "see, I'm in a spider's web and I can't get out". Thomas told me the story of Robocop: a man who had been remade into a machine: "He was hurt so badly, he didn't want it ever to happen again". I said perhaps he was also talking about a part of himself it felt very risky to allow to make contact with me, and so he built a wall between us to stop getting too close. It was hard for him to imagine we could be friendly without someone getting trapped or hurt.

As we talked about his heroes, who were the macho stars of popular films, Thomas began to have ideas about internal strengths that could develop once he had more of an experience in therapy of a relationship which could encompass dependency without overwhelming him. We worked steadily in the contained and consistent setting of the therapy room and he came to experience a paternal part of me that could both strengthen the maternal and protect it against his own powerful wishes to take over.

Meanwhile, his mother was receiving weekly support from a psychotherapist colleague for her own needs, so that Thomas was able to feel freer. Initially, she found it difficult not to intrude into her son's therapy, but over time and helped by the idea of my colleague and myself as a strong couple she was able to develop her own strengths. Her situation had been complicated by her entangled and problematic relationship with her own mother. Thomas made the secondary transfer amid concern among us all about his capacities to survive it, but he managed and has continued to do so. When the time felt right his therapy ended, while his mother continued to have support. We felt it was vital that Thomas knew his mother was being taken care of so that he was free to grow, to make new friends, go on school journeys and continue relatively unimpeded along the path towards adulthood.

Thomas's developmental impetus was hindered by a mother whose illness and, albeit slow, physical deterioration stirred up in him almost unbearable fears of her falling apart. He quite literally feared that she would fall and break her bones when he was away at school. The failure to separate at earlier stages had not begun to show until he was faced with the secondary transfer to a large school.

Another boy, 13-year-old Brian, who had ceased going to secondary school altogether during the first term of his transfer from primary education, lived alone with his mother, a partially recovered anorexic, who had been severely depressed since Brian's birth (he had been the product of a casual sexual encounter). She too, as we subsequently discovered, had a history of difficult and inadequate parenting. Brian had managed to go to school in the relatively sheltered setting of a good small primary school, but had found the task of negotiating the transition to a larger more uncontained environment too great.

As with Thomas, here again it could be said that the primary task of separation had not been achieved in infancy, but the difficulty had not surfaced in a direct way until Brian was assailed by the impact of a large secondary school. He complained of headaches and stomach aches and stayed at home with his mother where they both slept a good deal of the time. Since his absences from school were attributed to minor illnesses it was almost a year before the severity of the problem was recognised and indeed this is often a difficulty when physical illness masks the underlying fact of school refusal. As Jack Kahn has said, "physical symptoms are common in children with school phobia. There is no question of malingering, as the symptoms' emotional origin makes them no less distressing to experience".

Brian was silent in the presence of his mother but was more able to talk on his own with the therapist. He had some insight into his predicament and knew that he and his mother "compounded each other's problems" as he said.

Brian maintained that he had "never thought about" his father. However, by the time he had transferrd to a special unit for troubled adolescents he seemed to be in the grip of a full-blown depressive illness. When therapy was suggested and he came with his mother for a series of assessments, mother said she had to stay up all night in order that they could both get to the clinic for the morning appointment, since they both slept through alarms. He seemed to be a boy who managed on the surface to function in an articulate way (what we might see as a kind of 'skin' (Bick, 1968) to hold together more troubled underlying areas). I came to understand that for Brian beneath this 'skin' lay a mass of fears to do with separation and abandonment should he give up his position as feeder and provider for a depressed mother.

In Brian's therapy two themes stand out: he drew a house with a skeleton structure, which had no walls or roof, and I understood this both as the beginnings of something potentially stronger being built inside, and also as an indication of an impoverished semi-derelict world where he had been able to rely on no one. He found the idea of exploring his internal world quite terrifying (although this latent feeling was largely masked by his accusation to me that he was bored and therapy was boring). I think he only managed to sustain his therapy in the early stages because he incorporated into it his obsessive thinking about keeping to the same routes and routines. He described to me once how he had waited an hour in the snow for a bus that would take him by his usual route home, rather than catch another, involving an adjustment to his route, which would have got him home much earlier. In the course of the last term, before he re-entered mainstream school, he made with great skill an anorak, which he brought to show me in its various stages. "It's like a jacket, it's not a disaster", he said. I said I could see how proud he was that he could make something so difficult successfully and not mess it up. He talked about the wadding that he wouldn't use: it was to be a summer jacket (we were approaching the summer break). "The stripes on the inside go a different way, across and not down. It's not what you would think", he said. I said I thought this jacket meant a lot to him: that perhaps, too, things had changed quite a bit inside his mind, and he had been able to do better than he had thought, like go back to school some days in the week. The jacket and its symbolic equivalents seemed to be an appropriate and necessary defence for a boy who was depressed and had previously lacked hope.

As Anne Alvarez (1992) points out in *Live Company* "a manic experience . . . can signal the first glimmer of emergence from lifelong clinical depression".

Brian began to be interested in the survival of the rain forests and the preservation of whales, who could communicate long distances under the sea. His mother also saw a worker at the clinic and she became gradually able to connect with parental strengths and make a separation between Brian's needs and her own. She made a new relationship and started to work at a part-time job.

Brian ended his therapy very abruptly, after a lively and angry session shortly after an apparently successful re-entry into school. He said I had never been any use, and had never answered his questions. I had no recollection that he had ever asked me any. In this way I think I became in the transference the absent father: he left me rather than be left himself and while clearly this is only a partial solution it gave him the strength and energy to return to school. As far as I know there have been no recurrent difficulties, but I am aware that for Brian many issues were not worked through. Perhaps he will return for more help at another transitional stage.

Sexual preoccupations

Melanie Klein (1932) described how children's curiosity and anxieties about sexuality, especially that of their parents, may be the cause of serious problems.

A child may remain at home in order to prevent something dreadful happening to mother or father, or indeed between them. Sophie was referred at the age of 7, the eldest of five children with an almost precise 1-year age gap between each child. School refusal was one of a number of related symptoms reported in Sophie, as well as stomach aches, sleep disturbance and a general loss of interest in play. The family had also recently moved house. It emerged that the move had been precipitated by bad feeling in the local community after Sophie had accused a boy, who was later vindicated, of trying to pull her knickers down.

Sophie was offered individual sessions at the clinic and the parents were seen separately after an initial family interview: another new baby was imminent. Sophie showed many of the same symptoms in separating from her mother at the beginning of her individual sessions as she had shown when she got to the school gates. She began shaking, went deathly white and looked fearfully at the therapy room door, all this despite the fact that she had met the therapist several times before and had been comfortable when both of her parents were present.

Reaction such as this induces in a therapist what we would call a counter-transference concern: what has she done to produce such a terrified state? This mirrors the dilemma faced by both parents and school, where they may feel it is cruel to insist on school attendance in the face of such evident and extreme anxiety. Another possible outcome is that the therapist, parent or school becomes so stirred up by the child's anxiety that they act in an over-managing way, denying the meaning of the child's experience and can become sadistic.

When the therapist observed to Sophie that it seemed hard for her to leave her mother, Sophie said, "Mummy needs looking after . . . Mummy isn't well".

In later sessions, she said "Mummy is tired, she needs to rest". It became clear that Sophie's experience of her mother's frequent pregnancies was that they drained her mother of energy. She had not perhaps had sufficient time on her own on mother's lap to make space for a second child.

Sophie attended school for a term following the individual and family work but after the birth of the sixth baby, mother had a miscarriage. Sophie again refused to go to school.

It seemed as though there was no real solution for Sophie, events in the family continued to be traumatic for her and the symbolic place in the mind of her therapist was not enough to counteract this after the short-term work finished. It is also relevant that of all the children in this large family Sophie as the eldest was the one who suffered most and seemed most connected with her mother's predicament. She could indeed have benefited from longer-term psychotherapy.

Conclusion

As we have indicated in this chapter, school refusal is a complicated issue that very often involves family attitudes and history as well as personal vulnerability and panic at times of stress. What we feel is needed is for the family to experience a climate where understanding and authority can be integrated in order to help them move on. In our experience, school refusal is not a sudden eruption of a symptom but has been building up over time because of earlier failures to separate adequately. Individual psychotherapy may be offered to some children where appropriate, and the child psychotherapist can then work with the child on understanding their personal vulnerability and how it was that they got so stuck at home. The outcome is that the majority of children are then able to return to school. At best, psychotherapy allows the child to discover the enjoyable wisdom of disillusion about self and others, in a friendly sort of way.

Acknowledgements

Thanks to Pam Armbruster, Sue Brough and Maria Pozzi for material used in this chapter.

References

ALVAREZ, A. (1992) *Live Company*. London: Routledge.
BICK, E. (1968) The experience of the skin in early object relations. *International Journal of Psychoanalysis*, **49**, 484–486.

BOWLBY, J. (1973) *Attachment and Loss 2: Separation, Anxiety and Anger*. London: Hogarth.

DAWS, D. (1989) *Through the Night: Helping Parents and Sleepless Infants*. Free Association Books.

FONAGY, P., *et al* (1992) Measuring the ghost in the nursery. *Bulletin of the Anna Freud Centre*, **24**, 225–232.

FRAIBERG, S. (ed.) (1989) *Clinical Studies in Infant Mental Health*. London: Tavistock.

FREUD, S. (1920) *Beyond the Pleasure Principle*, Standard Edition XVIII. London: Hogarth.

GUEDENEY, A. & KREISLER, L. (1987) Sleep disorders in the first eighteen months of life. *Infant Mental Health Journal*, **8**, 307–318.

KAHN, J. & NURSTEN, J. (1981) *Unwillingly to School*, 3rd edn. Oxford: Pergamon.

KLEIN, M. (1932) *The Psychoanalysis of Children*. London: Hogarth.

RACKER, H. (1968) *Transference and Countertransference*. London: Hogarth.

SANDLER, J. with FREUD, A. (1945) *The Analysis of Defence*. New York: International University Press.

WINNICOTT, D. W. (1964) *The Child, the Family and the Outside World*. Penguin.

20 School refusal: a controlled 20–30 year follow-up study of Swedish urban children

NATALIA FLAKIERSKA-PRAQUIN,
MARIANNE LINDSTRÖM and
CHRISTOPHER GILLBERG

School non-attendance became a problem in Sweden in 1842 when school attendance became compulsory. School non-attendance that was not due to illness was then collectively referred to as truancy. During the 1930s, a distinction between various forms of school non-attendance was gradually made. Today one distinguishes between truancy and school refusal (previously referred to as school phobia or 'neurotic' school refusal).

School refusal (Johnson *et al*, 1941; Warren, 1948; Hersov & Berg, 1980; Broadwin, 1972; Waller & Eisenberg, 1980; Berg & Jackson, 1985; King & Tonge, 1992) is now generally considered a sign of emotional disorder. The essential problem is a prolonged or recurrent absence from school with the consent of the parents. In the mornings, the children complain of headache, stomach ache, nausea, dizziness, and so on, but if a medical examination is performed it does not usually establish an obvious cause for these symptoms. Teachers are often surprised to learn about the problems of the child, because they are not readily evident when the child is at school. A majority of the children are of average or above average intelligence and ambition. Some feel depressed about not being able to go to school. At home, the children can be demanding towards their parents. Outbursts of rage may occur, mostly towards the mother.

The purpose of the study presented here has been to follow up children treated for school refusal in the in-patient and out-patient psychiatric services for children and adolescents in Göteborg, Sweden, 20–30 years after initial contact. We have compared their further school attendance, social adjustment and need for psychiatric treatment with the same parameters in two comparison groups, one a group of psychiatric clinic attenders without school refusal and the other a group from the general population. Our hypotheses were that the school-refusal cases would continue to show more signs of emotional disorder than any of the two comparison groups and that, due to their socially avoidant behaviour, they might have fewer social contacts and children of their own in adult age.

Methods

Subjects: school refusal

The study encompassed all 35 children (16 boys, 19 girls) aged 7–12 years who had been treated as in-patients or out-patients at the University Clinic of Child and Adolescent Psychiatry in Göteborg, Sweden from 1961 to 1970. The clinic, at that time, provided all child and adolescent psychiatric services in the city of Göteborg. The 7–12 year age range was chosen so that the likelihood of any one child being treated within adult psychiatric services would be reduced to a minimum. All the children in the study were born in the years 1953–58. Of the patients 14 had been treated as in-patients and the remaining 21 had received out-patient treatment only; 14% (5/35) of the school-refusal children had applied for child psychiatric help for other problems before school refusal prompted referral.

The criteria for diagnosing school refusal were (a) prolonged or recurrent absence from school; (b) purported physical symptoms (such as headache or bellyache) and/or purported hostility from peers or teachers in the school (it was not required that such symptoms or such hostility be altogether lacking but that, judging from the case records, they had been perceived by the treating physician – and usually, after some time, by the family – as grossly out of proportion in relation to the duration and severity of the school refusal); (c) normal intelligence; (d) no obvious major/severe social or family dysfunction; and (e) no registered delinquency. All cases accepted for study met all 5 criteria. The cases were not selected according to registered diagnoses but according to detailed scrutiny of all 500 case records of 7–12-year-old children who had been treated at the in-patients or out-patients department of the University Clinic of Child and Adolescent Psychiatry in 1961–70 (Flakierska *et al*, 1988).

The selected cases have later been reanalysed with a view to establishing diagnoses according to DSM–III (American Psychiatric Association, 1980). It was found that all 35 cases complied with the criteria for separation anxiety disorder.

Subjects: other child psychiatric clinic attenders

Thirty-five non-school refusal children, matched pair-wise for age (±1 year) and sex and period of treatment (1961–70) who had been evaluated in the out-patient or in-patient departments of the University Clinic of Child and Adolescent Psychiatry as those with school refusal, were selected as a psychiatric comparison group. The diagnoses pertaining to this group are shown in Table 20.1.

Subjects: general population/'normal' comparison group

Thirty-five children matched pair-wise for age, sex and school area were selected when school health records of the school-refusal group were collected. These children constituted a general population 'normal' comparison group. As it turned out, this group was similar to the index group in respect of social class, as determined by the father's occupation. Five of the children in this group (14%) had been in contact with child and adolescent psychiatric services. This proportion of child and adolescent psychiatric clinic attenders accords well with Swedish data on children in the general population (Gillberg, 1985).

Information retrieval

The following information was retrieved for all index and comparison cases in 1990 (i.e. when the index and comparison cases were 32–37 years old, mean 34.3, s.d. 1.9 years, 95% confidence interval 33.9–34.7), 20–29 years after original treatment.

(a) All the case records from child and adolescent psychiatric clinics (out-patients, Göteborg; in-patients, Sweden) were examined in detail.
(b) School health records (the records of two school-refusal cases and eight cases from the psychiatric comparison group, who had moved from the region, could not be traced).
(c) Information from National Health Insurance records, containing details about numbers of days of registered illness and retirement due to medical/psychiatric illness.
(d) Information from national demographic registers, containing details about marriage, divorce, number of children and whether or not the subjects as adults were still living with their parents.
(e) Registration with the local social authorities of Göteborg.
(f) Registration on the state police register of Sweden.
(g) Registration (after the initial contact) at adult psychiatric clinics in the region.

The school-refusal cases are considered representative of school-refusal cases who applied for child psychiatric help during the mid-1960s. They constituted 7% of the total population of child psychiatric clinic attenders. This finding is in good accord with results obtained by Kahn & Nursten (1962), Chazan (1962) and Smith (1970). In order to trace all school-refusal cases, the 500 case records of all the child psychiatric clinic attenders were scrutinised conjointly by two of the authors. No attempt was made to diagnose panic disorder in a systematic fashion. In spite of the case records being very detailed in a majority of the cases, information on symptoms associated with panic disorder was scanty or

TABLE 20.1
Main diagnosis according to the DSM–III in the three study groups

Group/diagnosis	n
(1) School refusal	
DSM–III school refusal criteria met	35
Anxiety disorders	35
Separation anxiety disorder	(35)
(2) Other child psychiatric clinic attenders	
Conduct and oppositional defiant disorder	11
ADHD	1
Dysthymia	3
Uncomplicated bereavement	2
Anxiety disorders	6
Overanxious disorder	(4)
Generalised anxiety disorder	(1)
Separation anxiety disorder	(1)
OCD	1
Tic disorder	1
Reading skills disorder	1
Encopresis	2
Enuresis	2
Stereotypies	2
Sleep terror disorder	1
Adjustment disorder	2
(3) Normal comparison group	
Never consulted child psychiatrist	30
Conduct disorder	2
Anxiety disorders	2
Overanxious disorder	(2)
Parent–child problem (Battered child syndrome)	1

ADHD, attention deficit hyperactivity disorder; OCD, obsessive–compulsive disorder.

altogether lacking. At the time of initial evaluation, 31 out of 35 children were living with both biological parents. The remaining four were living with adoptive parents: since the age of 1 week and 5 months respectively (2), had a parent who had died (1), or parent who had divorced (1).

The group of other child psychiatric clinic attenders are considered representative of non-school-refusal child psychiatric patients who applied for help in the mid-1960s. The group of general population 'normal' comparison children were considered roughly representative of 7–12 year olds in 1953–58 and living in Göteborg in 1961–70.

Very good and very poor adjustment

An attempt was made to classify all 105 cases (index and comparison groups) according to overall adjustment.

Very good adjustment was defined as:

(a) completion of compulsory school;
(b) no registration on social or police registers;
(c) no further psychiatric care;
(d) no divorce;
(e) less than a mean of 15 days of registered sick-leave per year (census year inclusive).

Very poor adjustment was defined as registration on at least two official registers (social, police and psychiatric care).

Statistical methods

The sign test for matched pairs was used in the statistical analyses of the results. For some comparisons Student's *t*-test for matched pairs was used instead.

Results

Sex differences

There were no clear differences between boys and girls in respect of outcome status.

Position in sibship

Unfortunately, we do not have data on position in the sibship from the comparison groups. The results from the index group are presented in Table 20.1.

Almost half of the group of school refusers (16/35) were the youngest in a sibship of two, three or four. Exactly the same proportion were the eldest in sibships of corresponding sizes. Only three children (9%) had 'in-between' positions in the sibship. The proportions are similar to those in a normal group of 7-year-olds from the general population (Gillberg *et al*, 1992).

Child psychiatric care

All the school-refusal cases and the child psychiatric comparison group had received child psychiatric treatment (a prerequisite for entry into the study for these groups), some of them for prolonged periods, and a handful for several shorter periods over a number of years. Of the 35 school-refusal cases 14 had required in-patient treatment. The child psychiatric comparison group comprised a group of individuals who had been treated for a wide variety of child psychiatric disorders (Table 20.1). Three of these had required in-patient

TABLE 20.2
Follow-up data in school refusal and comparison groups

	School refusal	Other child psychiatric clinic attenders	Normal comparison	P < 0.05	P < 0.01
Interrupted compulsory school	6/33	2/27	2/35		
Completed compulsory school	27/33	25/27	33/35		
Completed senior high school	15/33	12/27	16/35		
Lowest health insurance class	6/33	2/33	3/33		
> 45 days' leave because of illness	7/33[1]	19/33	8/33	2/1, 2/3	2/1
Full-time pension	2/33	0/33	2/33		
Registered by social authorities	14/35	20/35	16/35		
Registered by state police	2/35	9/35	2/35	2/1, 2/3	
Adult psychiatric out-patient care	15/35	11/35	6/35	1/3	
Adult psychiatric in-patient care	2/35	3/35	2/35		
Still living with parents at follow-up	5/35	3/34	0/34		
Married at follow-up	14/34	13/34	20/34		
None	20/34	10/34	10/34		
One or more	14/34	24/34	24/34	1/2, 1/3	
Mean number of children	0.85	1.50	1.29	1/2, 1/3	
95% confidence interval	0.45–1.25	1.05–1.95	0.89–1.69		
Overall outcome					
Very good adjustment	11/35	6/35	13/35	2/3	
Intermediate outcome	14/35	14/35	13/35		
Very poor adjustment	10/35	15/35	9/35		

1. Student's *t*-test for matched pairs. All others sign-test for matched pairs.

treatment. Five (14%) of the comparison cases had been treated for child psychiatric disorders and problems (Severe conduct disorder (1), child abuse (1), emotional disorder (2) and truancy (1)). None of the children in this group had ever met criteria for school refusal.

School career

There were no significant differences (Table 20.2) in respect of further school attendance between the three groups (school health record data). However, there was a tendency towards the general population comparison children having completed compulsory school more often than the children with school refusal and those with other psychiatric disorders. Of the ten children who interrupted compulsory school (in the school-refusal cases this was usually 2–7 years after treatment), all but one were well known to social authorities in adulthood.

Registration by health, social and police authorities

There were few significant differences between the three groups in respect of medical health (as evidenced by information from national health insurance records), social adjustment (as measured by registration with local social authorities) or criminal offence (Table 20.2). However, the non-school-refusal psychiatric comparison group had significantly more days of sick-leave than both the other groups.

Adult psychiatric out-patient care

The school-refusal cases had applied for psychiatric out-patient help in adulthood significantly more often (Table 20.3) than the general population comparison cases (43% u 17%, P < 0.05). There was a trend towards the non-school-refusal comparison group being in between the other two groups.

Adult psychiatric in-patient care

There were two cases in each group who had been treated as in-patients at adult psychiatric clinics. One girl in the school-refusal group was diagnosed as suffering from 'neurotic depression', whereas one boy was said to suffer from a 'borderline condition' in adulthood. In the comparison group, one of the boys was given a diagnosis of 'anxiety neurosis' and the other of 'unspecified psychosis'.

Social and family relationships according to register data

At age 20–30 years, 14% of the school-refusal cases and 8% of other child psychiatric clinic attenders were still living with their parents (Table 20.4). This applied in none of the 'normal' comparison cases. The school-refusal cases had significantly fewer (P < 0.01) children of their own than did the comparison cases.

Overall adjustment

There were no significant differences between the groups with respect to overall adjustment (Table 20.2). For both boys and girls, the overall adjustment tended to be very good in those cases in which the parents had applied for help because of school refusal.

Discussion

Few studies of children with school refusal have reported results from more than 30 subjects plus acceptable comparison groups. Fewer still have

TABLE 20.3
Diagnoses according to adult psychiatric records: follow-up findings

Group/diagnosis	No. in contact with psychiatric services
(1) School refusal	15
Drug addiction	1
Alcoholism	1
Anxiety disorders	6
Panic disorder/agoraphobia/social phobia	(4)
Other anxiety disorders	(2)
Major depression	1
Chronic fatigue syndrome	2
Relationship problems	4
(2) Other psychiatric clinic attenders	11
Drug addiction	1
Alcoholism	1
Anxiety disorders	3
Panic disorder/agoraphobia/social phobia	(1)
Other anxiety disorders	(2)
Major depression	1
Chronic fatigue syndrome/dysthymia	1
Relationship problems	2
OCD	1
Suicide	1
(3) Normal comparison group	6
Drug addiction	1
Anxiety disorders	4
Panic disorder/agoraphobia/social phobia	(1)
Other anxiety disorders	(3)
Enuresis	1

OCD, obsessive–compulsive disorder.

presented clear diagnostic criteria (Berg, 1981). Only one or two reports have covered a follow-up period of 10 years or more (Coolidge *et al*, 1964; Berg, 1981). Our study details diagnostic criteria, makes use of two reasonable comparison groups, relies on register rather than subjective data, and the follow-up period exceeds 20 years.

Nevertheless, conclusions must be drawn with caution. The number of school-refusal cases is relatively small (35). Our sample is representative of Göteborg school-refusal cases requiring child psychiatric treatment, as the children constituted all such cases from one 10-year period. We believe that they are typical of severe school-refusal cases. It is unlikely that many severe cases could escape recognition in Sweden, where services and coverage are comprehensive. Our figure of 7% of the whole child psychiatric age-specific population suffering from school refusal accords well with previous findings (Chazan, 1962; Kahn & Nursten, 1962; Smith, 1970).

TABLE 20.4
Social and family relationships according to register data

Group	Living with parents at follow-up	Mean no. of children (s.d.)
School refusal	5/35	0.85* (1.18)
Other child psychiatric clinic attenders	3/34	1.50 (1.35)
Normal comparison group	0/34	1.29 (1.19)

*$P < 0.05$ School refusal *v* Other and School refusal *v* Normal comparison group.

Another important reason to keep a cautious attitude when discussing the results is the fact that we relied only on medical and health records and other register data. Although in many ways more 'objective' than interview and psychiatric assessment data, they cannot form the basis for a thorough opinion of the follow-up health status of our patients. A detailed psychiatric interview follow-up study at age 32–37 years of the school-refusal cases, the comparison group and the psychiatric non-school-refusal group is currently underway in our centre.

Bearing these important reservations in mind, there emerged three main findings from the present study.

Firstly, as regards general social adjustment and severe incapacitating psychiatric disorder, there were no clear differences between pre-adolescents with school refusal and comparison children with and without non-school-refusal psychiatric problems when followed up to a mean age of about 35 years.

Secondly, the school-refusal cases had applied for adult psychiatric out-patient treatment significantly more often than the normal comparison group. This finding too accords well with results from early studies in the field, in which it has been concluded that 'neurotic' disorders (i.e. less severe psychiatric problems) are relatively prevalent in adulthood following school refusal (Warren, 1960; Coolidge *et al*, 1964).

However, conclusions as regards a real increase in the frequency of emotional disorders in adulthood following school refusal must be tentative. All follow-up studies so far have been on children who once applied for child psychiatric help. The fact that they sought psychiatric help in childhood might make them more prone to seeking the help of adult psychiatric services, even in the absence of 'neurotic' symptoms. The normal comparison group cases only very occasionally had applied for psychiatric help in childhood.

Certainly, the trend towards more consultation was less pronounced when the school-refusal cases were contrasted with the non-school-refusal psychiatric clinic attender comparison group.

Third, we found that the school-refusal cases had fewer children of their own than both groups of comparison cases. Furthermore, almost 14% of the former group were living with their parents as adults, as compared with none in the normal comparison group. Both these findings might indicate a somewhat limited sphere of social relationships in grown-up school-refusal children. We have not been able to find any comparable data in the literature. Nevertheless, our conclusion receives indirect support from the study by Weiss & Burke (1967), who found 7 of 14 school phobics still to have social relationship problems after 5–10 years, in spite of their being well adjusted at school/work.

Our follow-up period is among the longest reported in the literature. Yet our study does not contribute to the elucidation of the 'ultimate' outcome of school refusal. Many adult psychiatric problems seem to have a peak age of onset in the fourth and fifth decades and our follow-up ends at about 35 years.

Tyrer and Tyrer (1974) found school refusal to be much more common in the background of adult psychiatric patients than in 'controls'. They also found an age trend in that children with school refusal in the early teens had a higher risk of becoming adult psychiatric patients than those with school refusal in primary school. Follow-up studies by Warren (1965) and Berg *et al* (1976) have found similar trends. The fact that we found so few severe disorders in our group is possibly related to the fact that our study group was relatively young at the time of diagnosis.

Atkinson *et al* (1989) recently presented preliminary evidence that among school refusers there are at least three subgroups: (I) those who are extensively disturbed and who have often experienced separation or loss (about 40% of cases); (II) those relatively few cases (20% of the whole group) who show the 'classical' separation anxiety and often had an overprotective, dependent mother; and (III) those who show perfectionism and fear of failure (about 40% of cases). If these findings are borne out by future study, they may pave the way for more fruitful division into homogeneous subgroups that might help predict outcome and choice of therapy with better precision in individual cases.

There have been claims for a connection between school phobia in childhood and agoraphobia in adulthood (Berg *et al*, 1974). This conclusion has mostly been based on the retrospective study of adult psychiatric patients or symptom sufferers. Also, separation anxiety disorder during childhood has been reported in patients who have been diagnosed as suffering from panic disorder in adult life (Klein, 1964; Sheehan *et al*, 1982). However, prospective evidence is largely lacking. All our school-refusal cases met DSM–III criteria for separation anxiety disorder. Separation anxiety disorder has recently been found to be an almost universal concomitant of panic disorder in psychiatrically hospitalised prepubertal children (Alessi & Magen, 1988). It is quite possible that several of the school-refusal cases actually suffered from panic attacks in childhood, but the medical reports were not detailed enough for a positive diagnosis to be made in all cases. It is also conceivable that a number of our school refusers are suffering from panic attacks in adult age, and indeed at least four had consulted adult psychiatrists for panic disorder. A tendency towards a higher rate of anxiety disorder in the school-refusal cases was noted, but differences fell short of statistical significance. Thus, we have not been able to confirm a clear relationship between school refusal and panic disorder but this could be due to the intermediate follow-up period or the fact that we relied on (admittedly crude) register and medical record data, rather than our personal interview data.

Our new follow-up study (in the late thirties to early forties), which includes a thorough psychiatric interview, will hopefully elucidate these matters. In that study we focus in detail on the possibility of continuities between childhood school refusal and panic disorder in adulthood.

In conclusion, we found an increased rate of consultation of adult psychiatric services and a low rate of parenting in a representative sample of treated school refusers 20–30 years after the first child psychiatric consultation. These findings appear to indicate some very long-term effects of a childhood diagnosis of school refusal on outcome in adult life.

Acknowledgement

This work was supported by grants from the Wilhelm and Martina Lundgren Foundation.

References

ALESSI, N. E. & MAGEN, J. (1988) Panic disorder in psychiatrically hospitalized children. *American Journal of Psychiatry*, **145**, 1450–1452.

AMERICAN PSYCHIATRIC ASSOCIATION (1980) *Diagnostic and Statistical Manual of Mental Disorders* (3rd edn) (DSM–III). Washington, DC: APA.

ATKINSON, L., QUARRINGTON, B., CYR, J. J., *et al* (1989) Differential classification in school refusal. *British Journal of Psychiatry*, **155**, 191–195.

BERG, I. (1981) When truants and school refusers grow up: comments. *British Journal of Psychiatry*, **141**, 208–210.

——, MARKS, I., McGUIRE, R., *et al* (1974) School phobia and agoraphobia. *Psychological Medicine*, **4**, 428–434.

——, BUTLER, A. & HALL, G. (1976) The outcome of adolescent school phobia. *British Journal of Psychiatry*, **128**, 80–85.

—— & JACKSON, A. (1985) School refusers grow up: a follow-up study of 168 subjects, 10 years on average after in-patient treatment. *British Journal of Psychiatry*, **147**, 366–370.

BROADWIN, I. T. (1972) A contribution to the study of truancy. *American Journal of Orthopsychiatry*, **2**, 253–259.

CHAZAN, M. (1962) School phobia. *British Journal of Educational Psychology*, **32**, 209–217.

COOLIDGE, J. C., BRODIER, D. & FEENEY, B. (1964) A 10-year follow-up of 66 school-phobic children. *American Journal of Orthopsychiatry*, **34**, 209–217.

FLAKIERSKA, N., LINDSTRÖM, M. & GILLBERG, C. (1988) School refusal: A 15–20-year follow-up study of 35 Swedish urban children. *British Journal of Psychiatry*, **152**, 834–837.

GILLBERG, C. (1985) Child psychiatric services in cities. *Läkartidningen*, **81**, 1618. (In Swedish).

———, GILLBERG, I. C. & STEFFENBURG, S. (1992) Siblings and parents of children with autism. A controlled population based study. *Developmental Medicine and Child Neurology*, **34**, 389–398.

HERSOV, L. & BERG, I. (eds) (1980) *Out of School: Modern Perspectives in Truancy and School Refusal*. New York: John Wiley.

JOHNSON, A. M., FALSTEIN, E. J., SZUREK, S. A., et al (1941) School phobia. *American Journal of Orthopsychiatry*, **11**, 702–711.

KAHN, J. H. & NURSTEN, J. P. (1962) School refusal: a comprehensive view of school phobia and other failures of school attendance. *American Journal of Orthopsychiatry*, **32**, 707–718.

KING, N. J. & TONGE, B. J. (1992) School refusal. *Journal of Paediatrics and Child Health*, **28**, 411–413.

KLEIN, D. F. (1964) Delineation of two drug responsive anxiety syndromes. *Psychopharmacologia*, **5**, 397–408.

SHEEHAN, D. V., SHEEHAN, K. E. & MINICHELLO, W. E. (1981) Age of onset of phobic disorders: a reevaluation. *Comprehensive Psychiatry*, **22**, 544–553.

SMITH, S. I. (1970) School refusal with anxiety: a review of sixty-three cases. *Canadian Psychiatry Association Journal*, **15**, 257–264.

TYRER, P. & TYRER, S. (1974) School refusal, truancy and adult neurotic illness. *Psychological Medicine*, **4**, 416–421.

WALLER, D. & EISENBERG, L. (1980) School refusal in childhood: a psychiatric–paediatric perspective. In *Out of School: Modern Perspectives in Truancy and School Refusal* (eds L. Hersov & I. Berg). Chichester: John Wiley.

WARREN, W. (1948) Acute neurotic breakdown in children with refusal to go to school. *Archives of Disease in Childhood*, **23**, 266–272.

——— (1960) Some relationships between the psychiatry of children and adults. *Journal of Mental Science*, **106**, 818–820.

——— (1965) A study of adolescent psychiatric in-patients and the outcome six or more years later. I: Clinical histories and hospital findings. *Journal of Child Psychology and Psychiatry*, **6**, 1–17.

WEISS, M. & BURKE, G. B. (1967) A 5–10 years follow-up of hospitalized school-phobic children and adolescents. *American Journal of Orthopsychiatry*, **37**, 294–295.

Index

Compiled by CAROLINE SHEARD